THE CITY & GUILDS TEXTBOOK

LEVEL 2 DIPLOMA IN
PLASTERING

THE CITY & GUILDS TEXTBOOK

LEVEL 2 DIPLOMA IN
PLASTERING

MIKE GASHE

MICHAEL MANN

COLIN FEARN

SERIES TECHNICAL EDITOR
MARTIN BURDFIELD

About City & Guilds

City & Guilds is the UK's leading provider of vocational qualifications, offering over 500 awards across a wide range of industries, and progressing from entry level to the highest levels of professional achievement. With over 8500 centres in 100 countries, City & Guilds is recognised by employers worldwide for providing qualifications that offer proof of the skills they need to get the job done.

Equal opportunities

City & Guilds fully supports the principle of equal opportunities and we are committed to satisfying this principle in all our activities and published material. A copy of our equal opportunities policy statement is available on the City & Guilds website.

First edition 2014

ISBN 978-0-85193-298-9

Publisher: Fiona McGlade
Development Editor: Claire Owen
Production Editor: Lauren Cubbage

Cover design by Design Deluxe
Illustrations by Barking Dog Art and Palimpsest Book Production Ltd
Typeset by Palimpsest Book Production Ltd, Falkirk, Stirlingshire
Printed in the UK by Cambrian Printers Ltd

British Library Cataloguing in Publication Data

A catalogue record for this book is available from the British Library.

Publications

For information about or to order City & Guilds support materials, contact 0844 534 0000 or centresupport@cityandguilds.com. You can find more information about the materials we have available at www.cityandguilds.com/publications.

Every effort has been made to ensure that the information contained in this publication is true and correct at the time of going to press. However, City & Guilds' products and services are subject to continuous development and improvement and the right is reserved to change products and services from time to time. City & Guilds cannot accept liability for loss or damage arising from the use of information in this publication.

City & Guilds
1 Giltspur Street
London EC1A 9DD

T 0844 543 0033

www.cityandguilds.com

publishingfeedback@cityandguilds.com

CONTENTS

FOREWORD

Whether in good times or in a difficult job market, I think one of the most important things for young people is to learn a skill. There will always be a demand for talented and skilled individuals who have knowledge and experience. That's why I'm such an avid supporter of vocational training. Vocational courses provide a unique opportunity for young people to learn from people in the industry, who know their trade inside out.

Careers rarely turn out as you plan them. You never know what opportunity is going to come your way. However, my personal experience has shown that if you haven't rigorously learned skills and gained knowledge, you are unlikely to be best placed to capitalise on opportunities that do come your way.

When I left school, I went straight to work in a butcher's shop, which was a fantastic experience. It may not be the industry I ended up making my career in, but being in the butcher's shop, working my way up to management level and learning from the people around me was something that taught me a lot about business and about the working environment.

Later, once I trained in the construction industry and was embarking on my career as a builder, these commercial principles were vital in my success and helped me to go on to set up my own business. The skills I had learned gave me an advantage and I was therefore able to make the most of my opportunities.

Later still, I could never have imagined that my career would take another turn into television. Of course, I recognise that I have had lucky breaks in my career, but when people say you make your own luck, I think there is definitely more than a grain of truth in that. People often ask me what my most life-changing moment has been, expecting me to say winning the first series of *Big Brother*. However, I always answer that my most life-changing moment was deciding to make the effort to learn the construction skills that I still use every day. That's why I was passionate about helping to set up a construction academy in the North West, helping other people to acquire skills and experience that will stay with them for their whole lives.

After all, an appearance on a reality TV show might have given me a degree of celebrity, but it is the skills that I learned as a builder that have kept me in demand as a presenter of DIY and building shows, and I have always continued to run my construction business. The truth is, you can never predict the way your life will turn out, but if you have learned a skill from experts in the field, you'll always be able to take advantage of the opportunities that come your way.

Craig Phillips

City & Guilds qualified bricklayer, owner of a successful construction business and television presenter of numerous construction and DIY shows

ABOUT THE AUTHORS

MIKE GASHE

CHAPTERS 3, 4 AND 6

I was brought up in a small village in the Snowdonia National Park, where I continue to live with my family. My plastering career started at the age of 16, attending Bangor Technical College under an apprentice scheme. During my time as a student at the college I won the Blue Circle Apprentice Award as well as the British Gypsum Young Apprentice Award.

Following my time at the college I went on to work as a self-employed plasterer for a number of years. For the past 20 years I have been a lecturer in the plastering section at Coleg Menai, now known as Grŵp Llandrillo Menai. During my time at the college many learners have been successful in a number of national awards and achievements.

I have recently been awarded the Master Plasterer qualification and I am also a freeman of The Worshipful Company of Plaisterers.

MICHAEL MANN

CHAPTERS 5, 7 AND 8

I was born in Birmingham where I still live with my wife and three children. I've been fortunate enough to have earned a living from plastering for the past 45 years since leaving school at 15. I still enjoy plastering as much now as ever. I believe it be a satisfying and rewarding job.

I came into teaching in my late forties and now teach at the same college where I was taught as an apprentice plasterer, where I gained my City & Guilds Advanced Craft Certificate in Plastering. I teach at all levels of plastering and find the role very fulfilling. My career aspiration is to pass on my work experience and knowledge to students who can then earn a good living, as well as to continue experiencing job satisfaction.

COLIN FEARN

CHAPTERS 1 AND 2

I was born, grew up and continue to live in Cornwall with my wife, three children and Staffordshire bull terrier.

As a qualified carpenter and joiner, I have worked for many years on sites and in several joinery shops.

I won the National Wood Award for joinery work and am also a Fellow of the Institute of Carpenters, holder of the Master Craft certificate and have a BA in Education and Training.

I was until recently a full-time lecturer at Cornwall College, teaching both full-time students and apprentices.

I now work full-time as a writer for construction qualifications, practical assessments, questions and teaching materials for UK and Caribbean qualifications.

In my spare time I enjoy walks, small antiques and 'keeping my hand in' with various building projects.

MARTIN BURDFIELD

SERIES TECHNICAL EDITOR

I come from a long line of builders and strongly believe that you will find a career in the construction industry a very rewarding one. Be proud of the work you produce; it will be there for others to admire for many years.

As an apprentice I enjoyed acquiring new knowledge and learning new skills. I achieved the C&G Silver Medal for the highest marks in the Advanced Craft Certificate and won the UK's first Gold Medal in Joinery at the World Skills Competition. My career took me on from foreman, to estimator and then works manager with a number of large joinery companies, where I had the privilege of working on some prestigious projects.

Concurrent with this I began working in education. I have now worked in further education for over 35 years enjoying watching learners' skills improve during their training. For 10 years I ran the Skillbuild Joinery competitions and was the UK Training Manager and Chief Expert Elect at the World Skills Competition, training the UK's second Gold Medallist in Joinery.

Working with City & Guilds in various roles over the past 25 years has been very rewarding.

I believe that if you work and study hard anything is possible.

HOW TO USE THIS TEXTBOOK

Welcome to your City & Guilds Level 2 Diploma in Plastering textbook. It is designed to guide you through your Level 2 qualification and be a useful reference for you throughout your career. Each chapter covers a unit from the 6708 Level 2 qualification, and covers everything you will need to understand in order to complete your written or online tests and to prepare for your practical assessments.

Please note that not all of the chapters will cover the learning outcomes in order. They have been put into a logical sequence as used within the industry and to cover all skills and techniques required.

Throughout this textbook you will see the following features:

Core

The term for the plaster that is sandwiched between both sides of the outer paper of the plasterboard

Useful words – Words in bold in the text are explained in the margin to help your understanding.

INDUSTRY TIP

Plasterboard and plaster manufacturers will only guarantee the joints against cracking if you use paper tape bedded in either plaster or jointing material.

Industry tips – Useful hints and tips related to working in the plastering industry.

ACTIVITY

Research two types of renders on the websites of manufacturers such as Sto, Weber and K Rend.

Activities – These are suggested activities for you to complete.

FUNCTIONAL SKILLS

Calculate the surface area of the two common types of plasterboard by multiplying their length by their width. Record your answer in metres squared.

Work on this activity can support FM2 (C2.7).

Functional Skills – These are activities that are tied to learning outcomes for the Functional Skills Maths, English and ICT qualifications.

Look at one of the ground floor rooms in 'Our House'. Measure the amount of paper tape to be used on the joints of plasterboard required for dry lining direct bond to the solid backgrounds.

'Our House' – These are activities that tie in directly with 'Our House' on SmartScreen to help you put the techniques in the book in context. Ask your tutor for your log-in details.

STEP 1 On the wall, measure from where the bottom of the board is going to sit up to the top and bottom of the box.

STEP 2 Transfer these measurements to each end of the plasterboard. Draw a line between these points to give you two parallel horizontal lines.

Step-by-steps – These steps illustrate techniques and procedures that you will need to learn in order to carry out plastering tasks.

Case Study: Jim

Jim recently went to assess a plastering job at the home of a friend's parents. When Jim got there they explained to him that a big crack had appeared over time in their living room ceiling. When Jim assessed the problem he noticed that the ceiling had not only cracked but also sagged down from the laths and that it was likely to collapse at any time. His immediate thought was to clear the room and make the place safe.

Case Studies – Each chapter ends with a case study of an operative who has faced a common problem in the industry. Some of these will reveal what the operative did and others provide you with the opportunity to solve a problem.

Drill and whisk

A powerful motorised drill with an attached whisk that mixes plaster with ease. It is a fast and efficient way of mixing lightweight plasters.

Trade dictionary – This feature lists key terms and tools that you will pick up from reading this book.

At the end of every chapter are some 'Test your knowledge' questions. These questions are designed to test your understanding of what you have learnt in that chapter. This can help with identifying further training or revision needed. You will find the answers at the end of the book.

INTRODUCTION

This book has been written to support students studying plastering at Level 2. By studying this book, you should receive a thorough grounding in the skills and knowledge you will need to complete your course and either progress to Level 3, or enter the workforce. You will learn about the wider construction industry and how it works, as well as the skills and techniques you will need in order to work as a plasterer. You will be able to work safely on site using the correct tools and equipment to apply plaster internally and externally, fix dry lining and plasterboards, lay sand and cement screeds and produce reverse moulds, and cast and fix fibrous plasterwork.

In addition to the features listed on the previous page, which are there to help you retain the information you will need to become a plasterer, this textbook includes a large trade dictionary. Use this for reference in class and in the workshop. Become familiar with the terms and techniques, and pay attention to the skills you need to master. If you put in the effort, you will be rewarded with a satisfying and successful career in plastering.

ACKNOWLEDGEMENTS

I would like to thank my dear wife Helen for her support in writing for this book. I dedicate my work to Matt, Tasha and Daisy, and not forgetting Floyd and Mrs Dusty.

Colin Fearn

Firstly I would like to thank City & Guilds and its Publishing team for giving me the opportunity to write three chapters for this book. Many thanks to Grŵp Llandrillo Menai for its continued support and to my colleagues in the plastering section, especially Wayne Taylor for his support and advice. Lastly thanks to NAPL members for their support and positive advice while writing the chapters. I would like to dedicate the chapters I wrote to all plastering learners who may benefit from my experience and knowledge of the plastering trade.

Mike Gashe

I would like to thank my wife Karen for the patience and encouragement whilst I contributed with others to produce this plastering book.

Michael Mann

To my gorgeous wife Clare, without whose constant support, understanding and patience I would not have been able to continue. To Matthew and Eleanor, for not being there on too many occasions: normal service will be resumed. Finally, my parents, to whom I will always be grateful.

Martin Burdfield

City & Guilds would like to sincerely thank the following:

For invaluable plastering expertise

Peter Gibson, Ian Pollitt, Jason Poole and Wayne Taylor.

For their help with photoshoots

Andrew Buckle (photographer), Mike Gashe and the staff and students at Grŵp Llandrillo Menai, Michael Mann and the staff and students at South and City College Birmingham.

For supplying pictures for the book cover

Andrew Buckle.

TRADE DICTIONARY

Industry term	Definition and regional variations
Additive Plasticiser	A substance that is added to plaster mixes to change their natural properties. For example, plasticiser is a liquid additive added to the plaster mix to make it workable. Other types of additives are: waterproofer, frostproofer/accelerator, salt inhibitors, SBR bonding slurry and mould remover.
Adhere/adhesion	How well a material bonds to its background.
Aggregate Granite	A 'filler', aggregate makes up the bulk of a mix. The size and type of aggregate are what determine the mix's strength. Used for external finishes such as pebbledash and rough cast.
Angle bead	Made from galvanised steel, stainless steel or plastic, these come in standard lengths of 2.4mm. Standard two coat angle beads are made to be used on two coat work. They are fixed with gypsum plaster dabs to provide a suitable thickness for float and set (two coat plasterwork).
Approved Code of Practice (ACoP) Managing health and safety in construction Construction (Design and Management) Regulations 2007	ACoP gives practical advice for those involved in the construction industry in relation to using machinery safely. ACoP has a special legal status and employers and employees are expected to work within its guidelines.

Industry term	Definition and regional variations
Architect 	A trained professional who designs a structure and represents the client who wants the structure built. They are responsible for the production of the working drawings. They supervise the construction of buildings or other large structures.
Architectural technician 	A draftsperson who works in an architectural practice. They usually prepare the location drawings for a building.
Beam cast 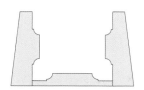	Cast beam cases are used to improve the appearance of concrete or steel beams that support upper floors but divide the lower-floor room, form part of a coffered ceiling and be part of a false ceiling to give the impression of a beamed ceiling. The design of a beam cast can vary, from plain sides (cheeks) and bottom (soffit), to panelled and moulded with inserts.
Bell cast  Timber rule method	Set above openings and the DPC line to form a drip and deflect rain water away from the wall surface. They can be made using pre-made beads, timber rules or roofing battens.
Bill of quantities 	Produced by the quantity surveyor and describes everything that is required for the job based on the drawings, specification and schedules. It is sent out to contractors and ensures that all the contractors are pricing for the job using the same information.
Binder  Cement	The binder is the active ingredient in a mix. It is what sets and holds the aggregate and other materials together. Gypsum, cement and lime are all types of binder.

Industry term	Definition and regional variations
Bolster with hand protection	There are different types of bolsters used for removing plaster, with various widths of blades. The safer and better ones will have a rubber hand-protector at the head. Bolsters with mushroom heads should not be used as these may chip off and cause injury when in use.
Bond	When the plaster sufficiently adheres to the background surface.
Bonding agents	A bonding adhesive applied with a brush, paddle, small shovel or roller to improve the bond between plaster or render and a background with a poor key.
Bound edge	The long edge of the plasterboard where the lining paper is wrapped up around the sides. *See also* Unbound edge.
Box rule	For ruling in screeds and checking the level.
British Standards Institute (BSI)	The authority that develops and publishes standards in the UK.
Broken in trowel	Describing a well-used or worn trowel, the corners have been rounded off and the edge is sharper. This makes applying finishing coats easier. You can buy 'ready to go' trowels with the edges rounded off to speed up the breaking in period.

Industry term	Definition and regional variations
Bucket 	Buckets have many uses for plastering, including transporting materials and clean water, and for mixing and cleaning. *Regional variation: tub*
Bucket trowel 	When mixing is in progress, this tool can be used to clean the rim of the mixing bucket, moving dry unmixed plaster back to the centre of the bucket with its wide, flat edge.
Building regulations	A series of documents that set out legal requirements for the standards of building work.
Busk 	Small rectangular tool used for making good fine jointing and minor defects. These can be different shapes, used depending on the shape and detail of the mould.
Casting 	Producing fibrous plasterwork by mixing fine casting plaster and water, then applying the mixed material over or into reverse moulds, to produce a positive mould. Casting is a process that can be completed with either a 'one gauge' or 'two gauge' mix, depending on the size of the cast to be produced.
Casting brush 	Used to brush plaster into enrichments in reverse moulding and then to brush and splash plaster when casting. *Regional variation: splash brush*
Ceiling rose 	A decorative, circular moulding attached to the ceiling, through which the electrical wires for a light pass. They can be cast from a flexible mould.

Industry term	Definition and regional variations
Cement 	Cement is used to bind and provide strength in the plastering mix. It is made from limestone and clay, and is used because of its faster setting time compared with lime mixes. Cement mixed with sand and water will begin to set after 45 minutes and will normally be completely set by the next day.
Cement-based plaster 	A more modern mix than lime-based, cement-based plaster is made up of 75% limestone and 25% clay, and contains cement as a binder.
Chalk line 	Snapped on floors and ceilings to form guidelines when installing wall boards.
Cherry picker 	Access equipment used in commercial buildings as the working height increases.
Class A plaster 	A type of plaster that sets quickly (approximately 20 minutes) and does not contain any retarder, unlike multi-finish plaster, which has a retarder added to allow more working time.
Claw hammer 	This hammer is used when preparing timber backgrounds that have been previously plastered. Its main function is to remove old nails that might be left in the timber surface, or to remove old lath work or damaged plasterboard.

Industry term	Definition and regional variations
Collated screws 	A quick way of fixing plasterboard to timber backgrounds, saving time and labour by speeding up the installation process. Collated screws are fixed using a mechanical drywall auto-feeder that is powered by 110V electricity or a battery. These screws vary in length from 25 to 50mm.
Comb scratcher 	Used to form a key on scratch coats. A comb scratcher is generally used on cement-based plasters. It is similar to a scarifier, but has fewer teeth.
Composite background 	A wall made up of two or more materials, eg brick- and blockwork.
Consolidate 	To close in the surface of a floating coat, render or floor screed with a float, which can make the surface flat, dense and compact.
Coping saw 	Used to shape the timber of the outline of a running mould.
Cordless drill 	Used for driving in and extracting drywall screws when fixing sheet materials such as plasterboard and EML.

Industry term	Definition and regional variations
Corner paper tape 	Used when taping joints in plasterboard. Corner paper tape is used on the external angles. It contains two corrosion-resistant metal strips along its length for strength and reinforcement, which means that this type of tape needs to be cut with a pair of tin snips.
Crow bar 	This is a long bar that can be used to lever materials that are wedged in place. It can also be used to remove stubborn nails and screws.
Curing 	In the context of screeds, curing means keeping the cement moist to allow the screed to fully harden. This is different from drying. Curing is an essential part of floor screeding as it allows the cement to reach full strength; the cement shouldn't be allowed to dry too quickly. Traditional damp hessian was used to help prevent moisture loss. Polythene sheeting can be used as well as additives to promote curing.
Dabs 	Drywall adhesive plaster applied to the background in dabs of about 75mm wide and 250mm in length. Drywall adhesive is compatible with most backgrounds.
Damp proof course (DPC) 	A layer or strip of watertight material placed in a joint of a wall to prevent the passage of water. Fixed at a minimum of 150mm above finished ground level. Two types of DPC are rigid and flexible.
Darby 	This tool has many uses. One is to rule and flatten scratch coat surfaces. Another is to form the angles of returns and reveals on uneven surfaces.

Industry term	Definition and regional variations
Data sheet	Data sheets are provided with a product by its manufacturer, and give you the necessary information on how to use the product. Data sheets also provide important health and safety information, such as correct manual handling when moving and transporting the product, any hazards associated with that product, and any specific first-aid issues.
Datum point	A fixed point or height from which to take reference levels. It may be a permanent Ordnance bench mark (OBM) or temporary bench mark (TBM). The datum point is used to transfer levels across a building site. It represents the finished floor level (FFL) on a dwelling.
Dead man prop	A useful piece of equipment when working on your own. It is a telescopic pole with pads on each end; the pole is adjusted to hold an item above your head just like an extra pair of hands.
Delaminate	To divide or become divided into layers. It indicates a failure of composite materials.
Devil float	A devil float is a plastic float with nails hammered through the top of one end so they stick through the face by 1mm. It is used to provide a key for a setting coat of plaster.
Drill and whisk	A powerful motorised drill with an attached whisk that mixes plaster with ease. It is a fast and efficient way of mixing lightweight plasters.
Drum mixer	A mechanical mixer for mixing materials. Sand and cement mixes are best mixed with a mechanical drum mixer. This type of mixing is carried out outdoors, as it can be noisy and the materials used will cause high dust levels. *Regional variation: Belle mixer*

Industry term	Definition and regional variations
Dry lining 	Lining masonry walls with plasterboards by directly bonding them with adhesive, known as 'dot and dab'. The term 'dry lining' comes from the plasterboards being a dry material as opposed to wet plaster.
Dry silo 	On most medium to large construction sites, dry silos are used to store pre-mixed materials such as mortar, render and floor screed materials. They are connected to the mains water supply, which is regulated to add the right amount of water to mix the materials to the correct consistency. The materials can then be drawn off as needed.
Drying time	The time that needs to pass between applying a plaster coat or coats and being able to decorate.
Drywall driver 	For driving in and extracting drywall screws. They come with various voltages including 110V, but 14.4V or 18V are probably the most practical. These drivers can either be battery-powered, so cordless, or powered by an electrical power cord.
Drywall knife 	A knife used when tape and jointing plasterboard. These knives are sometimes preferred instead of a hawk and trowel because their flexible aluminium blade is flat and good for finishing jointing materials but also sharp for cutting paper tape.

Industry term	Definition and regional variations
Dubbing out 	Filling out between uneven surfaces such as strong joints, building up the uneven surface until it is smooth.
Expanded metal lathing (EML) 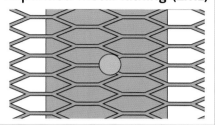	Sheet material in the form of diamond-shaped mesh that is used to reinforce a surface. This material can be fixed with screws and plugs, galvanised nails or it can be bedded into the plaster or render material.
Expansion beads 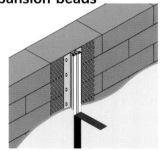	Expansion beads are used on walls that have expansion joints that allow slight movement in both sides of the wall to prevent cracking.
External angle 	A reveal or return of a wall forming a right angle and a corner. The very tip of an external angle is called an arris. *See also* Internal angle.
External corner towel 	For finishing external angles.
External rendering 	External rendering is a top coat finish that everyone can see, transforming wall surfaces using traditional or modern materials to the architect's, client's and environmental specifications. External rendering provides a desirable finish that will enhance the appearance of a building, and provides a protective surface, preventing passage of moisture that can penetrate the external wall and enter the building.

Industry term	Definition and regional variations
External wall insulation (EWI) 	External wall insulation is fixed to solid backgrounds mechanically, improving the insulation of a building.
Fall 	A sloping floor, which screeds can be laid to. This type of floor screed can be found in food preparation areas where washing down is required, in kennels and in walk-in wet shower rooms.
Fat	The residue on a trowel created from trowelling up. This is dead plaster that should be discarded. If used to fill holes and misses it will not set properly – it will shrink and become soft and dusty.
Feather edge 	A type of straight edge. Used for providing a firm and straight guide against which to cut. *See also* Straight edge.
Files 	A range of files is required to form both the timber and the zinc of a running mould. Files come in a variety of styles and sizes. A flat and a half round fine metal file are used for shaping the zinc or aluminium, and similar wood rasps for forming the timber.
Fine-toothed saw 	Used to cut plaster and timber for moulding.
Finishing blade 	A specifically designed tool for ruling undercoats and finishing setting plaster surfaces. They speed up some aspects of plastering and help achieve a consistently flat and smooth finish.

Industry term	Definition and regional variations
Firstings and seconds 	Two gauges of plaster used to cast moulds. The 'firstings' is the first application of plaster. Its purpose is to prevent reinforcing materials from penetrating and showing through the face of the cast. The 'seconds' is the second mix which will have hessian and laths incorporated during the casting process. This makes the cast stronger, meaning you can use less plaster and therefore the cast is lighter.
Fixing centres	The distance between fixings when installing plasterboard.
Flash set	Where gypsum plaster sets far more quickly than expected. Can be caused by using dirty or contaminated water, tools and equipment, or out-of-date or poorly stored plaster.
Flat brush 	For applying clean water when trowelling up.
Flat workbenches 	Flat workbenches are essential for making moulding work. Modern benches are made from a sturdy steel frame and a thick plywood top that needs to be sealed with shellac. Traditional benches were built with brick or blocks and contained a solid plaster top bench that was costly and time consuming to construct. *Regional variation: plasterer's bench*
Float 	Used to consolidate screed, as well as to provide a finish. These tools are generally made from polyurethane.
Floor laying trowel 	These are used to trowel the floor screed smooth. They differ from a plastering trowel as they are made from thicker steel and are at least 450mm long. Some have a pointed end to allow the plasterer to trowel into the corner of a room. *Regional variation: screeding trowel*
Flooring rule 	Used to compact sand and cement down to the screeds. This expels trapped air and compresses the sand and cement, making the screed more solid and helping avoid weak spots.

Industry term	Definition and regional variations
Floor scraper	A floor scraper is often used with a sweeping brush for cleaning the work area during and after working.
Foot lifter	Used to lift the plasterboard up to the ceiling line when fixing plasterboard to walls.
Foundation	Used to spread the load of a building to the sub-soil.
French chalk	This chalk is a fine powder, similar to talcum powder. It is used in producing reverse moulds, when the reverse is greased to find any misses.
Galvanised nail	When a protective zinc coating has been applied to steel nails to prevent corrosion or rusting which could cause unsightly staining on the finished plasterboard or cause the fixing to fail.
Gauging materials	The technical term for measuring materials, in particular the materials used in a plaster mix.
Gauging trowel	When mixing is in progress, this tool can be used to clean the rim of the mixing bucket, moving dry unmixed plaster back to the centre of the bucket. It is also used for cleaning and removing excess material off the straight edge and to clean plaster droppings by scraping the floor. *Regional variation: bullnose trowel*

Industry term	Definition and regional variations
Gaul	A hollow or miss on the surface of the finished plaster. It needs to be filled with fresh plaster for a neat finish.
Glue size	A traditional retarder used within the ornate plasterwork industry, glue size plaster retarder is made from animal skins and hooves. When added to gauging water it slows down the set of the plaster, allowing you more working time.
Green	Where plaster has set but not fully hardened. If you were to press a thumb into it you would not leave a dent, but if you were to drag your nail across it you would leave a scratch.
Hard hand brush	This type of brush is used for cleaning tools and equipment. It has harder bristles than a standard brush and will not wear down as quickly.
Hawk	Used to hold and transfer a workable amount of plaster from the spot board to the wall. The hawk is used in conjunction with the trowel to manipulate and apply the plaster directly onto the background surface. Hawks were traditionally made from timber, but modern ones are made from polyurethane or aluminium. *Regional variation: hand board*
Health and Safety Executive (HSE)	The national independent watchdog for work-related health, safety and illness. It works to reduce work-related death and serious injury in workplaces throughout Great Britain.
Heel	The back of a laying on trowel's blade. *See also* Toe.
Hemihydrate	Where a substance's natural water content has been reduced by 50–75%.
Hop-up	Purpose-made access equipment made of aluminium or timber that allows you to work up to standard ceiling heights. Its design allows you to step onto a platform from the ground without stretching.

Industry term	Definition and regional variations
Housekeeping 	Making sure that your work area is kept safe and tidy.
Independent scaffold 	This is a good type of scaffold to use when rendering outside surfaces because it is erected away from the wall. It is a sufficiently wide and solid working platform, allowing plenty of room to carry out your work.
Industrial Standards	Minimum standards of quality of completed work universally adopted within the industry.
Internal angle 	A corner that you can put things in. *See also* External angle.
Internal angle trowel 	For finishing internal angles. *Regional variation: corner trowel, twitcher*
Joint rule 	The joint rule has various uses in moulding work. Joint rules are flat blades and can be used for forming mitre joints. Another use is to form and align fibrous casts during fixing. Old joint rules can be used to scrape clean benches during and after the casting process, removing plaster droppings and splashes.
Joist centres	The distance from the centre of one joist to the centre of the next.
Kicking out	Where plaster forms a thicker ridge along the bottom of a wall. This makes it difficult for skirting boards to be fitted as they cannot sit flush to the wall.

Industry term	Definition and regional variations
Kinetic lifting	A method of lifting that ensures the risk of injury is reduced.
Laitance	A layer of weak material that comes to the top of concrete as it sets.
Large bristled brush	A large bristled brush has many uses, such as cleaning tools and equipment, or applying water or slurries to backgrounds. *Regional variation: hand brush*
Lath hammer	A traditional tool used by plasterers, before plasterboard was widely used, to cut wooden laths when lathing. Also used for hacking off old sand–lime plaster from walls and for hammering in plasterboard nails. *Regional variation: drywall hammer*
Laser level	This is a popular tool used when setting out guidelines. It is an accurate method of producing horizontal and vertical guides that can be used to work from.
Lime  Hydrated lime	Lime has many uses in plastering mixes. It is made by crushing limestone and heating it in a kiln. Lime comes in bags and should be stored on a pallet in dry conditions. There are two types used in plastering mixes: hydrated lime and hydraulic lime.

Industry term	Definition and regional variations
Lime-based plaster 	Traditional undercoat mixes used for applying pricking up, scratch and floating coats were referred to as 'lime mortar', a mix made of hydraulic lime putty as the binder, coarse sand as the aggregate and the addition of horse hair for reinforcement. There are two types of lime-based plaster mixes: non-hydraulic lime and hydraulic lime.
Lump hammer 	Lump hammers are made with timber, steel or fibreglass shafts (handles) that are inserted into a rectangular head with a flat face made from cast iron. Its purpose, like any hammer, is to cause impact, knocking against the head of the bolster to remove old plaster from backgrounds. *Regional variation: club hammer*
Manufacturers' instructions 	Manufacturers' instructions say what a product may be used for, how it is to be installed and what conditions it can be exposed to.
Materials schedule	This document lists the correct amount of different materials and components that are required to complete a build. For example, when applying plaster to interiors, the materials schedule will not only list the different types of undercoat and finishing plaster but also the number of different beads to be used to form returns and stops.
Mechanical breaker 	A breaker is a heavy-duty power tool generally used on hard, stubborn areas of plaster that are difficult to remove by hand using just a hammer and bolster. Mechanical breakers are very heavy and noisy when in use.
Mechanical key 	How rough or smooth a background surface is. Creating a rough surface, such as when using a comb scratcher, on a background helps the plaster adhere to it.
Method statement	A description of the intended method of carrying out a task, often linked to a risk assessment.

Industry term	Definition and regional variations
Mitre box 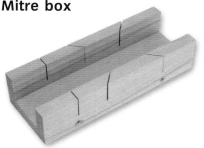	In fibrous plasterwork, it is used to cut mitres.
Mixing stand 	This is an essential piece of equipment to keep a mixing tool off the ground, preventing it from picking up dirt and contaminating the mix. This will also prevent trailing leads which can cause trip hazards.
Mortar (traditional) 	Coarse sand, hydraulic lime and horse or goat hair are the materials used for making traditional mortar. It is best mixed in a portable or small pan mixer.
Muffle 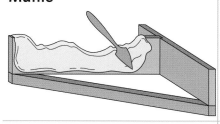	A false profile which can be built up from plaster, or a zinc plate which can be fixed temporarily to the stock profile to speed up the running process when running a mould. It should extend the original profile by approximately 5mm and can be made up from casting plaster or any sheet material such as zinc, plywood or hardboard.
Nodules 	Small balls of plaster left behind on the surface after devil floating. They are created from the plaster dragged out of the grooves by the nails of the devil float when forming the key. *Regional variation: snots*
Noggin	Timber fixed between joists or studs to support the edge and end of the plasterboard.

Industry term	Definition and regional variations
Ordinary Portland Cement (OPC) 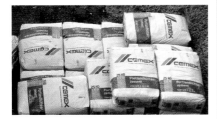	A type of cement used in mixes. It is used with PVA to become a slurry and strong bonding agent for cement-based plasters. It is also a binder when used in screeds. It has an initial setting time of no less than 45 minutes and a final set of no more than 10 hours.
Pad saw 	A saw 6–8 inches long, used for cutting out holes in plasterboards for electrical sockets and pipework, etc. Also used when making complex cuts.
Pan mixer 	Equipment used to mix materials on site. The pan mixer has a large pan with two steel wheels that rotate around a central column in the pan. The materials are placed in the pan and the rotary action of the wheel forces the materials together. When the mix is ready, a gate in the base of the pan is opened and the mix is pushed through the gate.
Paper tape 	Used when taping joints in plasterboard. This tape comes in roll form and has perforated holes and a centre crease in its design that helps align the tape to straight joints and internal angles.
Partition 	Walls used to separate and divide the overall space within a building into rooms.
Perimeter 2.2m 4.2m	The distance around an object or room.

Industry term	Definition and regional variations
Pein hammer 	A small lightweight hammer useful for securing the zinc profile onto the timber stock with nails when creating running moulds. *Regional variation: pin hammer*
Performance  Fireline	In a plasterboard context, this refers to plasterboards that have an extra characteristic compared with standard plasterboard, such as enhanced sound insulation, fire resistance, impact resistance or a combination of these. Their use will improve aspects of the performance of a room/building.
Perlite 	A lightweight aggregate used in pre-mixed plastering materials. It is a naturally occurring mineral that is mined, then crushed and heated.
Personal protective equipment (PPE) 	This is defined in the Personal Protective Equipment (PPE) at Work Regulations 1992 as 'all equipment (including clothing affording protection against the weather) which is intended to be worn or held by a person at work and which protects against one or more risks to a person's health or safety.' For example, safety helmets, gloves, eye protection, high-visibility clothing, safety footwear and safety harnesses.
Plain face 	An external render finish that has a flat, smooth, sandy look. This type of finish consists of several layers applied onto a solid background surface. It can be described as either two or three coat plastering/rendering work, depending on the unevenness of the background.

Industry term	Definition and regional variations
Plasterer's grease 	Plasterer's grease is used as a release agent to help prevent plaster sticking to the workbench or the plaster cast sticking to the reverse mould. It is made from a mix of beef dripping and paraffin at a ratio of approximately 50/50.
Plastering trowel 	The majority of plastering trowels are made from stainless steel and come in various sizes, 'pre-worn', and with different handle materials. There are various types and makes of trowels used in our industry today.
Plasticiser 	An additive used to improve the workability of a sand/cement mix.
Plated drywall screw 	A screw that has a rust-resistant zinc coating or black phosphate coating. They are sharp pointed and can be used to fix plasterboard to timber or steel channels.
Platform scaffold 	Access equipment suitable when applying plaster to ceilings. It gives you a continuous platform allowing you to apply and finish the setting plaster at regular intervals as the plaster sets without causing strain.
Plunger 	A traditional mixing tool used to mix plaster when added to water. During and after the mixing process it should be kept off the floor to prevent any bits of debris from sticking to the bottom of the tool, which could contaminate the next mix. *Regional variation: plasterer's mixing wheel*
Polymer	Strong glue-like substance used for improving adhesion of render surfaces.

Industry term	Definition and regional variations
Pre-cast plasterwork	Moulds that have been cast in a workshop before fixing.
Pre-mixed plaster	Plaster materials that have been mixed in a processing plant and are sold bagged, needing only clean water added for mixing. Modern pre-mixed plasters are a mixture of gypsum and lightweight aggregates (vermiculite and perlite).
Price work	Where the amount you are paid depends on the amount of work you complete.
Pricing for work	Calculating and costing for plastering work.
Primer	Used when taping joints in plasterboard. Applied after the joints and spots have dried out thoroughly, and the surface has been sanded. It seals the porous surface of the dry jointing material before the material receives decoration. *Regional variation: sealer*
Profile Cavetto	The shape and pattern of a mould outline. The desired profile is normally outlined in the working drawing, unless you are matching an existing pattern from an original. Examples are cavetto, ovolo, scotia, etc.
Prohibition notice	Issued by an HSE or local authority inspector when there is an immediate risk of personal injury. Receiving one means you are breaking health and safety regulations.
PVA	PVA is the abbreviation for polyvinyl acetate, a water-based glue that is used for preparing background surfaces by improving adhesion.
Ratio	The proportion of materials that are mixed together, eg six parts sand to one part cement.

Industry term	Definition and regional variations
Release agent	A substance applied to the surface of a mould to ease its removal after the plaster has set.
Render/bell beads	These are fixed to bridge the damp proof course (DPC), window and door heads to act as a drip. They are also used to break down large areas of render into more manageable working areas.
Retarder	A chemical additive that slows down the setting time of gypsum plasters, casting plaster and cement.
Reverse mould Plaster reverse mould	A mould that is the 'back to front' version of the shape or pattern that you want to produce. There are four processes that can be used for making reverse moulds: plaster, rubber and fibreglass reverse moulds, and positive moulds.
Risk assessment	An assessment of the hazards and risks associated with an activity and the reduction and monitoring of them.
RL247 Wax	This type of wax is a brush-on liquid wax release agent, which is also available in an aerosol canister.
Rotary kiln	A large kiln that is set at an angle. The heat source is at the bottom of the kiln so it is cooler towards the top. As the whole kiln rotates, the limestone and clay mixture inside travels through it.

Industry term	Definition and regional variations
Rubber bowls 	Plaster for fibrous plastering is generally mixed by hand in flexible rubber bowls that are easy to clean after use. *Regional variation: mixing bowl*
Sand 	Sand is an aggregate used to bulk a plastering mix. Well-graded sand will have small, medium and large grains that are angular in shape. There are several types of sand: dredged, pit and coarse/crushed aggregate.
SBR bonding slurry 	This type of slurry is applied to a background and while it is still tacky a scratch coat mix is applied over the top of it to ensure a good bond between the background and the applied material. SBR is the abbreviation for styrene-butadiene rubber. It is a strong bonding agent that is mixed with 1 part SBR to 2 parts cement to make a bonding slurry.
Scabbling 	The removal of the surface finish by mechanical means, producing a suitable key.
Scale	The ratio of the size on a drawing to the size of the real thing that it represents. It is impossible to fit a full-sized drawing of a building onto a sheet of paper, so it is necessary to scale the size of the building to enable it to fit. Scale rules are used to draw scaled-down buildings on paper.
Scarifier 	Like a comb scratcher, this is used to form a key on scratch coats. A scarifier is preferred on lightweight plaster surfaces. It has more teeth than a comb scratcher.
Screed rail 	To help keep the floor flat, to form a chequerboard framework or to use when forming falls.

Industry term	Definition and regional variations
Scrim 	Scrim is an open-weave material that comes in rolls from 50 to 100mm wide and can be stuck over all joints in plasterboard walls and ceilings. It can even be stuck over joints where they meet other walls, such as around the perimeter of a ceiling. The types shown here are hessian and self-adhesive.
Scrim cloth 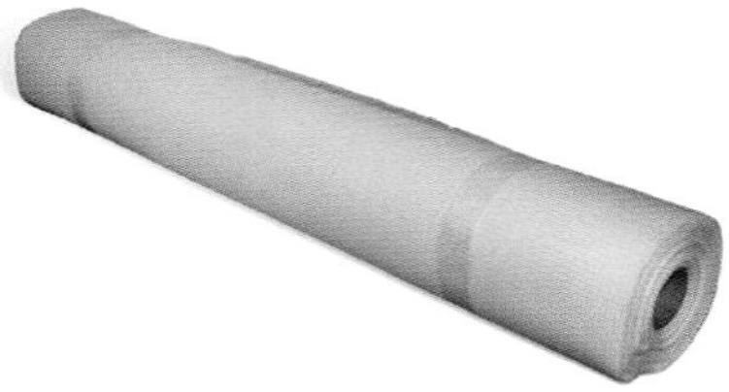	Used with render to reinforce it and bed it into the background surface it is being applied to.
Scrimming up 	Applying scrim to reinforce the joints when fixing plasterboards.
Scutch hammer 	This hammer has sharp teeth and can be used for removing plaster. It leaves a rough surface on backgrounds, so can also be used to provide a mechanical key when preparing to install fibrous plasterwork. *Regional variation: scutching hammer*
Services 	Those provided by utility companies, eg gas, electricity and water.
Setting time	The time between mixing cement or gypsum plaster with water and the mixture starting to harden.
Shank 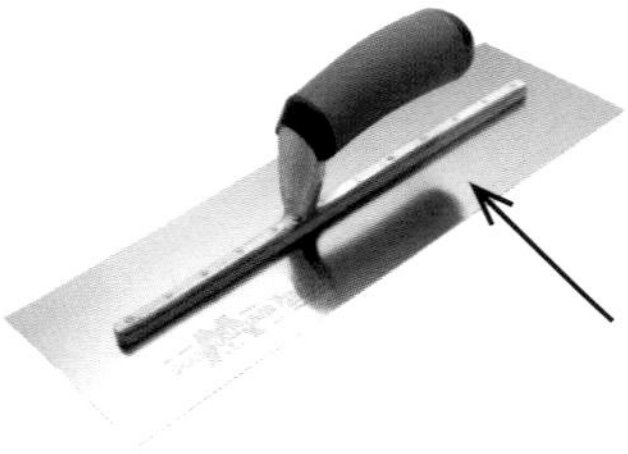	The part of a trowel that spreads out from the handle along the back of the flat face, attaching them together.

Industry term	Definition and regional variations
Sharp screeding sand 	Coarser than plastering sand, sharp screeding sand has the strength and durability required for a floor screed. The sand works by providing filler to the mix.
Shellac 	Liquid material applied with a brush to seal porous surfaces and form a protective skin in fibrous plasterwork.
Shellac brush 	Any good quality paint brush can be used to apply shellac. Any size can be used but 50mm is perhaps the most common.
Silt	Fine grains of sand. Too much silt in a plastering mix will prevent the cement from binding with the sand and cause the mix to be weak.
Slip sheet 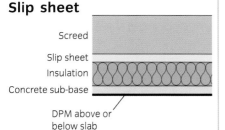	A slip sheet is laid between insulation and a floor screed, made from 1200 gauge polythene sheet. It should be lapped 150mm up the sides of the walls to form a vapour control.
Slurry 	A thin, sloppy cement applied to backgrounds in order to bond plaster to its surface.
Small brushes 	Used to clean detail work and sometimes used to apply wet plaster into the recess and joins of moulds where a small tool cannot reach.

Industry term	Definition and regional variations
Small tools leaf and square 	Used for minor moulding detail work. Also used for filling in joints in fibrous work.
Spatula 	To aid flattening and finishing of one coat plaster.
Speed taping tools 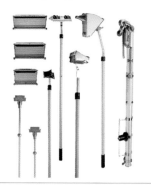	Tools used in the speed tape and box system, which is a quick method for applying jointing compound and paper tape at the same time when jointing plasterboard.
Spirit level 	Used to ensure a level surface, eg when checking a wall is plumb.
Spot board and stand 	These are used to hold a plaster mix. A good spot board should be made from 18mm thick plywood that will not warp or bend. The spot board stand is made from steel and will normally have four legs to take the weight of the spot board at each corner when loaded with the mix. Spot board stands are designed to be erected and dismantled with ease, so they take up less space when not in use. They should be set out as close as possible to the wall in order to reduce the need to transfer the material over long distances.
Spray finish plastering 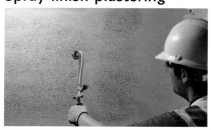	Developed by plastering manufacturers British Gypsum and Knauf, spray finish plasters can be sprayed directly onto the background, saving time and labour by improving efficiency.

Industry term	Definition and regional variations
Square	Used to square off frames and walls and for setting the screeds at the datum level.
Square edge plasterboard	Plasterboard that has its edges cut at a 90° angle from its face. *See also* Tapered edge plasterboard.
Staggered	Refers to the joint arrangement of plasterboards when they are fixed in place to timber or steel channel backgrounds – the vertical edges should not form a straight line.
Staple gun	Used for fixing beads to plasterboard.
Stock rotation	Making sure that older materials (such as bags of plaster) are at the front and/or top of the stack and so are used first, before their use-by date.
Stop beads	Stop beads are used when the plasterwork needs to stop at a different surface. This could be when it goes up to timber or decorative masonry. Stop beads can be fixed with galvanised nails or bedded into position, depending on how true the background is.
Straight edge	Made from aluminium, this tool has many uses. Its main use will be to rule plaster surfaces and check for straightness. Another use is to form angles or the edges of returns and reveals before fitting them with standard angle beads. *See also* Feather edge.
Strike off	The built-up plaster area on the back of a cast which will come into contact with the background surface when fitted in place.

Industry term	Definition and regional variations
Stud walling/studwork 	A partition wall constructed from lengths of timber that make a frame to fix sheet materials to.
Sub-contractor	A tradesperson that is not directly employed by a company but is employed for short periods to complete some aspects of the work. They are paid by the work completed at a set price
Substrate	A stable background onto which other materials can be applied.
Suction 	The rate at which a background absorbs moisture. No suction or low suction indicates that the background is hard or dense. High-suction backgrounds will absorb moisture from a plaster mix and may cause it to dry too quickly when applied.
Surform 	Used for smoothing off cut edges or trimming down boards that are slightly too long. Curved cuts can also be formed using this tool. *Regional variations: rasp, plasterboard plane*
Sweeping brush 	*See* Floor scraper.
Symbols Concrete	Used on drawings to indicate different types of building materials.
Tape measure 	For measuring accurately, particularly when cutting plasterboard. To prevent confusion and mistakes, use tape measures with metric-only scales.

Industry term	Definition and regional variations
Tapered edge plasterboard	Plasterboard that has its edges cut at a slant. *See also* Square edge plasterboard.
Tender	To submit a cost or price for work in an attempt to win the contract to do the work.
Tenon saw	A fine-toothed saw useful for cutting rebates into timber when creating running moulds.
Three coat work (external)	When plastering exteriors, this is applying three distinct layers of render dubbing out/pricking up, scratch and finish render surface.
Three coat work (internal)	Also known as 'scratch, float and set', in internal plastering this is three distinct layers of plaster. The first coat – the render or scratch – evens out an uneven background. The second coat – the float – provides a true flat surface for the third coat, which is called the set or finish.
Timber rule	A straight plane timber used as a guide to form the edge of a return. Before the introduction of aluminium feather edges, they were also used as straight edges.
Tin snips	Used to cut EML and beading, and to cut zinc/aluminium templates when constructing a running mould.
Toe	The front of a laying on trowel's blade. *See also* Heel.

Industry term	Definition and regional variations
Tool bag 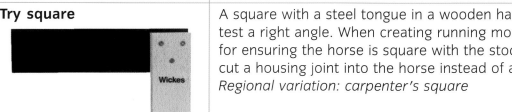	A plasterer's tool bag contains many items that will need to be maintained and cleaned after use. It can be used to store tools safely and securely, helping to keep them damage free and prolonging their life. *Regional variations: tool kit, holdall*
Trestle staging	This is a good scaffold for low level buildings and can be erected and dismantled with ease. A firm, flat base is always required for erecting trestles. Some sites will not allow trestles to be used; you should always check what type of access equipment can be used on the site where you will be working.
Trowelling up	The final procedure in the finishing process when a smooth texture is achieved.
Try square	A square with a steel tongue in a wooden handle, used to mark or test a right angle. When creating running moulds, this tool is useful for ensuring the horse is square with the stock, and if you decide to cut a housing joint into the horse instead of a butt joint. *Regional variation: carpenter's square*
Unbound edge	The short edge of a plasterboard sheet where the core is visible. *See also* Bound edge.
Undercut moulding members	A model or mould with overhang patterns. They can be difficult to remove when cast unless the reverse mould is made from flexible material.

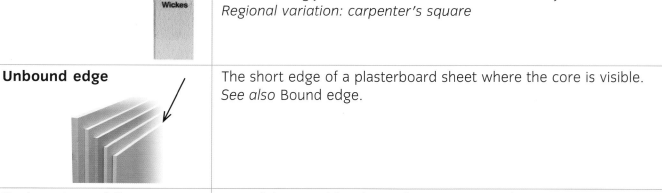

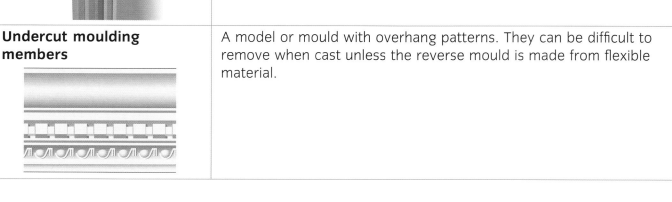

Industry term	Definition and regional variations
Utility knife	Used for cutting boards. Utility knifes can have fixed blades but, for safety reasons, ones with retractable blades are better. *Regional variations: board knife, craft knife*
Vermiculite	Like perlite, vermiculite is a naturally occurring mineral that is mined, then crushed and heated. It is a lightweight aggregate added to pre-mixed lightweight plaster to improve its bonding capabilities.
Wall plates	Timber that runs along the top of a wall, to which the roof is fixed. When timber wall plates need to be plastered, using EML is a good way of reinforcing the timber and providing a key.
Waste mould	Waste moulds are used to produce a one-off moulding from a clay model where the sculptor wishes to retain exclusiveness.
Water level	For setting a datum line, particularly in floor screeding.
Wet and dry abrasive paper	Can be used to smooth out high spots on zinc or aluminium profiles when constructing a running mould. *Regional variation: emery paper*

Industry term	Definition and regional variations
Wet screed 	A band of undercoat plaster screed being used as a floating guide while it is still wet.
Wire brush	This is a good tool for cleaning the face of backgrounds that still contain old dry plaster or flaking paint.
Wire brush attachment	This can be fitted to a power drill to remove paint and expose the background surface.
Wood saw	A sharp wood saw is used to cut the timber or plywood horse, stock and brace to size in a running mould.
Wooden laths	Thin strips of wood 1.5m long, 30mm wide and 6mm thick that were traditionally fixed to studwork and ceilings. They were used before the widespread use of plasterboards and EML to form a background for plasterwork.
Work schedule	A series of events where the order of activities and the amount of time involved has been planned out. This is usually shown in the form of a bar or Gantt chart. *Regional variation: programme of work, labour schedule*

Chapter 1
Unit 201: Health, safety and welfare in construction

A career in the building industry can be a very rewarding one, both personally and financially. However, building sites and workshops are potentially very dangerous places; there are many potential hazards in the construction industry. Many construction operatives (workers) are injured each year, some fatally. Regulations have been brought in over the years to reduce accidents and improve working conditions.

By reading this chapter you will know about:

1 The health and safety regulations, roles and responsibilities.
2 Accident and emergency reporting procedures and documentation.
3 Identifying hazards in the workplace.
4 Health and welfare in the workplace.
5 Handling materials and equipment safely.
6 Access equipment and working at heights.
7 Working with electrical equipment in the workplace.
8 Using personal protective equipment (PPE).
9 The cause of fire and fire emergency procedures.

HEALTH AND SAFETY LEGISLATION

According to the Health and Safety Executive (HSE) figures, in 2011/12:

- Forty-nine construction operatives were fatally injured. Twenty-three of these operatives were self-employed. This compares with an average of 59 fatalities over the previous five years, of which an average of 19 fatally injured construction operatives were self-employed.

- The rate of fatal injury per 100,000 construction operatives was 2.3, compared with a five-year average of 2.5.

- Construction industry operatives were involved in 28% of fatal injuries across all industry sectors and it accounts for the greatest number of fatal injuries in any industry sector.

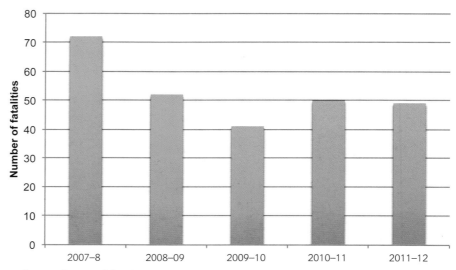

Number and rate of fatal injuries to workers in construction (RIDDOR)

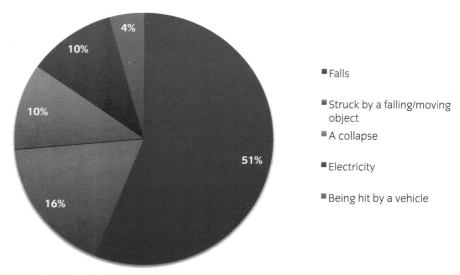

Proportion of fatalities in 2011/12 in construction

Health and safety legislation and great efforts made by the industry have made workplaces much safer in recent years. It is the responsibility of everyone involved in the building industry to continue to make it safer. Statistics are not just meaningless numbers — they represent injuries to real people. Many people believe that an accident will never happen to them, but it can. Accidents can:

- have a devastating effect on lives and families

- cost a lot financially in injury claims

- result in prosecution

- lead to job loss if an employee broke their company's safety policy.

Employers have an additional duty to ensure operatives have access to welfare facilities, eg drinking water, first aid and toilets, which will be discussed later in this chapter.

If everyone who works in the building industry pays close attention to health, safety and welfare, all operatives — including you — have every chance of enjoying a long, injury-free career.

UK HEALTH AND SAFETY REGULATIONS, ROLES AND RESPONSIBILITIES

In the UK there are many laws (legislation) that have been put into place to make sure that those working on construction sites, and members of the public, are kept healthy and safe. If these laws and regulations are not obeyed then prosecutions can take place. Worse still, there is a greater risk of injury and damage to your health and the health of those around you.

The principal legislation which relates to health, safety and welfare in construction is:

- Health and Safety at Work Act (HASAWA) 1974

- Control of Substances Hazardous to Health (COSHH) Regulations 2002

- Reporting of Injuries, Diseases and Dangerous Occurrences Regulations (RIDDOR) 2013

- Construction, Design and Management (CDM) Regulations 2007

- Provision and Use of Work Equipment Regulations (PUWER) 1998

- Manual Handling Operations Regulations 1992

- Personal Protective Equipment (PPE) at Work Regulations 1992

FUNCTIONAL SKILLS

Using the HSE website, find the most recent health and safety statistics. Of the total number of accidents that resulted in three or more days off work, what proportion (as a percentage) are those who were killed during that year? Work on this activity can support FM L2.3.1 and C2.4.

Standard construction safety equipment

- Work at Height Regulations 2005 (as amended)
- Lifting Operations and Lifting Equipment Regulations (LOLER) 1998
- Control of Noise at Work Regulations 2005
- Control of Vibration at Work Regulations 2005.

HEALTH AND SAFETY AT WORK ACT (HASAWA) 1974

The Health and Safety at Work Act (HASAWA) 1974 applies to all workplaces. Everyone who works on a building site or in a workshop is covered by this legislation. This includes employed and self-employed operatives, subcontractors, the employer and those delivering goods to the site. It not only protects those working, it also ensures the safety of anyone else who might be nearby.

KEY EMPLOYER RESPONSIBILITIES

The key employer health and safety responsibilities under HASAWA are to:

- provide a safe working environment
- provide safe access (entrance) and egress (exit) to the work area
- provide adequate staff training
- have a written health and safety policy in place
- provide health and safety information and display the appropriate signs
- carry out risk assessments
- provide safe machinery and equipment and to ensure it is well-maintained and in a safe condition
- provide adequate supervision to ensure safe practices are carried out
- involve trade union safety representatives, where appointed, in matters relating to health and safety
- provide personal protective equipment (**PPE**) free of charge, ensure the appropriate PPE is used whenever needed, and that operatives are properly supervised
- ensure materials and substances are transported, used and stored safely.

PPE

This is defined in the Personal Protective Equipment (PPE) at Work Regulations 1992 as 'all equipment (including clothing affording protection against the weather) which is intended to be worn or held by a person at work and which protects against one or more risks to a person's health or safety.'

Risk assessments and method statements

The HASAWA requires that employers must carry out regular **risk assessments** to make sure that there are minimal dangers to their employees in a workplace.

Risk assessment

An assessment of the hazards and risks associated with an activity and the reduction and monitoring of them

Risk Assessment

Activity / Workplace assessed: Return to work after accident
Persons consulted / involved in risk assessment
Date:
Reviewed on:

Location:
Risk assessment reference number:
Review date:
Review by:

Significant hazard	People at risk and what is the risk Describe the harm that is likely to result from the hazard (eg cut, broken leg, chemical burn etc) and who could be harmed (eg employees, contractors, visitors etc)	Existing control measure What is currently in place to control the risk?	Risk rating Use matrix identified in guidance note Likelihood (L) Severity (S) Multiply (L) * (S) to produce risk rating (RR)				Further action required What is required to bring the risk down to an acceptable level? Use hierarchy of control described in guidance note when considering the controls needed	Actioned to: Who will complete the action?	Due date: When will the action be complete by?	Completion date: Initial and date once the action has been completed
			L	S	RR	L/M/H				
Uneven floors	Operatives	Verbal warning and supervision	2	1	2	m	None applicable	Site supervisor	Active now	Ongoing
Steps	Operatives	Verbal warning	2	1	2	m	None applicable	Site supervisor	Active now	Ongoing
Staircases	Operatives	Verbal warning	2	2	4	m	None applicable	Site supervisor	Active now	Ongoing

		Likelihood			Likelihood 3 – Very likely 2 – Possible 1 – Unlikely
		1 Unlikely	2 Possible	3 Very likely	
Severity	1 Slight/minor injuries/minor damage	1	2	3	Severity 3 – Major injury/extensive damage 2 – Medium injury/significant damage 1 – Slight/minor damage
	2 Medium injuries/significant damage	2	4	6	
	3 Major injury/extensive damage	3	6	9	

1   – Low risk, action should be taken to reduce the risk if reasonably practicable
2, 3, 4 – Medium risk, is a significant risk and would require an appropriate level of resource
6 & 9 – High risk , may require considerable resource to mitigate. Control should focus on elimination of risk, if not possible control should be obtained by following the hierarchy of control

123 type risk assessment

A risk assessment is a legally-required tool used by employers to:

- identify work hazards

- assess the risk of harm arising from these hazards

- adequately control the risk.

Risk assessments are carried out as follows:

1 Identify the hazards. Consider the environment in which the job will be done. Which tools and materials will be used?

2 Identify who might be at risk. Think about operatives, visitors and members of the public.

3 Evaluate the risk. How severe is the potential injury? How likely is it to happen? A severe injury may be possible but may also be very improbable. On the other hand a minor injury might be very likely.

4 If there is an unacceptable risk, can the job be changed? Could different tools or materials be used instead?

5 If the risk is acceptable, what measures can be taken to reduce the risk? This could be training, special equipment and using PPE.

6 Keep good records. Explain the findings of the risk assessment to the operatives involved. Update the risk assessment as required – there may be new machinery, materials or staff. Even adverse weather can bring additional risks.

A **method statement** is required by law and is a useful way of recording the hazards involved in a specific task. It is used to communicate the risk and precautions required to all those involved in the work. It should be clear, uncomplicated and easy to understand as it is for the benefit of those carrying out the work (and their immediate supervisors).

Inductions and tool box talks

Any new visitors to and operatives on a site will be given an induction. This will explain:

- the layout of the site

- any hazards of which they need to be aware

- the location of welfare facilities

- the assembly areas in case of emergency

- site rules.

Tool box talks are short talks given at regular intervals. They give timely safety reminders and outline any new hazards that may have arisen because construction sites change as they develop. Weather conditions such as extreme heat, wind or rain may create new hazards.

KEY EMPLOYEE RESPONSIBILITIES

The HASAWA covers the responsibilities of employees and subcontractors:

- You must work in a safe manner and take care at all times.

- You must make sure you do not put yourself or others at risk by your actions or inactions.

Method statement

A description of the intended method of carrying out a task, often linked to a risk assessment

INDUSTRY TIP

The Construction Skills Certification Scheme (CSCS) was set up in the mid-90s with the aim of improving site operatives' competence to reduce accidents and drive up on-site efficiency. Card holders must take a health and safety test. The colour of card depends on level of qualification held and job role. For more information see www.cscs.uk.com

ACTIVITY

Think back to your induction. Write down what was discussed. Did you understand everything? Do you need any further information? If you have not had an induction, write a list of the things you think you need to know.

INDUSTRY TIP

Remember, if you are unsure about any health and safety issue always seek help and advice.

■ You must co-operate with your employer in regard to health and safety. If you do not you risk injury (to yourself or others), prosecution, a fine and loss of employment. Do not take part in practical jokes and horseplay.

■ You must use any equipment and safeguards provided by your employer. For example, you must wear, look after and report any damage to the PPE that your employer provides.

■ You must not interfere or tamper with any safety equipment.

■ You must not misuse or interfere with anything that is provided for employees' safety.

FIRST AID AND FIRST-AID KITS

First aid should only be applied by someone trained in first aid. Even a minor injury could become infected and therefore should be cleaned and a dressing applied. If any cut or injury shows signs of infection, becomes inflamed or painful seek medical attention. An employer's first-aid needs should be assessed to indicate if a first-aider (someone trained in first aid) is necessary. The minimum requirement is to appoint a person to take charge of first-aid arrangements. The role of this appointed person includes looking after the first-aid equipment and facilities and calling the emergency services when required.

First-aid kits vary according to the size of the workforce. First-aid boxes should not contain tablets or medicines.

Burn dressing

Resuscitation face shield

Nitrate gloves

Plasters

Eye wash

Foil blanket

Bandages

Cleaning wipes

Microporous tape

Safety pins

Scissors

First-aid kit

SOURCES OF HEALTH AND SAFETY INFORMATION

Source	How they can help
Health and Safety Executive (HSE)	A government body which oversees health and safety in the workplace. It produces health and safety literature such as the **Approved Code of Practice** (ACoP).
Construction Skills	The construction industry training body produces literature and is directly involved with construction training.
The Royal Society for the Prevention of Accidents (ROSPA)	It produces literature and gives advice.
The Royal Society for Public Health	An independent, multi-disciplinary charity which is dedicated to the promotion and protection of collective human health and wellbeing.
Institution of Occupational Safety and Health (IOSH)	A chartered body for health and safety practitioners. The world's largest health and safety professional membership organisation.
The British Safety Council	It helps businesses with their health, safety and environmental management.

Approved Code of Practice

ACoP gives practical advice for those in the construction industry in relation to using machinery

INDUSTRY TIP

There are many other trade organisations, eg the Timber Research and Development Association (TRADA) which also offer advice on safe practices.

ACTIVITY

You have been asked to give a tool box talk because of several minor injuries involving tripping on site. What topics would you include in this talk?

INDUSTRY TIP

To find out more information on the sources in the table, enter their names into a search engine on the internet.

HEALTH AND SAFETY EXECUTIVE (HSE)

The HSE is a body set up by the government. The HSE ensures that the law is carried out correctly and has extensive powers to ensure that it can do its job. It can make spot checks in the workplace, bring the police, examine anything on the premises and take things away to be examined.

If the HSE finds a health and safety problem that breaks health and safety law it might issue an **improvement notice** giving the employer a set amount of time to correct the problem. For serious health and safety risks where there is a risk of immediate major injury, it can issue a **prohibition notice** which will stop all work on site until the health and safety issues are rectified. It may take an employer, employee, self-employed person (subcontractor) or anyone else

Improvement notice

Issued by an HSE or local authority inspector to formally notify a company that improvements are needed to the way it is working

Prohibition notice

Issued by an HSE or local authority inspector when there is an immediate risk of personal injury. They are not issued lightly and if you are on the receiving end of one, you are clearly breaking a health and safety regulation involved with the building process to court for breaking health and safety legislation.

The HSE provides a lot of advice on safety and publishes numerous booklets and information sheets. One example of this is the Approved Code of Practice (ACoP) which applies to wood working machinery. The ACoP has a special legal status and employers and employees are expected to work within its guidelines.

The duties of the HSE are to:

- give advice

- issue improvement and prohibition notices

- caution

- prosecute

- investigate.

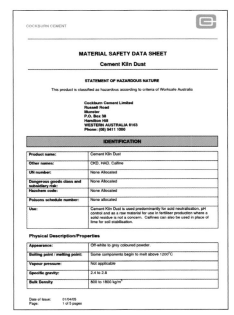

The Approved Code of Practice booklet is available free online

CONTROL OF SUBSTANCES HAZARDOUS TO HEALTH (COSHH) REGULATIONS 2002

The Control of Substances Hazardous to Health (COSHH) Regulations 2002 controls the use of dangerous substances, eg preservatives, fuel, solvents, adhesives, cement and oil-based paint. These have to be moved, stored and used safely without polluting the environment. It also covers hazardous substances produced while working, eg wood dust produced when sanding or drilling.

Hazardous substances may be discovered during the building process, eg lead-based paint or asbestos. These are covered by separate regulations.

When considering substances and materials that may be hazardous to health an employer should do the following to comply with COSHH:

- Read and check the COSHH safety data sheet that comes with the product. It will outline any hazards associated with the product and the safety measures to be taken.

- Check with the supplier if there are any known risks to health.

- Use the trade press to find out if there is any information about this substance or material.

- Use the HSE website, or other websites, to check any known issues with the substance or material.

Example of COSHH data sheet

When assessing the risk of a potentially dangerous substance or material it is important to consider how operatives could be exposed to it. For example:

- by breathing in gas or mist

- by swallowing it

- by getting it into their eyes

- through their skin, either by contact or through cuts.

Safety data sheets

Products you use may be 'dangerous for supply'. If so, they will have a label that has one or more hazard symbols. Some examples are given here.

These products include common substances in everyday use such as paint, bleach, solvent or fillers. When a product is 'dangerous for supply', by law, the supplier must provide you with a safety data sheet. Note: medicines, pesticides and cosmetic products have different legislation and don't have a safety data sheet. Ask the supplier how the product can be used safely.

Safety data sheets can be hard to understand, with little information on measures for control. However, to find out about health risks and emergency situations, concentrate on:

- Sections 2 and 16 of the sheet, which tell you what the dangers are;
- Sections 4-8, which tell you about emergencies, storage and handling.

Since 2009, new international symbols have been gradually replacing the European symbols. Some of them are similar to the European symbols, but there is no single word describing the hazard. Read the hazard statement on the packaging and the safety data sheet from the supplier.

Hazard checklist

☐ Does any product you use have a danger label?
☐ Does your process produce gas, fume, dust, mist or vapour?
☐ Is the substance harmful to breathe in?
☐ Can the substance harm your skin?
☐ Is it likely that harm could arise because of the way you use or produce it?
☐ What are you going to do about it?
   - Use something else?
   - Use it in another, safer way?
   - Control it to stop harm being caused?

CONTROL MEASURES

The control measures below are in order of importance.

1 Eliminate the use of the harmful substance and use a safer one. For instance, swap high **VOC** oil based paint for a lower VOC water-based paint.

2 Use a safer form of the product. Is the product available ready-mixed? Is there a lower strength option that will still do the job?

VOC

The measurement of volatile organic compounds shows how much pollution a product will emit into the air when in use

INDUSTRY TIP

Product data sheets are free and have to be produced by the supplier of the product.

3 Change the work method to emit less of the substance. For instance, applying paint with a brush releases fewer VOCs into the air than spraying paint. Wet grinding produces less dust than dry grinding.

4 Enclose the work area so that the substance does not escape. This can mean setting up a tented area or closing doors.

5 Use extraction or filtration (eg a dust bag) in the work area.

6 Keep operatives in the area to a minimum.

7 Employers must provide appropriate PPE.

Paint with high VOC content

ACTIVITY

Think of three substances in your workplace or place of training that might be hazardous to health. Can you find a COSHH data sheet for each? (They can often be found on the internet if you search for the product.)

European symbols

| Toxic | Very toxic | Harmful | Irritant |

Highly flammable   Extremely flammable   Explosive   Dangerous to the environment

Oxidising   Corrosive

New International symbols

Toxic   May explode when heated   Irritant

Causes fire   Explosive   Dangerous to the environment

Intensifies fire   Long term health hazard   Corrosive

COSHH symbols. The international symbols will replace the European symbols in 2015.

INDUSTRY TIP

For more detailed information on RIDDOR visit the HSE webpage at www.hse.gov.uk/riddor.

REPORTING OF INJURIES, DISEASES AND DANGEROUS OCCURRENCES REGULATIONS (RIDDOR) 2013

Despite all the efforts put into health and safety, incidents still happen. The Reporting of Injuries, Diseases and Dangerous Occurrences Regulations (RIDDOR) 2013 state that employers must report to the HSE all accidents that result in an employee needing more than seven days off work. Diseases and dangerous occurrences must also be reported. A serious occurrence which has not caused an injury (a near miss) should still be reported because next time it happens things might not work out as well.

Below are some examples of injuries, diseases and dangerous occurrences which would need to be reported:

- A joiner cuts off a finger while using a circular saw.

- A plumber takes a week off after a splinter in her hand becomes infected.

- A ground operative contracts **leptospirosis**.

- A labourer contracts dermatitis (a serious skin problem) after contact with an irritant substance.

- A scaffold suffers a collapse following severe weather, unauthorised alteration or overloading but no-one is injured.

Leptospirosis

Also known as Weil's disease, this is a serious disease spread by rats and cattle

The purpose of RIDDOR is to enable the HSE to investigate serious incidents and collate statistical data. This information is used to help reduce the number of similar accidents happening in future and to make the workplace safer.

INDUSTRY TIP

Accidents do not just affect the person who has the accident. Work colleagues or members of the public might be affected and so will the employer. The consequences may include:
- a poor company image (this may put potential customers off)
- loss of production
- insurance costs increasing
- closure of the site
- having to pay sick pay
- other additional costs.

New HSE guidelines require employers to pay an hourly rate for time taken by the HSE to investigate an accident. This is potentially very costly.

An F2508 injury report form

Although minor accidents and injuries are not reported to HSE, records must be kept. Accidents must be recorded in the accident book. This provides a record of what happened and is useful for future reference. Trends may become apparent and the employer may take action to try and prevent that particular type of accident occurring again.

CONSTRUCTION, DESIGN AND MANAGEMENT (CDM) REGULATIONS 2007

The Construction, Design and Management (CDM) Regulations 2007 focus attention on the effective planning and management of construction projects, from the design concept through to maintenance and repair. The aim is for health and safety considerations to be integrated into a project's development, rather than be an inconvenient afterthought. The CDM Regulations reduce the risk of harm to those that have to work on or use the structure throughout its life, from construction through to **demolition**.

ACTIVITY

You have identified a potential risk. What action should you take? Make notes.

The CDM Regulations play a role in safety during demolition

Demolition

When something, often a building, is completely torn down and destroyed

CDM Regulations protect workers from the construction to demolition of large and complex structures

The CDM Regulations apply to all projects except for those arranged by private clients, ie work that isn't in furtherance of a business interest. Property developers need to follow the CDM Regulations.

Under the CDM Regulations, the HSE must be notified where the construction work will take:

- more than 30 working days or

- 500 working days in total, ie if 100 people work for 5 days (500 working days) the HSE will have to be notified.

DUTY HOLDERS

Under the CDM Regulations there are several duty holders, each with a specific role.

Duty holder	Role
Client	This is the person or organisation who wishes to have the work done. The client will check that: - all the team members are competent - the management is suitable - sufficient time is allowed for all stages of the project - welfare facilities are in place before construction starts. HSE notifiable projects require that the client appoints a CDM co-ordinator and principal contractor, and provides access to a health and safety file.
CDM co-ordinator	Appointed by the client, the co-ordinator advises and assists the client with CDM duties. The co-ordinator notifies the HSE before work starts. This role involves the co-ordination of the health and safety aspects of the design of the building and ensures good communication between the client, designers and contractors.
Designer	At the design stages the designer removes hazards and reduces risks. The designer provides information about the risks that cannot be eliminated. Notifiable projects require that the designer checks that the client is aware of their CDM duties and that a CDM co-ordinator has been appointed. The designer will also supply information for the health and safety file.
Principal contractor	The principal contractor will plan, manage and monitor the construction in liaison with any other involved contractors. This involves developing a written plan and site rules before the construction begins. The principal contractor ensures that the site is made secure and suitable welfare facilities are provided from the start and maintained throughout construction. The principal contractor will also make sure that all operatives have site inductions and any further training that might be required to make sure the workforce is competent.
Contractor	Subcontractors and self-employed operatives will plan, manage and monitor their own work and employees, co-operating with any main contractor in relation to site rules. Contractors will make sure that all operatives have any further training that might be required to make sure they are competent. A contractor also reports any incidents under RIDDOR to the principal contractor.
Operatives	Operatives need to check their own competence: Can you carry out the task you have been asked to do safely? Have you been trained to do this type of activity? Do you have the correct equipment to carry out this activity? You must follow all the site health and safety rules and procedures and fully co-operate with the rest of the team to ensure the health and safety of other operatives and others who may be affected by the work. Any health and safety issues must be reported.

A client, a contractor and an operative looking over building plans ahead of construction

WELFARE FACILITIES REQUIRED ON SITE UNDER THE CDM REGULATIONS

The table below shows the welfare facilities that must be available on site.

Facility	Site requirement
Sanitary conveniences (toilets) 	■ Suitable and sufficient toilets should be provided or made available. ■ Toilets should be adequately ventilated and lit and should be clean. ■ Separate toilet facilities should be provided for men and women.
Washing facilities 	■ Sufficient facilities must be available, and include showers if required by the nature of the work. ■ They should be in the same place as the toilets and near any changing rooms. ■ There must be a supply of clean hot (or warm) and cold running water, soap and towels. ■ There must be separate washing facilities provided for men and women unless the area is for washing hands and the face only.

Facility	Site requirement
Clean drinking water 	▪ This must be provided or made available. ▪ It should be clearly marked by an appropriate sign. ▪ Cups should be provided unless the supply of drinking water is from a water fountain.
Changing rooms and lockers 	▪ Changing rooms must be provided or made available if operatives have to wear special clothing and if they cannot be expected to change elsewhere. ▪ There must be separate rooms for, or separate use of rooms by, men and women where necessary. ▪ The rooms must have seating and include, where necessary, facilities to enable operatives to dry their special clothing and their own clothing and personal effects. ▪ Lockers should also be provided.
Rest rooms or rest areas 	▪ They should have enough tables and seating with backs for the number of operatives likely to use them at any one time. ▪ Where necessary, rest rooms should include suitable facilities for pregnant women or nursing mothers to rest lying down. ▪ Arrangements must be made to ensure that meals can be prepared, heated and eaten. It must also be possible to boil water.

ACTIVITY

What facilities are provided at your workplace or place of training?

PROVISION AND USE OF WORK EQUIPMENT REGULATIONS (PUWER) 1998

The Provision and Use of Work Equipment Regulations (PUWER) 1998 place duties on:

▪ people and companies who own, operate or have control over work equipment

▪ employers whose employees use work equipment.

Work equipment can be defined as any machinery, appliance, apparatus, tool or installation for use at work (whether exclusively or not). This includes equipment which employees provide for their own use at work. The scope of work equipment is therefore extremely wide. The use of work equipment is also very widely interpreted and, according to the HSE, means 'any activity involving work equipment and includes starting, stopping, programming, setting, transporting, repairing, modifying, maintaining, servicing and cleaning.' It includes equipment such as diggers, electric planers, stepladders, hammers or wheelbarrows.

Under PUWER, work equipment must be:

- suitable for the intended use

- safe to use

- well maintained

- inspected regularly.

Regular inspection is important as a tool that was safe when it was new may no longer be safe after considerable use.

Additionally, work equipment must only be used by people who have received adequate instruction and training. Information regarding the use of the equipment must be given to the operator and must only be used for what it was designed to do.

Protective devices, eg emergency stops, must be used. Brakes must be fitted where appropriate to slow down moving parts to bring the equipment to a safe condition when turned off or stopped. Equipment must have adequate means of isolation. Warnings, either by signs or other means such as sounds or lights, must be used as appropriate. Access to dangerous parts of the machinery must be controlled. Some work equipment is subject to additional health and safety legislation which must also be followed.

Employers who use work equipment must manage the risks. ACoPs (see page 9) have been developed in line with PUWER. The ACoPs have a special legal status, as outlined in the introduction to the PUWER ACoP:

> *Following the guidance is not compulsory and you are free to take other action. But if you do follow the guidance you will normally be doing enough to comply with the law. Health and safety inspectors seek to secure compliance with the law and may refer to this guidance as illustrating good practice.*

> **INDUSTRY TIP**
>
> Abrasive wheels are used for grinding. Under PUWER these wheels can only be changed by someone who has received training to do this. Wrongly fitted wheels can explode!

> **ACTIVITY**
>
> All the tools you use for your work are covered by PUWER. They must be well maintained and suitable for the task. A damaged head on a bolster chisel must be reshaped. A split shaft on a joiner's wood chisel must be repaired. Why would these tools be dangerous in a damaged condition? List the reasons.

MANUAL HANDLING OPERATIONS REGULATIONS 1992

Employers must try and avoid manual handling within reason if there is a possibility of injury. If manual handling cannot be avoided then they must reduce the risk of injury by means of a risk assessment.

An operative lifting heavy bricks

LIFTING AND HANDLING

Incorrect lifting and handling is a serious risk to your health. It is very easy to injure your back – just ask any experienced builder. An injured back can be very unpleasant, so it's best to look after it.

Here are a few things to consider when lifting:

- Assess the load. Is it too heavy? Do you need assistance or additional training? Is it an awkward shape?

- Can a lifting aid be used, such as any of the below?

Wheelbarrow

Gin lift

Scissor lift

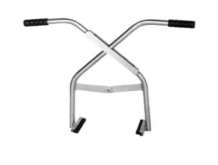

Kerb lifter

- Does the lift involve twisting or reaching?

- Where is the load going to end up? Is there a clear path? Is the place it's going to be taken to cleared and ready?

How to lift and place an item correctly

If you cannot use a machine, it is important that you keep the correct posture when lifting any load. The correct technique to do this is known as **kinetic lifting**. Always lift with your back straight, elbows in, knees bent and your feet slightly apart.

Kinetic lifting

A method of lifting that ensures that the risk of injury is reduced

Safe kinetic lifting technique

When placing the item, again be sure to use your knees and beware of trapping your fingers. If stacking materials, be sure that they are on a sound level base and on bearers if required.

Heavy objects that cannot easily be lifted by mechanical methods can be lifted by several people. It is important that one person in the team is in charge, and that lifting is done in a co-operative way. It has been known for one person to fall down and the others then drop the item!

CONTROL OF NOISE AT WORK REGULATIONS 2005

Under the Control of Noise at Work Regulations 2005, duties are placed on employers and employees to reduce the risk of hearing damage to the lowest reasonable level practicable. Hearing loss caused by work is preventable. Hearing damage is permanent and cannot be restored once lost.

EMPLOYER'S DUTIES UNDER THE REGULATIONS

An employer's duties are:

- To carry out a risk assessment and identify who is at risk.

- To eliminate or control its employees exposure to noise at the workplace and to reduce the noise as far as practicable.

- To provide suitable hearing protection.

- To provide health surveillance to those identified as at risk by the risk assessment.

- To provide information and training about the risks to their employees as identified by the risk assessment.

EMPLOYEES' DUTIES UNDER THE REGULATIONS

Employees must:

- Make full and proper use of personal hearing protectors provided to them by their employer.

- If they discover any defect in any personal hearing protectors or other control measures they must report it to their employer as soon as is practicable.

Ear defenders

Ear plugs

NOISE LEVELS

Under the Regulations, specific actions are triggered at specific noise levels. Noise is measured in decibels and shown as dB (a). The two main action levels are 80dB (a) and 85dB (a).

Requirements at 80dB (a) to 85dB (a):

- Assess the risk to operatives' health and provide them with information and training.

- Provide suitable ear protection free of charge to those who request ear protection.

Requirements above 85dB (a):

- Reduce noise exposure as far as practicable by means other than ear protection.

- Set up an ear protection zone using suitable signage and segregation.

- Provide suitable ear protection free of charge to those affected and ensure they are worn.

PERSONAL PROTECTIVE EQUIPMENT (PPE) AT WORK REGULATIONS 1992

Employees and subcontractors must work in a safe manner. Not only must they wear the PPE that their employers provide they must also look after it and report any damage to it. Importantly, employees must not be charged for anything given to them or done for them by the employer in relation to safety.

ACTIVITY

Think about your place of work or training. What PPE do you think you should use when working with cement or using a powered planer?

The hearing and respiratory PPE provided for most work situations is not covered by these Regulations because other regulations apply to it. However, these items need to be compatible with any other PPE provided.

The main requirement of the Regulations is that PPE must be supplied and used at work wherever there are risks to health and safety that cannot be adequately controlled in other ways.

The Regulations also require that PPE is:

- included in the method statement
- properly assessed before use to ensure it is suitable
- maintained and stored properly
- provided to employees with instructions on how they can use it safely
- used correctly by employees.

An employer cannot ask for money from an employee for PPE, whether it is returnable or not. This includes agency workers if they are legally regarded as employees. If employment has been terminated and the employee keeps the PPE without the employer's permission, then, as long as it has been made clear in the contract of employment, the employer may be able to deduct the cost of the replacement from any wages owed.

Using PPE is a very important part of staying safe. For it to do its job properly it must be kept in good condition and used correctly. If any damage does occur to an article of PPE it is important that this is reported and it is replaced. It must also be remembered that PPE is a last line of defence and should not be used in place of a good safety policy!

A site safety sign showing the PPE required to work there

INDUSTRY TIP

You can get chemical burns from cement. Always wear gloves when working with cement.

The following table shows the type of PPE used in the workplace and explains why it is important to store, maintain and use PPE correctly. It also shows why it is important to check and report damage to PPE.

PPE	Correct use
Hard hat/safety helmet 	Hard hats must be worn when there is danger of hitting your head or danger of falling objects. They often prevent a wide variety of head injuries. Most sites insist on hard hats being worn. They must be adjusted to fit your head correctly and must not be worn back to front! Check the date of manufacture as plastic can become brittle over time. Solvents, pens and paints can damage the plastic too.
Toe-cap boots or shoes  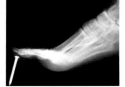 Safety boots A nail in a construction worker's foot	Toe-cap boots or shoes are worn on most sites as a matter of course and protect the feet from heavy falling objects. Some safety footwear has additional insole protection to help prevent nails going up through the foot. Toe caps can be made of steel or lighter plastic.
Ear defenders and plugs   Ear defenders Ear plugs	Your ears can be very easily damaged by loud noise. Ear protection will help prevent hearing loss while using loud tools or if there is a lot of noise going on around you. When using earplugs always ensure your hands are clean before handling the plugs as this reduces the risk of infection. If your ear defenders are damaged or fail to make a good seal around your ears have them replaced.
High-visibility (hi-viz) jacket 	This makes it much easier for other people to see you. This is especially important when there is plant or vehicles moving in the vicinity.
Goggles and safety glasses   Safety goggles Safety glasses	These protect the eyes from dust and flying debris while you are working. It has been known for casualties to be taken to hospital after dust has blown up from a dry mud road. You only get one pair of eyes, look after them!

PPE	Correct use
Dust masks and respirators   Dust mask Respirator	Dust is produced during most construction work and it can be hazardous to your lungs. It can cause all sorts of ailments from asthma through to cancer. Wear a dust mask to filter this dust out. You must ensure it is well fitted. Another hazard is dangerous gases such as solvents. A respirator will filter out hazardous gases but a dust mask will not! Respirators are rated P1, P2 and P3, with P3 giving the highest protection.
Gloves  Latex glove Nitrile glove  Gauntlet gloves Leather gloves	Gloves protect your hands. Hazards include cuts, abrasions, dermatitis, chemical burns or splinters. Latex and nitrile gloves are good for fine work, although some people are allergic to latex. Gauntlets provide protection from strong chemicals. Other types of gloves provide good grip and protect the fingers.  **A chemical burn as a result of not wearing safety gloves**
Sunscreen 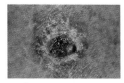 Suncream Melanoma	Another risk, especially in the summer months, is sunburn. Although a good tan is sometimes considered desirable, over-exposure to the sun can cause skin cancer such as melanoma. When out in the sun, cover up and use sunscreen (ie suncream) on exposed areas of your body to prevent burning.
Preventing HAVS 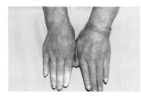	Hand–arm vibration syndrome (HAVS), also known as vibration white finger (VWF), is an industrial injury caused by using vibrating power tools (such as a hammer drill, vibrating poker and vibrating plate) for a long time. This injury is controlled by limiting the time such power tools are used. For more information see page 31.

ACTIVITY

You are working on a site and a brick falls on your head. Luckily, you are doing as you have been instructed and you are wearing a helmet. You notice that the helmet has a small crack in it. What do you do?

1 Carry on using it as your employer will charge you for a new one, after all it is only a small crack.

2 Take it to your supervisor as it will no longer offer you full protection and it will need replacing.

3 Buy a new helmet because the old one no longer looks very nice.

INDUSTRY TIP

The most important pieces of PPE when using a disc cutter are dust masks, glasses and ear protection.

WORK AT HEIGHT REGULATIONS 2005 (AS AMENDED)

The Work at Height Regulations 2005 (as amended by the Work at Height (Amendment) Regulations 2007) put several duties upon employers:

- Working at height should be avoided if possible.

- If working at height cannot be avoided, the work must be properly organised with risk assessments carried out.

- Risk assessments should be regularly updated.

- Those working at height must be trained and competent.

- A method statement must be provided.

Workers wearing safety harnesses on an aerial access platform

Several points should be considered when working at height:

- How long is the job expected to take?

- What type of work will it be? It could be anything from fitting a single light bulb, through to removing a chimney or installing a roof.
  - How is the access platform going to be reached? By how many people?
  - Will people be able to get on and off the structure safely? Could there be overcrowding?

- What are the risks to passers-by? Could debris or dust blow off and injure anyone on the road below?

- What are the conditions like? Extreme weather, unstable buildings and poor ground conditions need to be taken into account.

A cherry picker can assist you when working at height

ACCESS EQUIPMENT AND SAFE METHODS OF USE

The means of access should only be chosen after a risk assessment has been carried out. There are various types of access.

Ladders

Ladders are normally used for access onto an access platform. They are not designed for working from except for light, short-duration work. A ladder should lean at an angle of 75°, ie one unit out for every four units up.

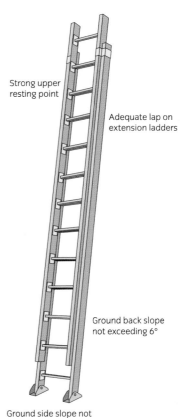

Strong upper resting point

Adequate lap on extension ladders

Ground back slope not exceeding 6°

Ground side slope not exceeding 16°, clean and free of slippery algae and moss

Using a ladder correctly

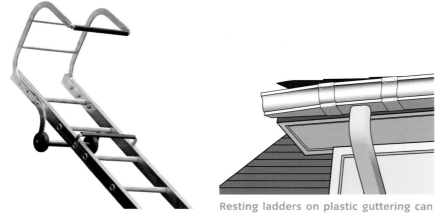

Roof ladder

Resting ladders on plastic guttering can cause it to bend and break

The following images show how to use a ladder or stepladder safely.

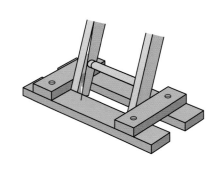

A ladder secured at the base.

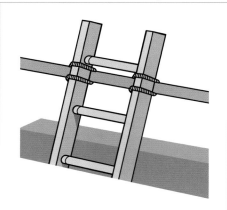

A ladder secured at the top of a platform for working from.

Access ladders should extend 1m above the landing point to provide a strong handhold.

Certain stepladders are unsafe to work from the top three rungs.

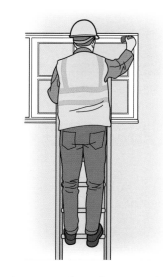

Don't overreach, and stay on the same rung.

Grip the ladder when climbing and remember to keep three points of contact.

INDUSTRY TIP

Always complete ladder pre-checks. Check the stiles (the two uprights) and rungs for damage such as splits or cracks. Do not use painted ladders because the paint could be hiding damage! Check all of the equipment including any stays and feet.

Stepladders

Stepladders are designed for light, short-term work.

Working from the side can make stepladders unstable. Do not overreach

Don't stand on the top three steps

Stepladder is fully open

Locked open firm and level on the ground

Using a stepladder correctly

FUNCTIONAL SKILLS

Using information on stepladders on the HSE website, write down two examples of what sort of job stepladders could be used for and two jobs they should not be used for.

Work on this activity can support FICT 2.A and FE 2.2.2.

Trestles

This is a working platform used for work of a slightly longer duration.

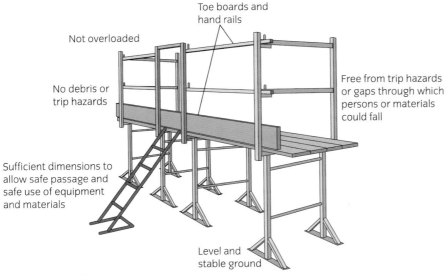

Not overloaded

Toe boards and hand rails

No debris or trip hazards

Free from trip hazards or gaps through which persons or materials could fall

Sufficient dimensions to allow safe passage and safe use of equipment and materials

Level and stable ground

Parts of a trestle

Tower scaffold

These are usually proprietary (manufactured) and are made from galvanised steel or lightweight aluminium alloy. They must be erected by someone competent in the erection and dismantling of mobile scaffolds.

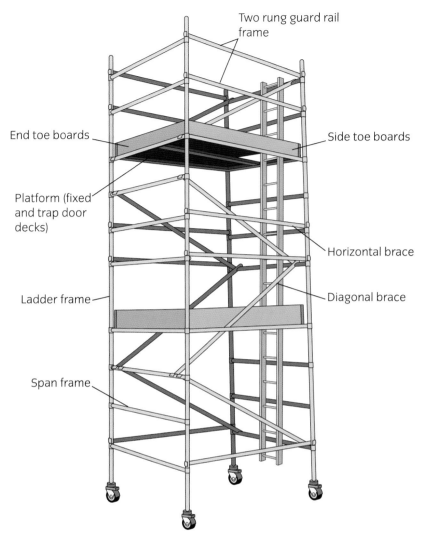

Two rung guard rail frame

End toe boards

Side toe boards

Platform (fixed and trap door decks)

Horizontal brace

Ladder frame

Diagonal brace

Span frame

Parts of a tower scaffold

To use a tower scaffold safely:

- Always read and follow the manufacturer's instruction manual.
- Only use the equipment for what it is designed for.
- The wheels or feet of the tower must be in contact with a firm surface.
- Outriggers should be used to increase stability. The maximum height given in the manufacturer's instructions must not be exceeded.
- The platform must not be overloaded.
- The platform should be unloaded (and reduced in height if required) before it is moved.
- Never move a platform, even a small distance, if it is occupied.

INDUSTRY TIP

Remember, even a mobile access tower should have toe boards and guard rails fitted at all times when in use.

Tubular scaffold

This comes in two types:

- independent scaffold has two sets of standards or uprights

- putlog scaffold is built into the brickwork.

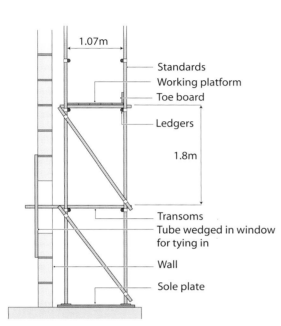

Independent tubular scaffold

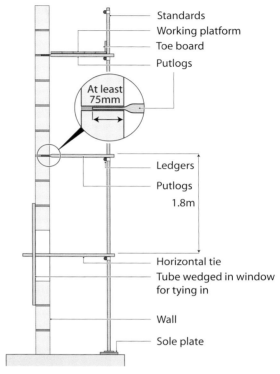

Putlog tubular scaffold

Tubular scaffold is erected by specialist scaffolding companies and often requires structural calculations. Only trained and competent scaffold erectors should alter scaffolding. Access to a scaffold is usually via a tied ladder with three rungs projecting above the step off at platform level.

OUR HOUSE

You have been asked to complete a job that requires gaining access to the roof level of a two-storey building. What equipment would you choose to get access to the work area? What things would you take into consideration when choosing the equipment? Take a look at 'Our House' as a guide for working on a two-storey building.

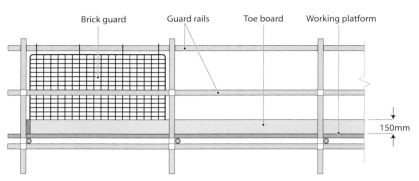

A safe working platform on a tubular scaffold

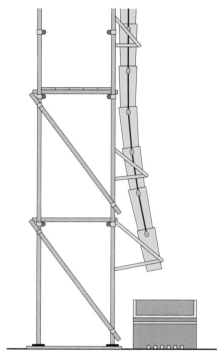

A debris chute for scaffolding

All scaffolding must:

■ not have any gaps in the handrail or toe boards

■ have a safe system for lifting any materials up to the working height

■ have a safe system of debris removal.

Fall protection devices include:

■ harnesses and lanyards

■ safety netting

■ air bags.

A harness and lanyard or safety netting will stop a person falling too far, leaving them suspended in the air. Air bags (commonly known as 'bouncy castles') are set up on the ground and inflated. If a person falls, they will have a soft landing. Air bags have fallen out of favour somewhat as some operatives use them as an easy way to get off the working platform – not the purpose they were intended for!

Using a scissor lift at height

LIFTING OPERATIONS AND LIFTING EQUIPMENT REGULATIONS (LOLER) 1998

The Lifting Operations and Lifting Equipment Regulations (LOLER) 1998 put responsibility upon employers to ensure that the lifting equipment provided for use at work is:

■ strong and stable enough for the particular use and marked to indicate safe working loads

■ positioned and installed to minimise any risks

■ used safely, ie the work is planned, organised and performed by competent people

■ subject to on-going thorough examination and, where appropriate, inspection by competent people.

THE CONTROL OF VIBRATION AT WORK REGULATIONS 2005

Vibration white finger or hand-arm vibration syndrome (HAVS), see page 23, is caused by using vibrating tools such as hammer drills, vibrating pokers or hand held breakers over a long period of time. The most efficient and effective way of controlling exposure to hand–arm vibration is to look for new or alternative work methods which remove or reduce exposure to vibration.

Follow these steps to reduce the effects of HAVS:

- Always use the right tool for each job.

- Check tools before using them to make sure they have been properly maintained and repaired to avoid increased vibration caused by faults or general wear.

- Make sure cutting tools are kept sharp so that they remain efficient.

- Reduce the amount of time you use a tool in one go, by doing other jobs in between.

- Avoid gripping or forcing a tool or work piece more than you have to.

- Encourage good blood circulation by:
  - keeping warm and dry (when necessary, wear gloves, a hat, waterproofs and use heating pads if available)
  - giving up or cutting down on smoking because smoking reduces blood flow
  - massaging and exercising your fingers during work breaks.

Damage from HAVS can include the inability to do fine work and cold can trigger painful finger blanching attacks (when the ends of your fingers go white).

An operative taking a rest from using a power tool

Don't use power tools for longer than you need to

CONSTRUCTION SITE HAZARDS

DANGERS ON CONSTRUCTION SITES

Study the drawing of a building site. There is some demolition taking place, as well as construction. How many hazards can you find? Discuss your answers.

Dangers	Discussion points
Head protection	The operatives are not wearing safety helmets, which would prevent them from hitting their head or from falling objects.
Poor housekeeping	The site is very untidy. This can result in slips, trips and falls and can pollute the environment. An untidy site gives a poor company image. Offcuts and debris should be regularly removed and disposed of according to site policy and recycled if possible.
Fire	There is a fire near a building; this is hazardous. Fires can easily become uncontrollable and spread. There is a risk to the structure and, more importantly, a risk of operatives being burned. Fires can also pollute the environment.

Dangers	Discussion points
Trip hazards	Notice the tools and debris on the floor. The scaffold has been poorly constructed. There is a trip hazard where the scaffold boards overlap.
Chemical spills	There is a drum leaking onto the ground. This should be stored properly – upright and in a lockable metal shed or cupboard. The leak poses a risk of pollution and of chemical burns to operatives.
Falls from height	The scaffold has handrails missing. The trestle working platform has not been fitted with guard rails. None of the operatives are wearing hard hats for protection either.
Noise	An operative is using noisy machinery with other people nearby. The operative should be wearing ear PPE, as should those working nearby. Better still, they should be working elsewhere if at all possible, isolating themselves from the noise.
Electrical	Some of the wiring is 240V as there is no transformer, it's in poor repair and it's also dragging through liquid. This not only increases the risk of electrocution but is also a trip hazard.
Asbestos or other hazardous substances	Some old buildings contain **asbestos** roofing which can become a hazard when being demolished or removed. Other potential hazards include lead paint or mould spores. If a potentially hazardous material is discovered a supervisor must be notified immediately and work must stop until the hazard is dealt with appropriately.

Asbestos

A naturally occurring mineral that was commonly used for a variety of purposes including: **insulation**, fire protection, roofing and guttering. It is extremely hazardous and can cause a serious lung disease known as asbestosis

Insulation

A material that reduces or prevents the transmission of heat

Cables can be a trip hazard on site

FUNCTIONAL SKILLS

Using the data you collected in the Functional Skills task on page 3, produce a pie chart to show the proportion of occupational cancer that is caused by asbestosis.
Work on this activity can support FM L2.3.1 and C2.4.

Boiler suit

Hand cleaner

PERSONAL HYGIENE

Working in the construction industry can be very physical, and it's likely to be quite dirty at times. Therefore you should take good care with your personal hygiene. This involves washing well after work. If contaminants are present, then wearing a protective suit, such as a boiler suit, that you can take off before you go home will prevent contaminants being taken home with you.

You should also wash your hands after going to the toilet and before eating. This makes it safer to eat and more pleasant for others around you. The following step-by-steps show a safe and hygienic way to wash your hands.

STEP 1 Apply soap to hands from the dispenser.

STEP 2 Rub the soap into a lather and cover your hands with it, including between your fingers.

STEP 3 Rinse hands under a running tap removing all of the soap from your hands.

STEP 4 Dry your hands using disposable towels. Put the towels in the bin once your hands are dry.

WORKING WITH ELECTRICITY

Electricity is a very useful energy resource but it can be very dangerous. Electricity must be handled with care! Only trained, competent people can work with electrical equipment.

THE DANGERS OF USING ELECTRICAL EQUIPMENT

The main dangers of electricity are:

- shock and burns (a 230V shock can kill)

- electrical faults which could cause a fire

- an explosion where an electrical spark has ignited a flammable gas.

VOLTAGES

Generally speaking, the lower the voltage the safer it is. However, a low voltage is not necessarily suitable for some machines, so higher voltages can be found. On site, 110V (volts) is recommended and this is the voltage rating most commonly used in the building industry. This is converted from 230V by use of a transformer.

110V 1 phase – yellow

230V (commonly called 240V) domestic voltage is used on site as battery chargers usually require this voltage. Although 230V is often used in workshops, 110V is recommended.

400V (otherwise known as 3 phase) is used for large machinery, such as joinery shop equipment.

Voltages are nominal, ie they can vary slightly.

230V 1 phase – blue

BATTERY POWER

Battery power is much safer than mains power. Many power tools are now available in battery-powered versions. They are available in a wide variety of voltages from 3.6V for a small screwdriver all the way up to 36V for large masonry drills.

400V 3 phase – red

The following images are all examples of battery-powered tools you may come across in your workplace or place of training.

Battery drill   Battery-powered planer   Battery-powered jigsaw

WIRING

The wires inside a cable are made from copper, which conducts electricity. The copper is surrounded by a plastic coating that is colour coded. The three wires in a cable are the live (brown), which works with the neutral (blue) to conduct electricity, making the appliance work. The earth (green and yellow stripes) prevents electrocution if the appliance is faulty or damaged.

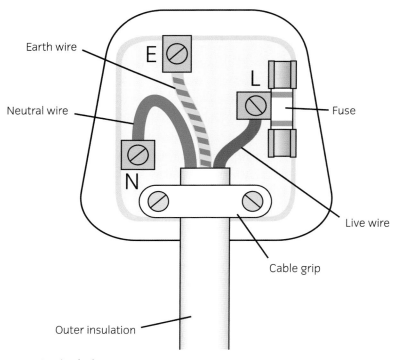

A wired plug

POWER TOOLS AND CHECKS

Power tools should always be checked before use. Always inform your supervisor if you find a fault. The tool will need to be repaired, and the tool needs to be kept out of use until then. The tool might be taken away, put in the site office and clearly labelled 'Do not use'.

Power tool checks include:

- *Look for the portable appliance testing (PAT) label*: PAT is a regular test carried out by a competent person (eg a qualified electrician) to ensure the tool is in a safe electrical condition. A sticker is placed on the tool after it has been tested. Tools that do not pass the PAT are taken out of use.

PAT testing labels

- *Cable*: Is it damaged? Is there a repair? Insulation tape may be hiding a damaged cable. Damaged cables must be replaced.

- *Casing*: Is the casing cracked? Plastic casings ensure the tool is double-insulated. This means the live parts inside are safely shielded from the user. A cracked casing will reduce the protection to the user and will require repair.

- *Guards and tooling*: Are guards in place? Is the tooling sharp?

- *Electricity supply leads*: Are they damaged? Are they creating a trip hazard? You need to place them in such a way that they do not make a trip hazard. Are they protected from damage? If they are lying on the floor with heavy traffic crossing them, they must be covered.

- *Use appropriate equipment for the size of the job*: For example, too many splitters can result in a web of cables.

- *Storage*: After use, power tools and equipment should be stored correctly. Tools must be returned to the boxes, including all the guards and parts. Cables need to be wound onto reels or neatly coiled as they can become tangled very easily.

Cable protection

Cable reel

INDUSTRY TIP

Remember, always fully unroll an extension lead before use because it could overheat and cause a fire.

FIRE

Fire needs three things to start; if just one of them is missing there will be no fire. If all are present then a fire is unavoidable:

1 *Oxygen*: A naturally occurring gas in the air that combines with flammable substances under certain circumstances.

2 *Heat*: A source of fire, such as a hot spark from a grinder or naked flame.

3 *Fuel*: Things that will burn such as acetone, timber, cardboard or paper.

The fire triangle

If you have heat, fuel and oxygen you will have a fire. Remove any of these and the fire will go out.

PREVENTING THE SPREAD OF FIRE

Being tidy will help prevent fires starting and spreading. For instance:

■ Wood offcuts should not be left in big piles or standing up against a wall. Instead, useable offcuts should be stored in racks.

■ Put waste into the allocated disposal bins or skips.

■ Always replace the cap on unused fuel containers when you put them away. Otherwise they are a potential source of danger.

■ Flammable liquids (not limited to fuel-flammable liquids) such as oil-based paint, thinners and oil must be stored in a locked metal cupboard or shed.

■ Smoking around flammable substances should be avoided.

■ Dust can be explosive, so when doing work that produces wood dust it is important to use some form of extraction and have good ventilation.

FIRE EXTINGUISHERS AND THEIR USES

You need to know where the fire extinguishers and blankets are located and which fire extinguishers can be used on different fires. The table below shows the different classes of fire and which extinguisher to use in each case.

Class of fire	Materials	Type of extinguisher
A	Wood, paper, hair, textiles	Water, foam, dry powder, wet chemical
B	Flammable liquids	Foam, dry powder, CO_2
C	Flammable gases	Dry powder, CO_2
D	Flammable metals	Specially formulated dry powder
E	Electrical fires	CO_2, dry powder
F	Cooking oils	Wet chemical, fire blanket

Fire blanket

INDUSTRY TIP

Remember, although all fire extinguishers are red, they each have a different coloured label to identify their contents.

CO_2 extinguisher

Dry powder extinguisher

Water extinguisher

Foam extinguisher

It is important to use the correct extinguisher for the type of fire as using the wrong one could make the danger much worse, eg using water on an electrical fire could lead to the user being electrocuted!

EMERGENCY PROCEDURES

In an emergency, people tend to panic. If an emergency were to occur, such as fire, discovering a bomb or some other security problem, would you know what to do? It is vital to be prepared in case of an emergency.

It is your responsibility to know the emergency procedures on your work site:

- If you discover a fire or other emergency you will need to raise the alarm:
  - You will need to tell a nominated person. Who is this?
  - If you are first on the scene you will have to ring the emergency services on 999.

- Be aware of the alarm signal. Is it a bell, a voice or a siren?

- Where is the assembly point? You will have to proceed to this point in an orderly way. Leave all your belongings behind, they may slow you or others down.

- At the assembly point, there will be someone who will ensure everyone is out safely and will do so by taking a count. Do you know who this person is? If during a fire you are not accounted for, a firefighter may risk their life to go into the building to look for you.

- How do you know it's safe to re-enter the building? You will be told by the appointed person. It's very important that you do not re-enter the building until you are told to do so.

Emergency procedure sign

ACTIVITY

What is the fire evacuation procedure at your workplace or place of training?

SIGNS AND SAFETY NOTICES

The law sets out the types of safety signs needed on a construction site. Some signs that warn us about danger and others tell us what to do to stay safe.

The following table describes five basic types of sign.

Type of sign	Description
Prohibition 	These signs are red and white. They are round. They signify something that must *not* be done.
Mandatory	These signs are blue. They are round. They signify something that *must* be done.

Type of sign	Description
Caution 	These signs are yellow and black. They are triangular. These give warning of hazards.
Safe condition 	These signs are green. They are usually square or rectangular. They tell you the safe way to go, or what to do in an emergency.
Supplementary 	These white signs are square or rectangular and give additional important information. They usually accompany the signs above.

Case Study: Miranda

A site has a small hut where tools are stored securely, and inside the hut there is a short bench that has some sharpening equipment including a grinding wheel.

Miranda wished to grind her plane blade, but before using it found that the grinding wheel was defective as the side of the wheel had been used, causing a deep groove.

She found another old grinding wheel beneath the bench which looked fine. She fitted it to the grinder and used it.

Afterwards, she wondered if she should have asked someone else to change the wheel for her.

- What health and safety issues are there with this scenario?

- What training could Miranda undertake?

Work through the following questions to check your learning.

1 Which one of the following must be filled out prior to carrying out a site task?

   a Invoice.

   b Bill of quantities.

   c Risk assessment.

   d Schedule.

2 Which one of the following signs shows you something you **must** do?

   a Green circle.

   b Yellow triangle.

   c White square.

   d Blue circle.

3 Two parts of the fire triangle are heat and fuel. What is the third?

   a Nitrogen.

   b Oxygen.

   c Carbon dioxide.

   d Hydrogen sulphite.

4 Which of the following types of fire extinguisher would **best** put out an electrical fire?

   a CO_2.

   b Powder.

   c Water.

   d Foam.

5 Which piece of health and safety legislation is designed to protect an operative from ill health and injury when using solvents and adhesives?

   a Manual Handling Operations Regulations 1992.

   b Control of Substances Hazardous to Health (COSHH) Regulations 2002.

   c Health and Safety (First Aid) Regulations 1981.

   d Lifting Operations and Lifting Equipment Regulations (LOLER) 1998.

6 What is the correct angle at which to lean a ladder against a wall?

   a 70°.

   b 80°.

   c 75°.

   d 85°.

7 Which are the **most** important pieces of PPE to use when using a disc cutter?

   a Overalls, gloves and boots.

   b Boots, head protection and overalls.

   c Glasses, hearing protection and dust mask.

   d Gloves, head protection and boots.

8 Which one of the following is **not** a lifting aid?

   a Wheelbarrow.

   b Kerb lifter.

   c Gin lift.

   d Respirator.

9 Which one of the following is a 3 phase voltage?

   a 400V.

   b 230V.

   c 240V.

   d 110V.

10 Above what noise level must you wear ear protection?

   a 75dB (a).

   b 80dB (a).

   c 85dB (a).

   d 90dB (a).

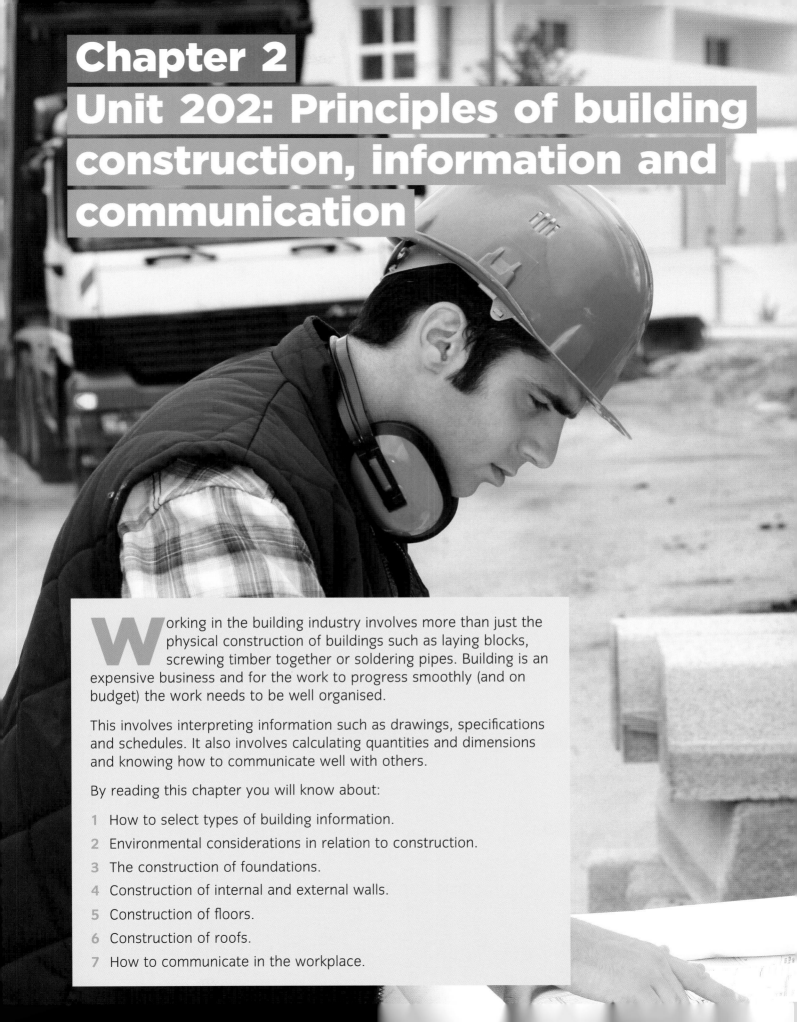

Chapter 2
Unit 202: Principles of building construction, information and communication

Working in the building industry involves more than just the physical construction of buildings such as laying blocks, screwing timber together or soldering pipes. Building is an expensive business and for the work to progress smoothly (and on budget) the work needs to be well organised.

This involves interpreting information such as drawings, specifications and schedules. It also involves calculating quantities and dimensions and knowing how to communicate well with others.

By reading this chapter you will know about:

1 How to select types of building information.
2 Environmental considerations in relation to construction.
3 The construction of foundations.
4 Construction of internal and external walls.
5 Construction of floors.
6 Construction of roofs.
7 How to communicate in the workplace.

TECHNICAL INFORMATION

This section will discuss the three main sources of technical information that are used when constructing buildings:

- working drawings and **specifications**
- schedules
- **bill of quantities**.

These are all essential information and form the contract documents (those that govern the construction of a building). All documentation needs to be correctly interpreted and correctly used. The contract documents need to be looked after and stored (filed) correctly and safely. If documents are left lying around they will become difficult to read and pages may be lost, leading to errors. The contract documents will need to be **archived** at the end of the contract, so they can be referred back to in case of any query or dispute over the work carried out or the materials used.

DRAWING SCALES

It is impossible to fit a full-sized drawing of a building onto a sheet of paper, so it is necessary to **scale** (shrink) the size of the building to enable it to fit. The building has to be shrunk in proportion; this makes it possible to convert measurements on the drawing into real measurements that can be used. Scale rules are made specifically for this purpose.

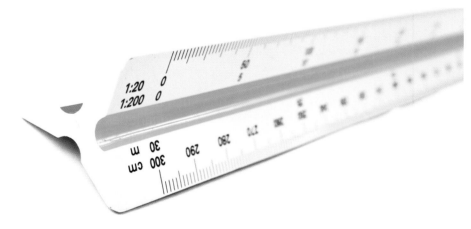

Triangular scale rule

How do scale rules work? Let's say we are using a scale of 1:5. That means that what we draw – using the sizes on the scale rule – will be five times smaller on the drawing than the object's actual size. So, a line 30mm long will represent an object 150mm long (30 × 5 = 150).

Specification

A contract document that gives information about the quality of materials and standards of workmanship required

Bill of quantities

A document containing quantities, descriptions and cost of works and resources

Archived

Kept in storage

Scale

The ratio of the size on a drawing to the size of the real thing that it represents

INDUSTRY TIP

Do not scale from photocopies because these can easily become distorted in the process of photocopying.

INDUSTRY TIP

If a drawing has **dimensions**, use these instead of using a scale rule to take a measurement.

Dimension

A measurement

The British Standards Institute's BS 1192 (Drawing office practice) gives a range of standard scales that are used for various drawing types and scale rules are manufactured to meet this purpose.

British Standards Institute

The British Standards Institute (BSI) is the UK authority that develops and publishes standards in the UK

SCALES IN COMMON USE

Scale	Use
1:1	Full size (used for rods)
1:2 1:5 1:10	Building details
1:20 1:50 1:100 1:200	Plans, elevations and sections
1:200 1:500 1:1250	Site plans
1:1250 1:2500	Location plans

The documents these scales are used for are described on pages 49–51.

The documents these scales are used for are described on pages 49–51.

FUNCTIONAL SKILLS

Work out the following:

Scale size	Scale	Actual size
10mm	1:10	100mm
25mm	1:20	a)
b)	1:50	300mm
50mm	1:200	c)

Work on this activity can support FM L2.3.2 and C2.3.

Answers: a) 500mm, b) 6mm, c) 10m

DATUM POINTS

Heights of buildings and the relative heights of components within the building are calculated from a common **datum point**. Datum points are determined by transferring a known fixed height from a bench mark. There are two types of datum point:

- A permanent Ordnance bench mark (OBM) is a given height on an Ordnance Survey map. This fixed height is described as a value, eg so many metres above sea level (as calculated from the average sea height at Newlyn, Cornwall).

- A temporary bench mark (TBM) is set up on site.

Datum point

A fixed point or height from which reference levels can be taken. The datum point is used to transfer levels across a building site. It represents the finished floor level (FFL) on a dwelling

Ordnance and temporary bench marks

ACTIVITY

Find your local OBM or your site TBM. What is the height of your OBM or TBM?

BASIC DRAWING SYMBOLS (HATCHINGS)

Standard symbols, also known as hatching symbols, are used on drawings as a means of passing on information simply. If all the parts of a building were labelled in writing, the drawing would soon become very crowded. Additionally, it is important to use standard symbols so that everyone can read them and they mean the same to everyone. The following images are just some of the standard symbols used.

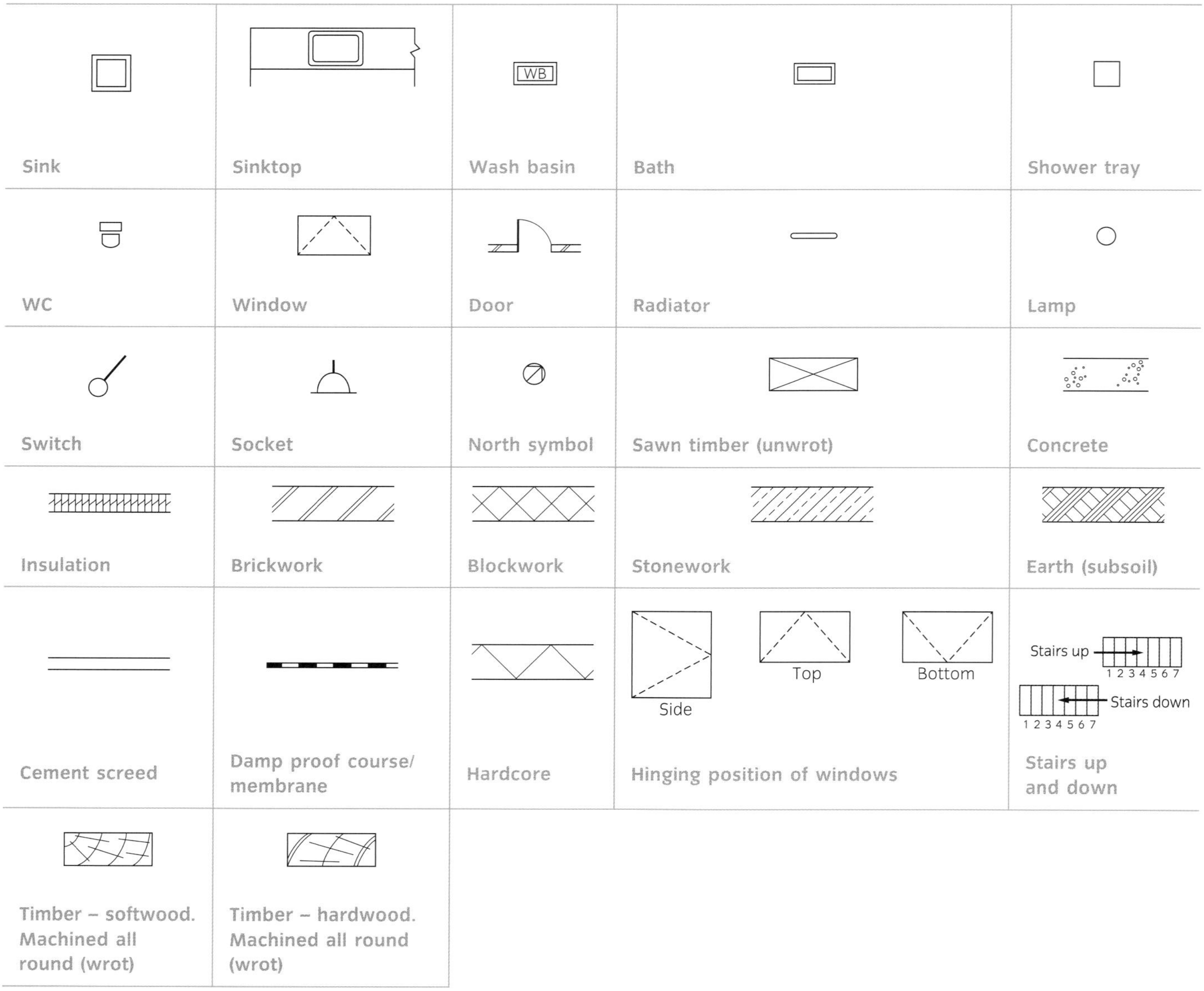
WB
Sink
Sinktop
Wash basin
Bath
Shower tray
WC
Window
Door
Radiator
Lamp
Switch
Socket
North symbol
Sawn timber (unwrot)
Concrete
Insulation
Brickwork
Blockwork
Stonework
Earth (subsoil)
Cement screed
Damp proof course/ membrane
Hardcore
Side
Top
Bottom
Hinging position of windows
Stairs up
1 2 3 4 5 6 7
Stairs down
1 2 3 4 5 6 7
Stairs up and down
Timber – softwood. Machined all round (wrot)
Timber – hardwood. Machined all round (wrot)

INFORMATION SOURCES

Type of drawing	Description
Location drawings	Usually prepared by an **architect** or **architectural technician**. Show the location of the building plot, position of the building and areas within the building. The term location drawings covers all of the drawings in this table.
Block plans 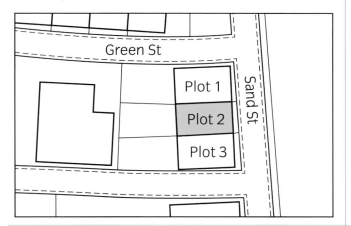	Show the proposed development in relation to its surrounding properties. The scales used are 1:1250 or 1:2500. Very little detail is available from this type of plan. The direction North is usually shown.
Site plans 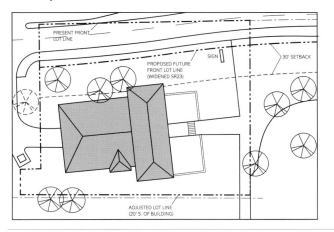	Show the plot in more detail, with drain runs, road layouts and the size and position of the existing building (and any extensions proposed) in relation to the property boundary. A scale of 1:200 or 1:500 is used. The Planning Portal sometimes refers to site plans as block plans, but the two types of plan have been distinguished in this book.

Architect

A trained professional who designs a structure and represents the client who wants the structure built. They are responsible for the production of the working drawings. They supervise the construction of buildings or other large structures

Architectural technician

A draftsperson who works in an architectural practice

Type of drawing	Description
Floor plans 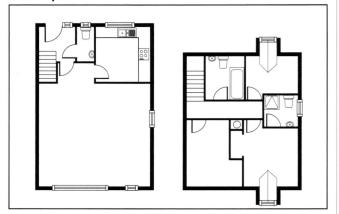	Show the positioning of walls, size of rooms along with the positioning of elements within the building such as units.
Elevations 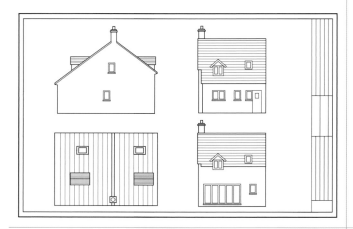	Show a building from a particular side and show the positioning of features such as doors and windows.
Sections 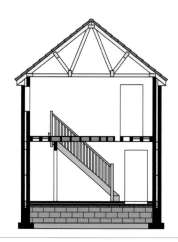	Show in greater detail what the section of a component looks like and how it might fit in relation to another component. A typical example would be a cross-section of a window showing the size of the features and how they fit together. Using these drawings it is possible to determine the positions of rooms, windows, doors, kitchen units and so on. Elevations are shown. These drawings are more detailed, and are often scaled to provide construction measurements. Some of the scales used are 1:200, 1:100, 1:50, 1:10, 1:5 and 1:1. A scale of 1:1 is full size.

Type of drawing	Description
Construction drawings (detail drawings) Detail showing typical exterior corner detail External walls — Exterior cladding — Breather membrane paper Exterior cladding — Wall plate stud — Breather membrane paper — Vapour control membrane on the inside of the timber frame	Show details of construction, normally as a cross-section.

PERMITS TO WORK

The permit to work is a documented procedure that gives authorisation for certain people to carry out specific work within a specified time frame. It sets out the precautions required to complete the work safely, based on a risk assessment. The following is an example of permit-to-work documentation that must be filled out.

PERMIT TO WORK

1. Area	2. Date
3. Work to be Done	4. Valid From
	5. Valid To
6. Company	
7. Man in Charge	8. No of Men

9. Safety Precautions

10. Safety Planning Certificate (cancelled if alarm sounds)

I have inspected the above job which has been safely prepared according to requirements of a safety planning certificate

Signed ....

11. Approval of Permit to Work

I am satisfied that this permit is properly authorised, that safe access is provided, and that all persons affected by this job have been informed

Signed ....

12. Electrical Equipment

All power has been isolated/locked/tagged/tried*
Circuits are live for troubleshooting only

Signed ....

13. Acceptance of Permit to Work

I/we* have read and understood the above precautions and will observe them. All equipment complies with relevant standards. I understand the site emergency plan.

Signed ....

14. Completion of Permit to Work

I/we* certify that this job is complete/incomplete*, all guards have been replaced and secured and all equipment has been removed. The job site has been left clean and tidy.

Permit to work

SIGNS AND NOTICES

As mentioned in Chapter 1, signs are used to keep operatives safe, and the law sets out the types of safety signs needed on a construction site. Some signs warn us about danger and others tell us what to do to stay safe. There are five basic types of sign on a site: prohibition, mandatory, caution, safe condition and supplementary. For more information on the colour, shape and use of these signs, see Chapter 1, pages 41–42.

Examples of safe condition and caution signs

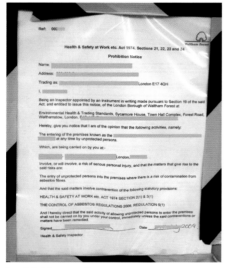

Prohibition notice

Notices are also used on construction sites, and again these are covered in Chapter 1, page 8. Two that you need to know are improvement notices and prohibition notices, both of which are issued by the HSE. An improvement notice is issued by an HSE or local authority inspector to formally notify a company that improvements are needed to the way it is working. A prohibition notice is issued by an HSE or local authority inspector when there is an immediate risk of personal injury. They are not issued lightly and if you receive one, you are clearly breaking a health and safety regulation. The HASAWA workplace notice is also important.

SPECIFICATIONS

A specification accompanies the working drawings. It gives further information that cannot be shown on the drawings because the drawings need to be clear and not covered in notes. A specification would include information such as:

- the colour of paint required

- a specific timber species

- the brick type required

- the plaster finish required.

It is prepared by construction professionals such as architects and building services engineers. They can be produced from previous project specifications, in-house documents or master specifications such as the National Building Specification (NBS). The NBS is owned by the Royal Institute of British Architects (RIBA).

Example of a specification

COMPONENT RANGE DRAWINGS

A component range drawing shows the range of components available from a manufacturer. It includes:

- sizes available

- coding for ordering purposes

- availability (whether it can be bought off the shelf or whether pre-ordering is required).

Availability is particularly important when planning delivery dates. Schedules reference this type of drawing.

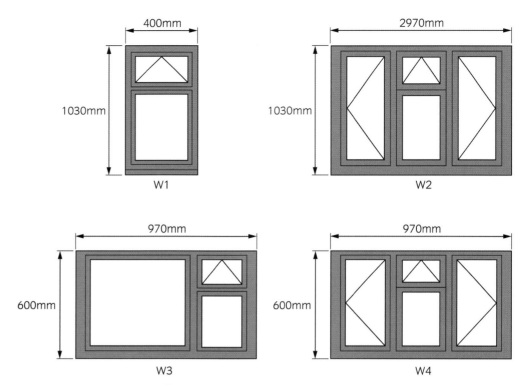

Component range drawing of windows

SCHEDULES

A schedule is used to record repeated design information that applies to a range of components or fittings, such as:

- windows
- doors
- kitchen units
- joinery fittings.

A schedule is mainly used on bigger sites where there are multiples of several designs of houses, with each type having different components and fittings. It avoids a house being given the wrong component or fitting.

A schedule is usually used in conjunction with a component range drawing, a detail drawing and a floor plan.

A detail drawing shows just that – a detail of a particular part of a building and how it is constructed.

In a typical plan, the doors and windows are labelled D1, D2, W1, W2 etc. These components would be included in the schedule, which would provide additional information on them. For example, see the following schedule.

Master Internal Door Schedule							
Ref:	Door size	S.O. width	S.O. height	Lintel type	FD30	Self closing	Floor level
D1	838 × 1981	900	2040	BOX	Yes	Yes	GROUND FLOOR
D2	838 × 1981	900	2040	BOX	Yes	Yes	GROUND FLOOR
D3	762 × 1981	824	2040	BOX	No	No	GROUND FLOOR
D4	838 × 1981	900	2040	N/A	Yes	No	GROUND FLOOR
D5	838 × 1981	900	2040	BOX	Yes	Yes	GROUND FLOOR
D6	762 × 1981	824	2040	BOX	Yes	Yes	FIRST FLOOR
D7	762 × 1981	824	2040	BOX	Yes	Yes	FIRST FLOOR
D8	762 × 1981	824	2040	N/A	Yes	No	FIRST FLOOR
D9	762 × 1981	824	2040	BOX	Yes	Yes	FIRST FLOOR
D10	762 × 1981	824	2040	N/A	No	No	FIRST FLOOR
D11	686 × 1981	748	2040	N/A	Yes	No	SECOND FLOOR
D12	762 × 1981	824	2040	BOX	Yes	Yes	SECOND FLOOR
D13	762 × 1981	824	2040	100 HD BOX	Yes	Yes	SECOND FLOOR
D14	686 × 1981	748	2040	N/A	No	No	SECOND FLOOR

Example of a schedule

BILLS OF QUANTITIES

A bill of quantities is produced by the quantity surveyor and describes everything that is required for the job based on the drawings, specification and schedules. A bill of quantities contains the following information:

- *Preliminaries*: General information including the names of the client and architect, details of the work and descriptions of the site.

- *Preambles*: Like the specification, this outlines the quality and description of materials and workmanship, etc.

- *Measured quantities*: A description of how each task and material is to be measured, with measurements in metres (linear and square), hours, litres, kilogrammes and the number of components required.

The completed document is sent out to contractors who then price the work and enter the costs into the blank spaces. The bill of quantities ensures that all the contractors are pricing for the job using the same information.

BILL OF QUANTITIES

Number	Item Description	Unit	Quantity	Rate	Amount	
					£	p
	CLASS A: GENERAL ITEMS					
	Specified Requirements					
	Testing of Materials					
A250	Testing of recycled and secondary aggregates	sum				
	Information to be provided by the Contractor					
A290	Production of Materials Management Plan	sum				
	Method Related Charges					
	Recycling Plant/Equipment					
A339.01	Mobilise; Fixed	sum				
A339.02	Operate; Time-Related	sum				
A339.03	De-mobilise; Fixed	sum				
	CLASS D: DEMOLITION AND SITE CLEARANCE					
	Other Structures					
D522.01	Other structures; Concrete	sum				
D522.02	Grading/processing of demolition material to produce recycled and secondary aggregates	m³	70			
D522.03	Disposal of demolition material offsite	m³	30			
	CLASS E: EARTHWORKS					
	Excavation Ancillaries					
E542	Double handling of recycled and secondary aggregates produced from demolition material	m³	70			
	Filling					
E615	Importing primary aggregates for filling to structures	m³	15			
E619.1	Importing recycled and secondary aggregates for filling to structures	m³	15			

WORK SCHEDULES

It is very important indeed that the progress of work is planned out. A work schedule or programme of work is an easy way of showing what work is to be carried out and when. This is usually shown in the form of a bar chart called a Gantt chart. The chart lists the tasks that need to be done on the left-hand side and shows a timeline across the top. The site manager or trade supervisors can quickly tell from looking at this chart:

- if work is keeping to schedule

- what materials, equipment and labour are required

- when they are required.

Materials very often have a **lead-in time** and so cannot be delivered immediately. These need to be ordered and delivered at the correct time. Labour planning is also required otherwise the trades may be working elsewhere when needed.

Task	Time (days)						
	1	2	3	4	5	6	7
Prepare the ground	▨	▨					
Spread foundations			▨	▨			
Lay cables for services				▨	▨		
Build walls up to DPC						▨	▨
	Proposed time in orange						

Gantt chart

CALCULATING QUANTITIES FOR MATERIALS

Calculations are required throughout the building process. It is important that these calculations are accurate, as mistakes can be very expensive. A company can lose a lot of money if it underestimates:

- the amount of materials required

- how much they cost

- how long it will take to complete a job.

It could also lead to the company gaining a bad reputation for not being able to complete a job on time and in budget.

Materials are usually better priced if bought in bulk, whereas a buy-as-you go approach can cost more.

Lead-in time

The time taken between ordering an item and it being delivered

Consider these points when buying materials:

- Is there sufficient storage room for delivered materials?

- Is there a risk of the materials being damaged if there is nowhere suitable to store them or if they are delivered too early?

- Will it be a problem to obtain the same style, colour or quality of product if they are not all ordered at the same time?

- Will over-ordering cause lots of wastage?

These and many other considerations will help determine when and in what quantity materials are ordered.

Some wastage is unavoidable. Allowances must be made for wastage, eg cut bricks that cannot be re-used, short ends of timber, partly full paint cans. Up to 5% waste is allowed for bricks and blocks and 10% for timber and paint.

It may be that all the materials are ordered by the office or supervisory staff, but you still need to know how to recognise and calculate material requirements. Deliveries have to be checked before the delivery note is signed and the driver leaves. Any discrepancies in the type or quantity of materials, or any materials that have arrived damaged, must be recorded on the delivery note and reported to the supervisor. Any discrepancies will need to be followed up and new delivery times arranged.

You must be able to identify basic materials and carry out basic calculations. You will often have to collect sufficient materials to carry out a particular operation. Being able to measure accurately will mean you can make the most economic use of materials and therefore reduce waste.

INDUSTRY TIP

Wastage is impossible to avoid, so make sure enough materials are ordered as it might be difficult to order additional materials that match exactly, such as tiles or wallpaper.

Deliveries must be checked before signing the delivery note

UNITS OF MEASUREMENT

The construction industry uses metric units as standard; however, you may come across some older measures called imperial units.

Units for measuring	Metric units	Imperial units
Length	millimetre (mm) metre (m) kilometre (km)	inch (in) or " eg 6" (6 inches) foot (ft) or ' eg 8' (8 foot)
Liquid	millilitre (ml) litre (l)	pint (pt)
Weight	gramme (g) kilogramme (kg) tonne (t)	pound (lb)

ACTIVITY

Look online to find out:
- What other imperial units are still commonly used?
- How many millimetres are there in an inch?
- How many litres are there in a gallon?

Units for measuring	Quantities	Example
Length	There are 1,000mm in 1m There are 1,000m in 1km	1mm × 1,000 = 1m 1m × 1,000 = 1km 6,250mm can be shown as 6.250m 6,250m can be shown as 6.250km
Liquid	There are 1,000ml in 1l	1ml × 1,000 = 1l
Weight	There are 1,000g in 1kg There are 1,000kg in 1t	1g × 1,000 = 1kg 1kg × 1,000 = 1t

INDUSTRY TIP

Although everything supplied in the construction industry is measured in metric units, many materials still use the imperial equivalent. For example, a plywood sheet will be 1.22m × 2.44m. This is actually the equivalent of an 8 foot by 4 foot board. It is worth noting these differences as they can cause problems.

CALCULATIONS

Four basic mathematical operations are used in construction calculations.

ADDITION

The addition of two or more numbers is shown with a plus sign (**+**).

Example

A stack of bricks 3 bricks long and 2 bricks high contains 6 bricks.

$$3 + 3 = 6$$

More examples:

$$5 + 2 = 7$$

$$19 + 12 = 31$$

$$234 + 105 = 339$$

Pallet of bricks

SUBTRACTION

The reduction of one number by another number is shown with a minus sign (**–**).

Example

A pallet containing 100 bricks is delivered on site, but you need only 88 bricks. How many are left over?

$$100 - 88 = 12$$

More examples:

$$5 - 2 = 3$$

$$19 - 12 = 7$$

$$234 - 105 = 129$$

MULTIPLICATION

The scaling of one number by another number is shown with a multiplication sign (×).

> **Example**
>
> A stack of bricks is 3 bricks long and 2 bricks high. It contains 6 bricks.
>
> $$3 \times 2 = 6$$
>
> More examples:
>
> $$19 \times 12 = 228$$
>
> $$234 \times 10 = 2,340$$
>
> $$234 \times 105 = 24,570$$

In the last two examples, the comma (,) is used to show we are in the thousands. In words we would say, twenty-four thousand, five hundred and seventy.

DIVISION

Sharing one number by another number in equal parts (how many times it goes into the number) is shown with a division sign (÷).

> **Example**
>
> $$4 \div 2 = 2$$
>
> $$36 \div 12 = 3$$
>
> $$600 \div 4 = 150$$

LINEAR MEASUREMENTS

Linear means how long a number of items would measure from end to end if laid in a straight line. Examples of things that are calculated in linear measurements are:

- skirting board
- lengths of timber
- rope
- building line
- wallpaper.

We use this form of measurement when working out how much of one of the materials listed above we need, eg to find out how much

The quantity of skirting required is calculated using linear measurements

A joiner measuring a room

Perimeter

The distance around an object or room

skirting board is required for a room. First, we need to measure the **perimeter** (sides) of a room. To find the linear length we add the length of all four sides together. This can be done in two ways: adding or multiplying.

Example 1

A site carpenter has been asked how many metres of skirting are required for the rooms below.

They can add all the sides together:
2.2 + 4.2 + 2.2 + 4.2 = 12.8m

Or, they can multiply each side by 2, and add them together:
(2.2 × 2) + (4.2 × 2) = 12.8m

Either way, **12.8m** is the correct answer.

Example 2

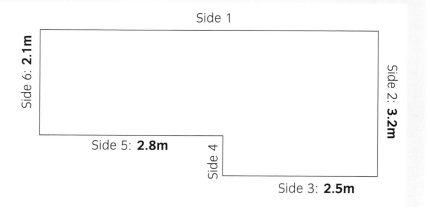

To work out the perimeter of this room we need to add all the sides together. In this example each side has been given a reference number, so all we need to do is add all the sides together, like this:

side 1 (side 3 + side 5) + side 2 + side 3 + side 4 (side 2 − side 6) + side 5 + side 6

Now, let's show the working out: (2.8 + 2.5) + 3.2 + 2.5 + (3.2 − 2.1) + 2.8 + 2.1 = 17m

The amount of skirting board required is **17m**.

Now let's put some door openings in. This symbol ⟵⟶ represents an opening.

Example 3

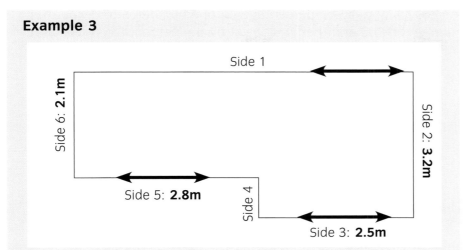

On side 1 there is an opening 0.9m wide, on side 3 there is an opening 1.5m wide and on side 5 there is an opening 2.1m wide.

We know from Example 2 that the perimeter of the room is 17m. We now need to remove the openings. Skirting board will not be needed for the openings.

Step 1

Add together the lengths of the three combined openings:

0.9 + 1.5 + 2.1 = 4.5m

Step 2

Deduct this from 17m:

17 − 4.5 = 12.5m

The linear length of skirting board required is 12.5m.

Step 3

However, this calculation does not take into account any waste. We would normally add 10% extra to allow for waste:

12.5 + 10% = 12.5 + 1.25 = 13.75m

The total amount of skirting board required is **13.75m**.

PERCENTAGES

An easy way to find a percentage (%) of a number is to divide the number by 100 and then multiply it by the percentage you require.

Example

Increase 19m by 12%

$19 \div 100 = 0.19$

$0.19 \times 12 = 2.28$

$19 + 2.28 = 21.28m$

Total required **21.28m**.

AREA

Floors

The structured layers of a building, eg ground floor, first floor, second floor

To find out how much material is required to cover a surface such as a **floor** or wall you need to calculate its area. Area is the measurements of a two-dimensional surface, eg the surface of floors, walls, glass or a roof.

To find the area of a surface you need to multiply its length by its width (L × W) or one side by the other. This will give you an answer which is expressed in square units (^{2}). For example, mm², m² or km².

Example 1

A bricklayer has been asked to work out the area of the floor below.

Side 1: **2.2m**

Side 2: **4.4m**

side 1 × side 2 = floor area

$2.2 \times 4.4 = 9.68m^2$

The total floor area is **9.68m²**.

Irregularly shaped areas can be calculated by breaking up the area into sections that can be worked out easily, and then adding them together.

Example 2

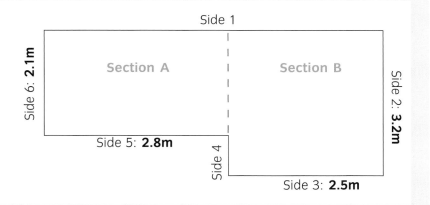

Irregularly shaped rooms can be split into sections to calculate the area

Step 1

Divide the area into two parts, and then calculate the area of each part. The easiest way to do this is to divide it into two smaller sections:

Step 2

Work out the areas of section A and section B:

section A = 2.1 × 2.8 = 5.88m²

section B = 2.5 × 3.2 = 8m²

Step 3

Add the areas of section A and section B together:

section A + section B = total floor area

5.88 + 8 = 13.88m²

The total floor area is 13.88m².

A tiler tiling a floor

INDUSTRY TIP

Remember, there are 1,000mm in a metre so we show the sum as 0.305m in Example 3.

ACTIVITY

Find the area of the following measurements:

1   2.1m × 2.4m
2   0.9m × 2.7m
3   250mm × 3.4m

Answers: 1) 5.04m², 2) 2.43m², 3) 0.85m²

Now let's say the floor requires tiling. The tiler needs to calculate the number of floor tiles required.

Example 3

The size of each floor tile is 305mm × 305mm. We can also show this as 0.305m × 0.305m.

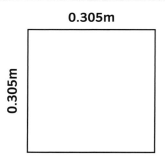

0.305m

0.305m

How many floor tiles are required for the floor area in Example 2? The total floor area is 13.88m².

Step 1

Calculate the area of one tile. As the floor area is given in m², we need to calculate the size of the tile in the same unit, ie m².

0.305 × 0.305 = 0.093m²

Step 2

Now you need to divide the total floor area by the area of one tile to find out the total number of tiles required.

total floor area ÷ area of one tile = total number of tiles

13.88 ÷ 0.093 = 149.247 tiles

This number is rounded up to the next full tile, so a total of 150 floor tiles are required.

Step 3

However, this total does not allow for any waste.

Add 5% to allow for waste:

150 + 5% = 158 tiles (to the next full tile)

Let's look at the working out:

150 ÷ 100 = 1.5 tiles (this is 1%)

1.5 × 5 = 7.5 tiles (this is 5%)

5% of 150 tiles, rounded up to the next full tile, is 8 tiles.

Therefore **158 tiles** are required.

AREA OF A TRIANGLE

Sometimes you will be required to work out an area that includes a triangle.

Example 1

A painter has been asked to work out how much paint will be needed to paint the front of this house.

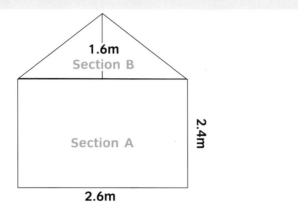

1.6m
Section B

2.4m

Section A

2.6m

Step 1

Divide the area up into a rectangular section (section A) and a triangular section (section B).

Step 2

Find the area of section A:

2.4 × 2.6 = 6.24m²

The area of section A is 6.24m².

Step 3

Find the area of section B.

The area of a triangle can be found by multiplying the base by the height, then dividing by 2.

(base × height) ÷ 2 = area

2.6 × 1.6 = 4.16

4.16 ÷ 2 = 2.08m²

The area of section B is 2.08m².

Step 4

area of section A + area of section B = total wall area

6.24 + 2.08 = 8.32m²

The total wall area is **8.32m²**.

ACTIVITY

Look at the diagram. Work out the area of the wall in order to arrange the delivery of sufficient paint.

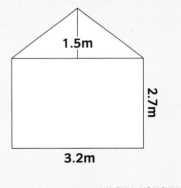

1.5m

2.7m

3.2m

Answer: 11.04m²

RIGHT-ANGLED TRIANGLE

Now let's look at the right-angled triangle below. It has three sides, A, B and C. Pythagorean theorem tells us that in a right-angled triangle the **hypotenuse** is equal to the sum of the square of the lengths of the two other sides, in other words $a^2 + b^2 = c^2$. In this example the hypotenuse is side C.

Using the Pythagorean theorem we can work out the length of any side.

Hypotenuse

The longest side of a right-angled triangle. It is always opposite the right angle

Example 1

If side A is 3m long and side B is 4m long, what is the length of side C?

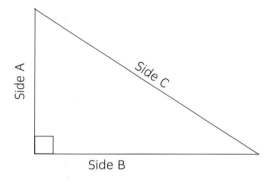

$3 \times 3 = 9$

$4 \times 4 = 16$

$9 + 16 = 25$

$\sqrt{25} = 5$

($\sqrt{}$ means square root. A square root of a number is the number that is multiplied by itself to make that number, in this case $5 \times 5 = 25$)

Side C is **5m** long.

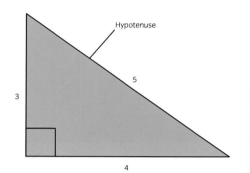

The hypotenuse

INDUSTRY TIP

If a triangle has a small square in the corner, this shows you the corner is a right angle.

Example 2

A joiner has been asked to work out the length of a roof (side C).

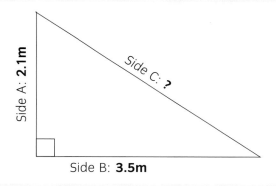

2.1×2.1 (side A) = 4.41

3.5×3.5 (side B) = 12.25

$4.41 + 12.25 = 16.66$

$\sqrt{16.66} = 4.08$m

The length of side C is **4.08m**.

Example 3

A bricklayer needs to find the rise of a roof (side A).

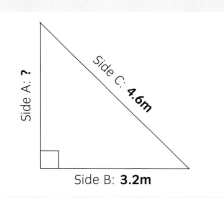

3.2×3.2 (side B) = 10.24

4.6×4.6 (side C) = 21.16

$21.16 - 10.24 = 10.92$

$\sqrt{10.92} = 3.30$m

The length of side A is **3.3m**.

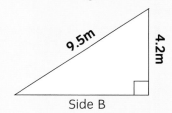
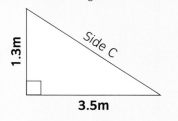

PERIMETERS AND AREAS OF CIRCLES

Circumference

The distance around the edge of a circle

Diameter

The length of a straight line going through the centre of a circle connecting two points on its circumference

Sometimes you are required to find the perimeter or **circumference** of a circle.

circumference of a circle = π × **diameter**

$$C = πd$$

π (or 'pi') is the number of times that the diameter of a circle will divide into the circumference.

π = 3.142

This is equal to the number of diameters in one revolution of a circle. It is the same for any sized circle.

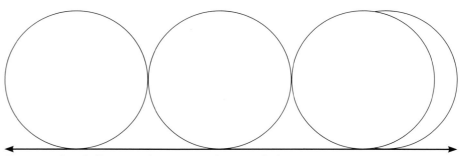

There are 3.142 diameters in one complete revolution

Example 1

A joiner is making a circular window that has a diameter of 600mm. Its circumference is:

0.600 × 3.142 = **1.885m**

The diameter of a circle from a given circumference is:

diameter = circumference ÷ π

Example 2

A window has a circumference of 2.250m. Its diameter is:

2.250 ÷ 3.142 = **0.716m** (or 716mm)

Radius

The length of a line from the centre to a point on the circumference of a circle. It is exactly half the length of the diameter

The area of a circle is found by:

area of a circle = π × **radius**² (radius is equal to half the diameter)

Example 3

A painter needs to paint a circle that is 1.2m in diameter and is required to find the area of the circle to enable them to order the correct quantity of paint.

1.2 ÷ 2 = **0.6m** (the radius)

3.142 × 0.6m² = **1.13m²**

VOLUME

The volume of an object is the total space it takes up, eg a tin of paint, a foundation for a wall or the capacity of a concrete mixer, and is shown as m³ (cubic metres). To find the volume of an object you must multiply length by width by height.

$$\text{volume} = \text{length} \times \text{width} \times \text{height}$$

Example 1

Each side of this cube is 1m. The total space it takes up is 1m³.

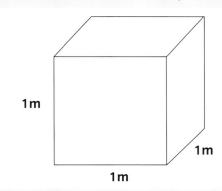

1m × 1m × 1m = **1m³**

Example 2

A bricklayer has been asked to work out how many m³ of **concrete** is required for a strip foundation. The size of the foundation is 3.2m long, 0.600m wide and 0.900m deep.

length × width × height = volume

3.2 × 0.600 × 0.900 = 1.728m³

The volume of concrete needed for the strip foundation is **1.728m³**.

INDUSTRY TIP

Remember r² is the same as r × r (r= radius).

A bricklayer taking levels

Concrete

Composed of cement, fine aggregate (sand) and course aggregate (stone) of varying sizes and in varying proportions

To work out the volume of a cylinder:

$$\text{volume} = \pi r^2 h \ (\pi \times r^2 \times h)$$

ACTIVITY

A bricklayer has been given two tasks:
1 Measure the volume of a strip foundation measuring 4.250m long, 1.1m wide and 1m deep.
2 Find the volume of four pile foundations (see page 83) each measuring 2.5m deep, with a diameter of 0.9m.

Work out the answers to the tasks.

Answers: 1) 4.675m³, 2) 6.36m²

Example 3

A joiner has a tin of preservative and needs to know its volume. The tin has a diameter of 250mm and a height of 700mm.

$\pi r^2 h \ (\pi \times r^2 \times h) = \text{volume}$

The radius (r) is half the diameter:

$250 \div 2 = 125\text{mm}$

$3.142 \times 0.125^2 \times 0.700 = 0.034\text{m}^3$

The volume of the tin of paint is **0.034m³**.

COMMUNICATION

Good communication is vital to the smooth running of any building project.

Communication involves sharing thoughts, information and ideas between people. For communication to be effective, information must be:

- given in a clear way
- received without misunderstanding.

It has been said that to be a good communicator it is just as important to be a good listener as it is to be a good speaker! Good communication leads to a safer and more efficient workplace, not to mention helping to maintain a pleasant working environment.

Most sites will have policies and procedures in place that govern the chain of command and communication between supervisory staff and workers.

INDUSTRY TIP

Before communicating something, it is good to gather your thoughts. Have relevant information to hand, eg a drawing, and take notes if required.

ACTIVITY

A customer has asked for the best steps to take before painting the skirting board in their new home. You have been asked to reply to the customer and give advice on the best way for them to do this.

Decide on the best form of communication and list all the information you should give along with the stages they should follow.

WRITTEN COMMUNICATION

There are many methods of communication within the building industry. In this chapter we have discussed drawings, schedules and specifications etc. The architect uses these methods to communicate details about the building to the team who will **tender** for and erect the building.

Communication is usually electronic via email (with or without attachments) or through intranet sites. Drawings are very commonly distributed in electronic formats which are printed on to paper when required. Messages are often given via text.

Sometimes communication will be via a memorandum (memo), a written form of communication.

Site rules, risk assessments and method statements (see Chapter 1) communicate safety information.

SITE PAPERWORK

Communication on site is aided by the use of paperwork and without it no building site could operate. It is an important method of communication between operatives and supervisory staff, builders, architects and clients.

Tender

To supply a client with a fixed quotation for work

INDUSTRY TIP

Messages that are passed on by word of mouth are open to interpretation, so written messages can often be clearer.

FUNCTIONAL SKILLS

Thinking about the garage that you worked out the costs for on page 57 and using a computer, write a letter to the client outlining the cost and other details such as when the work would start and any basic terms regarding payment.

Work on this activity can support FE 2.3.1.

Type of paperwork	Description
Timesheet **Timesheet** Employer: CPF Building Co. / Employee Name: Louise Miranda / Week starting: 17/6/14 Date: 21/6/13 *(see table below)*	Used to record the hours completed each day, and is usually the basis on which pay is calculated. Timesheets also help to work out how much the job has cost in working hours, and can give information for future estimating work when working up a tender.

Timesheet

Employer:	Employee Name:	Week starting:
CPF Building Co.	Louise Miranda	17/6/14

Date: 21/6/13

Day	Job/Job Number	Start Time	Finish Time	Total Hours	Overtime
Monday	Penburthy, Falmouth 0897	9am	6pm	8	
Tuesday	Penburthy, Falmouth 0897	9am	6pm	8	
Wednesday	Penburthy, Falmouth 0897	8.30am	5.30pm	8	
Thursday	Trelawney, Truro 0901	11am	8pm	8	2
Friday	Trelawney, Truro 0901	11am	7pm	7	1
Saturday	Trelawney, Truro 0901	9am	1pm	4	
Totals				43	3

Employee's signature:_____

Supervisor's signature: _____

Type of paperwork	Description
Job sheet **CPF Building Co** **Job sheet** **Customer name:** Henry Collins **Date:** 9/12/14 **Address:** 57 Green St Kirkham London **Work to be carried out** Finishing joint work to outer walls **Instructions** Use weather struck and half round	Gives details of a job to be carried out, sometimes with material requirements and hours given to complete the task.
Variation order **Confirmation notice** **Architect's instruction** **CPF Building Co** **Variation order** **Project Name:** Penburthy House, Falmouth, Cornwall **Reference Number:** 80475 **Date:** 14/11/14 **From: :** _____ **To:** _____ **Reason for change:** **Tick** Customer requirements ☑ Engineer requirements ☐ Revised design ☐ **Instruction:** Entrance door to be made from Utile hardwood with brushed chrome finished ironmongery (changed from previous detail, softwood with brass ironmongery). Signature _____	Sometimes alterations are made to the contract which changes the work to be completed, eg a client may wish to move a door position or request a different brick finish. This usually involves a variation to the cost. This work should not be carried out until a variation order and a confirmation notice have been issued. Architect's instructions are instructions given by an architect, first verbally and then in writing to a site agent as work progresses and questions inevitably arise over details and specifications.

Type of paperwork	Description
Requisition order	Filled out to order materials from a supplier or central store. These usually have to be authorised by a supervisor before they can be used.

CPF Building Co
Requisition order

Supplier Information: Construction Supplies Ltd   **Date:** 9/12/14

Contract Address/Delivery Address: Penburthy House, Falmouth, Cornwall

Tel number: 0207294333

Order Number: 26213263CPF

Item number	Description	Quantity	Unit/Unit Price	Total
X22433	75mm 4mm gauge countersunk brass screws slotted	100	30p	£30
YK7334	Brass cups to suit	100	5p	£5
V23879	Sadikkens water based clear varnish	1 litre	£20.00	£20.00
Total:				£55.00

Authorised by: Denzil Penburthy

Delivery note	Accompanies a delivery. Goods have to be checked for quantity and quality before the note is signed. Any discrepancies are recorded on the delivery note. Goods that are not suitable (because they are not as ordered or because they are of poor quality) can be refused and returned to the supplier.

Construction Supplies Ltd
Delivery note

Customer name and address:
CPF Building Co
Penburthy House
Falmouth
Cornwall

Delivery Date: 16/12/14
Delivery time: 9am

Order number: 26213263CPF

Item number	Quantity	Description	Unit Price	Total
X22433	100	75mm 4mm gauge countersunk brass screws slotted	30p	£30
YK7334	100	Brass cups to suit	5p	£5
V23879	1 litre	Sadikkens water based clear varnish	£20	£20

Subtotal	£55.00
VAT	20%
Total	£66.00

Discrepancies: ....

Customer Signature: ....

Print name: ....

Date: ....

Type of paperwork	Description
Delivery record **Davids & Co** **Monthly delivery record** Customer name and address: CPF Building Co, Penburthy House, Falmouth, Cornwall Customer order date: 28th May 2014 	Item number	Quantity	Description	Unit Price	Date Delivered
BS3647	2	1 tonne bag of building sand	£60	3/6/14
CM4324	12	25kg bags of cement	£224	17/6/14 | Customer Signature: .... Print name: .... Date:	Every month a supplier will issue a delivery record that lists all the materials or hire used for that month.
Invoice **Davids & Co** **Invoice** Invoice number: 75856 PO number: 4700095685 Date: 2nd January 2014 Company name and address: Davids & Co, 228 West Retail Park, Ivybridge, Plymouth Customer name and address: CPF Building Co, Penburthy House, Falmouth, Cornwall VAT registration number: 663694542 For: 	Item number	Quantity	Description	Unit Price
BS3647	2	1 tonne bag of building sand	£30
CM4324	12	25kg bags of cement	£224
Subtotal	£2748.00
VAT	20%
Total	£3297.60	 Please make cheques payable to Davids & Co Payment due in 30 days	Sent by a supplier. It lists the services or materials supplied along with the price the contractor is requested to pay. There will be a time limit within which to pay. Sometimes there will be a discount for quick payment or penalties for late payment.
Site diary 	This will be filled out daily. It records anything of note that happens on site such as deliveries, absences or occurrences, eg delay due to the weather.

VERBAL COMMUNICATION

Often, managers, supervisors, work colleagues and trades communicate verbally. This can be face to face or over a telephone. Although this is the most common form of communication, it is also the most unreliable.

Mistakes are often made while communicating verbally. The person giving the information might make an error. The person receiving the information might misunderstand something because the information is unclear or it is noisy in the background, or because they later forget the details of the conversation.

Confusion can be minimised by recording conversations or by using a form of written communication. If there is a record it can be used for future reference and help to clear up any misunderstandings.

TAKING A TELEPHONE MESSAGE

It is a good idea to take down details of telephone calls and many companies provide documentation for this purpose. When taking a message it is important to record the following details:

- *Content*: This is the most important part of the message – the actual information being relayed. Take and write down as many details as possible.

- *Date and time*: Messages are often **time sensitive**, and may require an urgent response.

- *Who the message is for*: Ensure the person gets the message by giving it to them or leaving it in a place where they will find it.

- *Contact name and details*: Write down the name of the person leaving the message, and how to get back to them with a response.

UNACCEPTABLE COMMUNICATION

When communicating, it is very important to stay calm. Think about what you are going to say. An angry word will often encourage an angry response. However, keeping calm and composed will often diffuse a stressful situation. A shouting match rarely ends with a good or productive result.

There are several types of communication that are unacceptable and could result in unemployment. Unacceptable communication includes:

- aggressive communication such as swearing or using inappropriate hand gestures

An operative taking notes during a phone call

Time sensitive
When something must be dealt with quickly

- racist or sexist comments or gestures

- showing prejudice against people with disabilities.

This type of behaviour shows a lack of respect for others and does not create a safe or pleasant working environment. It will also give your company a poor image if customers see or hear this behaviour. Acting in this way is likely to result in trouble for you and your employer and could even result in a **tribunal** and loss of employment.

Tribunal

A judgement made in court

KNOWLEDGE OF THE CONSTRUCTION INDUSTRY AND BUILT ENVIRONMENT

Buildings come in a wide variety of types in relation to appearance and methods of construction. Despite the variety of buildings, they all have design features in common. In this section we will discuss various parts of buildings and their purpose.

We will also discuss sustainable construction – how buildings can be designed to sit better within the environment, with lower pollution levels and energy requirements both during the building process and when in use.

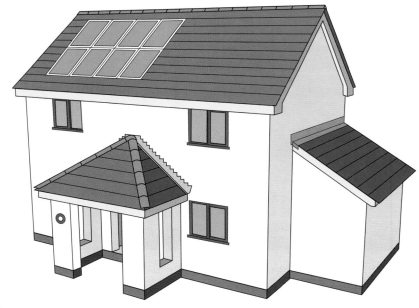

A house with solar panels

FOUNDATIONS

Foundation

Used to spread the load of a building to the subsoil

Foundations serve as a good base on which to put the building. They need to be capable of carrying the weight of the building and any further load that may be put upon it. These are known as **dead loads** and **imposed loads**.

Foundations must be designed to resist any potential movement in the ground on which the building will sit. Ground conditions can vary widely. Soil samples are taken to help decide on the type of foundation to use. This usually takes the form of bore holes dug or drilled around the site. These samples are sent away for testing in a laboratory. The results will identify:

- the soil condition (clay or sandy)

- the depth of the soil

- the depth of the water table

- if any contaminations are present.

The soil condition is important: clay soil drains poorly and can move if it gets waterlogged or dries out completely. Sandy soils drain very well, but can become unstable. A foundation that is suitable for the ground type and load of the building will be designed.

CONCRETE

Foundations are made from concrete. Concrete is made from fine and coarse aggregate (crushed stone), sand and cement mixed with water. Water reacts with the cement causing it to harden. This process is called hydration and it locks the aggregates together. Concrete is very strong under compression (when weight is put upon it) but is weak when it is pulled (put under tension). Tension can be caused in a foundation when it has to bridge softer sections of ground or when ground conditions are unstable. To prevent failure of the foundation, the concrete may need to be reinforced with steel which is cast into the concrete before it hardens.

Dead load

The weight of all the materials used to construct the building

Imposed load

Additional loads that may be placed on the structure, eg people, furniture, wind and snow

INDUSTRY TIP

The type of foundation to be used will usually be decided by the architect and a structural engineer and will be the result of tests.

INDUSTRY TIP

Remember, cement will give chemical burns so use the correct PPE while using and mixing it.

Concrete with steel reinforcement

Sulphate-resisting cement

Sulphate-resisting cement, such as Sulphate Resisting Portland Cement, is more resistant than ordinary cement to the action of mineralised water containing sulphates. It also hardens more slowly and has a higher frost resistance. The ratio of cement to aggregate in concrete will also affect its strength. Concrete can be mixed in a number of ratios to suit the type of foundation design and the strength of foundation needed to cope with different ground conditions. The ratios are outlined below.

Concrete name	Ratio	Usage
C7.5 (low strength)	1:3:6 or 7 (cement:sand: coarse aggregate)	For general non-structural use.
C10 to C15 (medium strength)	1:4:6 to 1:4:5 (cement:sand: medium aggregate)	Used in typical house foundations.
C20 (strong)	1:2:4 (cement:sand: medium aggregate)	Used as a foundation mix in house construction in softer ground and for slabs.
C25 (stronger)	1:1.5:3 (cement:sand: medium aggregate)	Can be used for foundations to larger houses and for creating floors.
C30 (very strong)	1:2:3 (cement:sand: fine aggregate)	A general-purpose, strong concrete.
C35 (industrial strength)	1:1.5:2.5 (cement: sand:fine aggregate)	Structural concrete.

Additives are used to slow down or speed up the curing process if required (known as retardants and accelerants respectively) and for frost resistance as frost can damage concrete that has not had a chance to harden sufficiently.

TYPES OF FOUNDATION

Different types of structures, such as detached houses, high-rise and low-rise buildings, all require different types of foundation.

High-rise building

Low-rise building

Detached house

OUR HOUSE

What type of foundation does the building you are sitting in have? How can you tell? Why was that foundation type chosen? Look at the foundations used in 'Our House' as a further guide.

Strip foundations

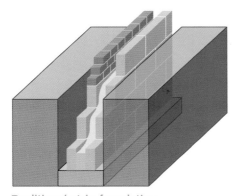

Traditional strip foundation

A strip foundation is the traditional type of foundation used for residential developments (ordinary houses). It is formed by digging a trench to the required width and depth as determined by the soil conditions and the weight of the structure. It is either filled with concrete or a layer of concrete is poured into the bottom. This layer must be a minimum of 150mm thick and is commonly 225mm thick.

Footings

The substructure below ground level. These are projecting courses at the base of a wall

Damp proof course (DPC)

A layer of plastic that prevents damp rising up through a wall needs to be positioned at least 150mm above ground level

Footings are brought up to the level of the **damp proof course** (DPC) using concrete blocks or bricks. These are set out from the centre of the strip of concrete in order to spread the weight evenly. A variety of specialist bricks and blocks are used for this purpose. They need to be able to resist water penetration and therefore frost damage.

Engineering brick

Trench block

It can be economical to fill the trench up to the top with concrete rather than build a substructure – this is known as trench fill. Sometimes it is necessary to build on the edge of the concrete – this is known as an eccentric foundation.

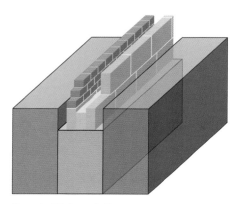

Trench fill foundation

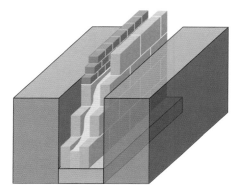

Eccentric foundation

Wide strip foundations

A wide strip foundation is very similar to a strip foundation in most of its aspects. The main difference between the two is that a wide strip foundation has steel reinforcements placed within the concrete. The steel gives considerably more strength to the foundation and enables greater loads to be placed on it. Without the steel reinforcements the foundation would need to be much deeper and would need vast amounts of concrete.

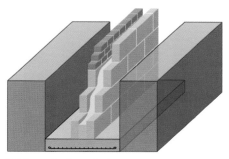

Wide strip foundation

Pad foundations

A pad foundation is used to support a point load such as a column in a steel-framed building. This type of foundation often has bolts set into the top ready for fixing the steel.

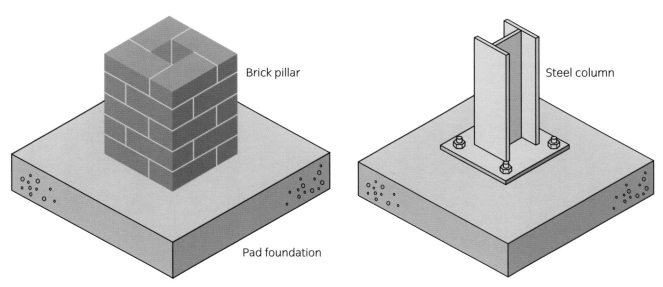

Pad foundation

Pad foundation with bolts

Pile foundations

Deep **piles** are used to transfer the load through unsuitable soil layers into the harder layers of ground below, even down to rock if required (known as end bearing). Some piles use **friction** to provide support. This is known as skin friction. Tall buildings (and especially narrow buildings such as chimneys or towers) have large lateral forces due to side winds and pile foundations resist these forces well.

Pile

A cylindrical foundation used on large, heavy buildings, or where the ground has poor load-bearing capabilities

Friction

Resistance between the surface of the concrete foundation and the soil around it

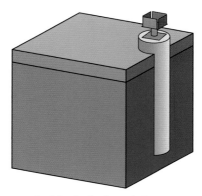

A cylindrical pile foundation

Raft foundations

A raft foundation is often laid over an area of softer soil that would be unsuitable for a strip foundation. A raft foundation is a slab of concrete covering the entire base of the building; it spreads the weight of the building over a wider area but still maintains a deeper base around the load-bearing walls.

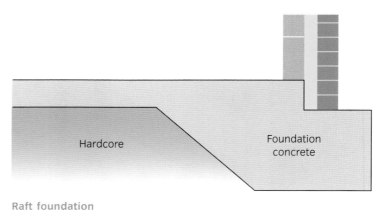

Hardcore

Foundation concrete

Raft foundation

FLOORS

Floors can be divided into two main categories:

- ground floors
- upper floors.

Floors are required to be load bearing, and there is a wide variety of construction methods depending on the type of building and potential load that will be imposed upon the floor. Floors also may need to prevent:

- heat loss
- transfer of sound
- moisture penetration.

GROUND FLOORS

These may be either solid ground floors or suspended floors.

Solid floors

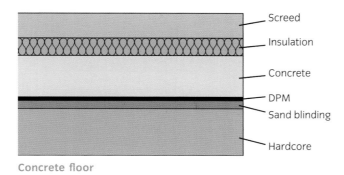

Screed
Insulation
Concrete
DPM
Sand blinding
Hardcore

Concrete floor

Solid concrete floors are laid upon **hardcore** and have a **damp proof membrane** (DPM) built into them to prevent damp coming up through the floor. **Insulation** is also laid into the floor to reduce heat loss. It is important that the insulation is not affected by the high water content of the wet concrete when being poured.

A finish to a concrete floor is called a screed. It can be laid 'lean' which consists of a mix of sand and cement that has only a little water added to it. Another type is known as 'self-levelling' which is mixed up very wet and finds its own level. It can be bought in bags as a powder that needs to be mixed, or delivered in a lorry and poured in.

As mentioned earlier, steel reinforcement can also be used within the concrete to increase strength and reduce cracks.

Hollow and suspended floors

Upper floors and some ground floors are suspended or hollow, meaning that instead of resting on the ground beneath, the load is transferred via beams to the walls.

Two types of beam used are Posi-Joist and I-beam. Posi-Joists are strong yet lightweight as they are made from two smaller beams connected with metal struts. It is easier to accommodate large services such as soil pipes when using this type of floor. Timber I-beams are similar to Posi-Joists, but the middle of the beam is made from a timber sheet material. Timber joists are usually covered with either chipboard or solid timber floorboards. A sleeper wall is built beneath the floor to carry the joists, making the floor stronger and reducing movement.

Hardcore

A mixture of crushed stone and sand laid and compacted to give a good base for the concrete

Damp proof membrane (DPM)

An impermeable layer that prevents damp coming up through the floor. A layer of sand known as blinding is placed below the DPM to prevent any sharp stones below piercing the membrane when the concrete is poured

Insulation

Materials used to retain heat and improve the thermal value of a building; may also be used for managing sound transfer

Modern timber frame

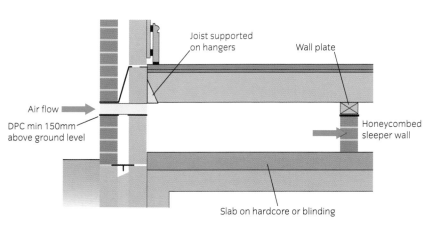

Joist supported on hangers

Wall plate

Air flow

DPC min 150mm above ground level

Honeycombed sleeper wall

Slab on hardcore or blinding

Suspended wood floor

Posi-Joist

I-beam

Suspended concrete floors can be made using two methods. They can either be cast 'in situ', which means that formwork (a mould) is set up and concrete is poured into it. Alternately, precast floors involve using concrete beams or rafts that have been made off site in a factory and are set onto walls. Concrete is then poured on top to finish the floor.

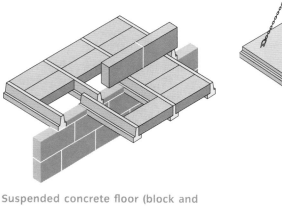

Suspended concrete floor (block and beam)

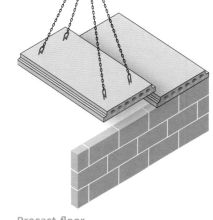

Precast floor

UPPER FLOORS

In most domestic dwellings timber floor joists are used and laid in the same way as hollow timber ground floors, while in large commercial and industrial buildings solid concrete floors are used.

INDUSTRY TIP

Timber joists normally run across the shortest span.

WALLS

Walling for a building can usually be divided in two categories:

- external

- internal.

Walling can be load or non-load bearing. Load-bearing walls carry the weight of the floors and roof and transfer this weight down to the foundations. A non-load-bearing wall carries no weight.

Walls often have openings in them, eg doors and windows, which will weaken them if they are not constructed correctly. Openings require support (via a **lintel** or arch) across the top to give the wall support and **bond** it together.

Lintel

A horizontal member for spanning an opening to support the structure above

Bond

The arrangement or pattern of laying bricks and blocks to spread the load through the wall, also for strength and appearance

EXTERNAL WALLING

External walls need to:

- keep the elements (wind and rain) out of the building

- look good

- fit into the surrounding landscape.

Several methods of construction are used for external walling. Common construction methods are:

- **solid wall**

- **cavity wall**

- timber framing.

Solid walls

Many older traditional buildings have solid walls made from brick, block or stone – see the table on the next page. Solid walls have the disadvantage of being more easily penetrated by damp. Older solid walls are often upgraded by having insulating and waterproofing layers applied to the outside of the wall.

ACTIVITY

What are the walls in the building you are sitting in made from? Why do you think these materials were chosen? What are the advantages or disadvantages of these materials?

Solid wall

Walls of a thickness of one brick and greater

Cavity wall

Walling built in two separate skins (usually of different materials) with a void held together by wall ties

Solid wall

Material used	Description
Bricks 	A very traditional building material made from fired clay, calcium silicate or concrete. A standard sized brick is 215mm × 102.5mm × 65mm.
Blocks 	These are made of either concrete (crushed stone and cement) or a lightweight cement mixture. They are much bigger than a brick, and are available in various sizes. The most commonly used size is 440mm × 215mm × 100mm. Wider blocks are used for walls where more strength or improved sound insulation is required. Lightweight blocks made from aerated concrete are easier to lay and cut and have greater thermal resistance. However, they are more costly and do not have the same structural properties as standard dense concrete blocks.
Stone 	A natural building material which varies widely in use and appearance from area to area. Stone may be cut to a uniform size before use or used in its quarried state.
Mortar 	This is used between bricks, blocks and stones to bind them together and increase the strength of the wall. It is a mixture of soft sand and cement mixed with water and other additives if required, eg **plasticiser**, colouring or **lime**. It is important that the strength of the mortar is correct for the type of material that is being used to construct the wall. If the mortar has too much cement in the mix it will be so strong that it will not allow movement in the walling due to settlement, and the bricks could crack resulting in the wall needing to be rebuilt. Other additives (retardant and accelerant) can slow down or accelerate this curing process and help protect from frost. Mortars are mixed to a ratio of materials, eg 1:6. The first number is the proportion of cement with the second being the proportion of sand. A typical mix ratio for masonry walling is 1:5.

Plasticiser

An additive that is used to make the mortar more pliable and easier to work with

Lime

A fine powdered material traditionally used in mortar

Bonding is the interlocking pattern that the brick and block **leaves** are laid in, which increases the strength of the wall. There are many bond types. Here are three common examples.

Leaves

The two walls or skins that make up a cavity wall to comply with current building regulations

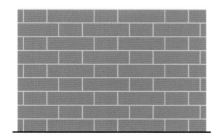

Flemish bond

English bond

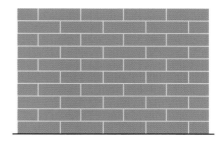

Stretcher bond

Cavity walls

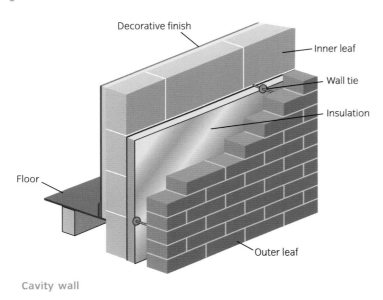

Cavity wall

The most common type of external walling used today is cavity wall construction.

Cavity walls are two masonry walls built side by side to form an inner and outer leaf (sometimes called skins). The leaves are held together with wall ties. These ties are made from rust- and rot-proof material and are built in as the walls are being constructed. The cavity is partially filled with insulation (typically fibreglass batts or polystyrene boards) as required by the **building regulations**. This reduces heat loss and saves energy.

The inner leaf usually carries any loads from the roof and floors down to the foundations and has a decorative finish on the inside, typically plaster which is either painted or papered. The outer leaf resists the elements and protects the inside of the building.

Building regulations

A series of documents that set out legal requirements for the standards of building work

ACTIVITY

State the minimum performance standards required for a cavity wall to meet current building regulations.

ACTIVITY

Find out the current minimum width of cavity allowed.

Timber framing

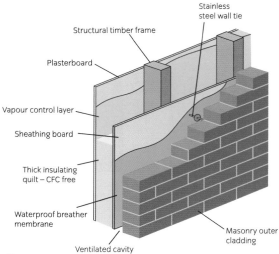

Timber frame wall

Elizabethan oak frame

Timber framing is both a traditional and modern method of building. Traditional buildings using timber framing were made mostly from oak with various in-fills such as brick or plaster to form the walls. Modern timber frame homes are generally built from softwood and have an outer skin of masonry or are clad with timber or plaster to waterproof the structure. Oak framing, as a traditional building method, is becoming increasingly popular again.

Prefabricated walls

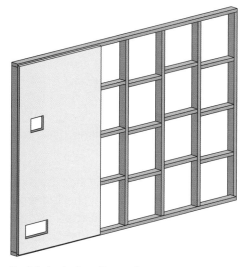
Prefabricated wall panel

Services

Those provided by the utility companies, eg gas, electric and water

There are a variety of prefabricated products available, generally made in a factory and then transported to site to be erected. These products enable quick and easy building. Often the **services** are pre-installed.

INTERNAL WALLING

Internal walling can be load or non-load bearing. Internal partitions divide large internal spaces into smaller rooms.

Internal partitions can be made from studwork or masonry. Studwork partitions consist of studs (which can be made from timber or metal) covered with a sheet material (usually plasterboard).

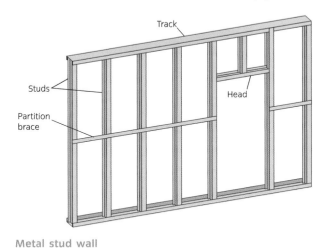

Metal stud wall

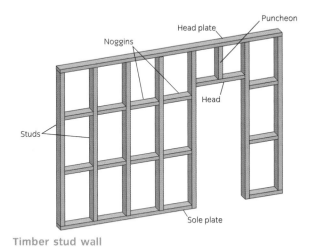

Timber stud wall

WALL FINISHES

External walls made from brick usually have no further finishes added while ones made from blocks are rendered. This is a covering of sand and cement mortar which is then finished with masonry paint.

Internal walls are most often plastered with a thin layer of gypsum plaster over plasterboard; this gives a very smooth hardwearing finish which is then usually finished with emulsion paint or papered coverings.

It is important to **size** new plaster to give a good base before applying further coverings of paint or paper coverings. This first coat of paint or paste is usually thinned down by 10% with clean water.

INDUSTRY TIP

At least two coats of emulsion are usually required for new plaster.

Size

To apply a watered-down or mist-coat of paint or paste to new plaster

ROOFS

Roofs are designed to protect the structure below by keeping the weather out. As heat rises, the roof must be well insulated to prevent heat loss and improve the energy efficiency of the building.

TYPES OF ROOFS

Roofs come in a wide variety of designs, but they come under two main categories of 'flat' and 'pitched'.

INDUSTRY TIP

A flat roof has an incline of up to 10° while a pitched roof has an incline over 10°.

Flat roofs

Flat roofs are similar in design to floors, in that they are made from joists decked with timber sheet material. A waterproof layer such as bituminous felt (made from tar), plastic or fibreglass is also used. Although flat roofs tend to be cheaper to install than pitched roofs, they do not last as long and they can suffer from leaks.

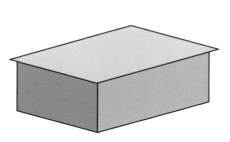

Flat roof

House with a flat roof

Pitched roofs

Pitched roofs are constructed using rafters, and come in a variety of designs. The simplest design of pitched roof is the 'lean-to', where a roof leans up against a wall. 'Gable-ended roofs' are a very common design, with walls covering the ends of the roof. These walls are known as gables or gable ends, which gives the roof its name. The weather can drive into these gables, and very often lengths of timber known as bargeboards are used to keep the elements out. 'Hipped roofs' are more complex (and rather more expensive). The roof ends are covered, making the roof more resistant to the elements. It is common to find a combination of the above roofs in the same building.

House with a pitched roof

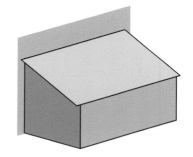

Lean-to roof

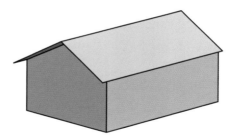

Gable-ended roof

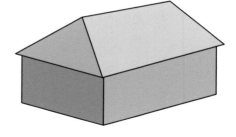

Hipped roof

ROOF COMPONENTS

You will need to know the different components of roofs. Study the illustrations below to learn what these are and how they are used to assemble a roof.

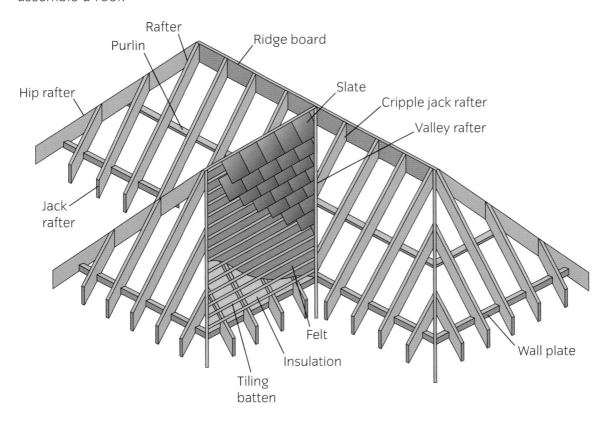

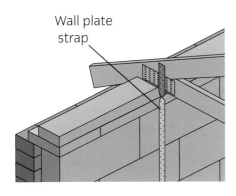

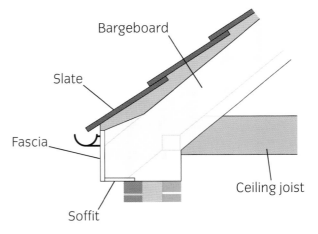

Roofs are usually constructed using **truss rafters**. This method of building a roof is quicker to install than a cut roof (where all of the components are cut and assembled on site). Roofs can be constructed using a combination of trusses and cut rafters. One type of commonly used truss is called a Fink truss (see next page).

Truss rafters

Rafters that are already cut and fixed together before being delivered on site

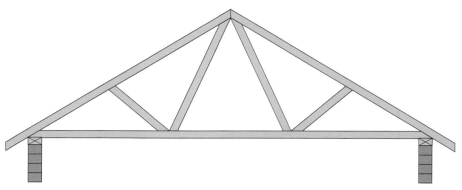

Commonly used standard Fink truss

Roofs are commonly covered with slates or tiles. Slates are a natural product. Slate is a type of mineral that can be split into thin sheets. Artificial cement fibre slates are also available; these are thin and uniform. Tiles can be made from clay or concrete.

Slate

Cement fibre slate

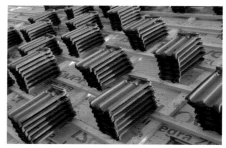

Roof tiles

A felt is laid below the roofing material to provide additional protection in case some water gets through the tiles.

Flashings are commonly made from lead and are used to provide waterproofing at joints where roofing materials meet walls and around chimneys.

Flashing providing waterproofing

Flashing around a chimney

Timber requires protection from the elements (rain, wind and sun) and this is done using timber coatings. Knotting is applied to prevent heat from the sun drawing resin out of knots in the timber. Primer is applied to give a good key to the paint or stain that is used to provide a finish. Paint also requires undercoat to be applied to give a good finish. Paint and stain can be water- or solvent-borne (water- or oil based).

SERVICES

Buildings contain services such as:

- water

- electricity

- gas supplies.

Additionally, waste such as sewage and water run-off have to be considered.

WATER

Water is brought into a building using pipes. Supply pipes used are usually made of plastic, with internal domestic plumbing being made from plastic or copper. Plumbing is installed using a variety of fittings including tees, elbows and reducers. Bathrooms, kitchens and most heating systems require plumbing.

Copper pipe

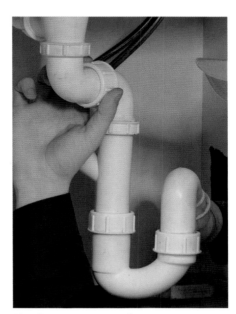

Plastic waste water pipe

Pipe fittings: Tee

Elbow

Reducer

ACTIVITY

What services are being used in the building you are sitting in? How are they brought into the building?

Not only is water carried into a building, it is also taken away. Rainwater run-off is collected into gutters and taken away via downpipes and drains and returned to the ground. It may also be stored for later use in raintanks; this is known as rainwater harvesting.

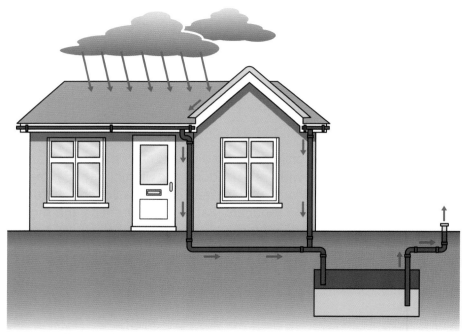
Rainwater flowing down pipes and into an underground raintank

SEWAGE

Sewage is taken away from the building via drains and is disposed of either into a sewer or into a septic tank/sewage treatment plant.

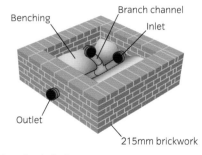
Benched drain

Septic tank

Sewage treatment plant

ELECTRICITY

Electricity is an important service provided to buildings. It powers lighting and heating. It is brought into a building through cables.

GAS

Gas is brought into a building using pipes. Gas powers heating systems and provides fuel for cooking.

OTHER SERVICES

Other services that are installed include telephone systems and other data cables for broadband and entertainment systems.

Electricity cables, switches and socket

SUSTAINABILITY

Our planet is a fixed size. Fossil fuels, eg oil and coal, that we take from the ground are not infinite, ie they will run out one day. However, the wind, the sun and the tides will always be there. These are sustainable sources of energy.

Pipework to boiler

Building materials can be sustainable if they are chosen carefully. For example, the process of manufacturing concrete uses a lot of fuel and produces a lot of carbon dioxide (a gas that some say is damaging the climate).

On the other hand, trees absorb carbon dioxide as they grow, look nice and the timber they produce is an excellent building material. However, some timber is harvested from rainforests without thought for the surrounding environment, or is harvested to such an extent that certain species are close to extinction. Managed forests where trees are replanted after harvesting provide a sustainable source of timber.

Here are some questions to consider regarding sustainability in construction.

MATERIALS

- How far have the materials been brought? Locally sourced materials do not have to be transported far, thus reducing fuel use.

- Are the materials sustainably sourced? Has the timber come from a managed forest or has it come from a rainforest with no regard to the environment?

- Have the materials been manufactured with the minimum of energy and waste?

DESIGN

Is there an alternative design that can be used that uses more sustainable materials? For example, a timber frame could be used instead of concrete block or brick.

The table below shows some sustainable materials.

Material	Image
Straw bales	
Cob (soil)	
Timber

Redwood   Spruce   Oak |
| Bamboo | |

Material	Image
Lime	
Sheep wool	

ENERGY EFFICIENCY

Energy is expensive and is only going to get more expensive. As the population increases, more and more energy will be required. This needs to come from somewhere and its production can be damaging to the environment. The less power a building uses the better and if it can produce its own that is a bonus. Energy-saving measures can save a lot of power consumption.

Insulation

Light, air-filled materials tend to have better thermal insulation properties than heavy, dense materials. This means that heat cannot easily pass from one side to another, and so if these materials are used in a building it will require less heating during the winter and will remain cooler during the summer.

The following drawing shows how much heat a typical home loses through different parts of the property. Better insulation will reduce the amount of heat lost.

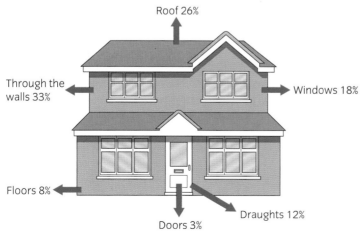

Roof 26%
Through the walls 33%
Windows 18%
Floors 8%
Doors 3%
Draughts 12%

Sources of heat loss from a house

INDUSTRY TIP

There are many ways of reducing the energy consumption of buildings, such as the use of low-energy light bulbs or lights that come on only when a sensor detects movement and turn off when there is no one about.

OUR HOUSE

What insulation has been used in the building you are sitting in? Is the building energy efficient? Is it cold? Does it take a lot of heating? Take a look at 'Our House' and identify the insulation measures used there.

The table below shows some examples of insulation.

Type of insulation	Description
Blue jean and lambswool 	Lambswool is a natural insulator. Blue jean insulation comes from recycled denim.
Fibreglass/mineral wool 	This is made from glass, often from old recycled bottles or mineral wool. It holds a lot of air within it and therefore is an excellent insulator. It is also cheap to produce. It does however use up a fair bit of room as it takes a good thickness to comply with building regulations. Similar products include plastic fibre insulation made from plastic bottles and lambswool.
PIR (polyisocyanurate) 	This is a solid insulation with foil layers on the faces. It is lightweight, rigid and easy to cut and fit. It has excellent insulation properties. Polystyrene is similar to PIR. Although polystyrene is cheaper, its thermal properties are not as good.
Multifoil 	A modern type of insulation made up of many layers of foil and thin insulation layers. These work by reflecting heat back into the building. Usually used in conjunction with other types of insulation.

Type of insulation	Description
Double glazing and draught proofing measures 	The elimination of draughts and air flows reduces heat loss and improves efficiency.

MAKING BETTER USE OF EXISTING AND FREE ENERGY

Solar power

The sun always shines and during the day its light reaches the ground (even on cloudy days). This energy can be used. A simple use of this is to allow sunlight to enter a building. With a little thought in design, light can reach deep into a building via roof lights and light tunnels. This means that internal artificial lighting requirements are reduced, therefore saving energy.

Solar panels can generate hot water or electricity, and once the cost of installation has been covered the energy they produce is totally free.

Solar panel

A panel that absorbs sun rays to generate electricity or hot water

Solar panels

Air-conditioning unit

Turbines

A machine designed to allow continuous movement to create electrical energy

Heat source and recovery

Humans give off a fair bit of energy as they go through a normal day (eg body heat, heat given off by hairdryers, cookers, refrigerators and other activities) and this can be conserved. Modern air-conditioning systems take the heat from stale air and put it into the fresh air coming in.

Heat can be taken from the ground and even the air outside.

Wind power

Wind power is becoming more widespread. However, some people feel that wind **turbines** are damaging the visual environment as they spoil the appearance of the countryside. Individuals will have their own opinion on whether wind power is a good thing or not as there are many considerations to be taken into account.

Wind turbines

Water power

Water is another source of power, whether that be hydro-electric (water from dams turning turbines) or wave power (which is currently under development).

Another method is through extracting heat energy contained in the air and ground. This can be extracted by the use of a heat exchanger. Water in pipes buried in the ground circulates, picking up heat, which is then taken out and used in the building. This can also be achieved with air from outside.

Biomass heating

Biomass heating (using wood and other non-fossil fuels) is also becoming more popular as these systems can heat water efficiently as well as heat rooms, and of course a well-insulated building does not require a lot of heating.

Energy-efficient goods and appliances

Energy-efficient electrical goods (eg low-energy light bulbs) and appliances (eg dishwashers, fridges and washing machines) which use a reduced amount of power and less water are available.

PROTECTING THE ENVIRONMENT

Building work can create a lot of waste, and can pollute the environment. To avoid this, careful consideration needs to be given to how waste is disposed of. There are many regulations that control the management of waste (ie COSHH, see Chapter 1, page 9) that also need to be followed.

Proper stock control and efficient use of materials reduces waste. Dust and fumes can be reduced by using water or LEV (local exhaust ventilation), which sucks dust from the air. Materials such as glass or plastics can be recycled, very often into other building materials. Timber can be reused instead of being thrown away or taken to a salvage yard. The waste that is left (the waste that cannot be recycled or reused) then needs to be disposed of carefully in a skip. Hazardous waste such as asbestos is usually removed by specialists.

A hydro-electric dam

Biomass fuel

An energy-efficient light bulb

Case Study: Tristan

Tristan has been asked to help design and produce specifications for a house. He has been asked to research how to make the house energy efficient. The house will have four bedrooms and has a gable-ended roof that faces south.

Tristan consulted manufacturers' catalogues and websites to determine the most efficient system for generating energy. As the roof faces south, Tristan decides that panels on the roof are a good option. Tristan decides that five solar thermal collectors will be enough to provide hot water for the occupants of the house. Ground source heat pumps will provide additional heating for the house.

The walls, roof, windows and floor are to be insulated. The building regulations provide minimum requirements that Tristan refers to. Again, using manufacturers' information he decides which is the best insulation systems to use, balancing effectiveness with cost.

- Do you agree with Tristan's design?

- Could it be improved?

- Are there any drawbacks to his design?

Work through the following questions to check your learning.

1   Which one of the following identifies the details of materials needed for a project?

a   Specification.

b   Programme of work.

c   Delivery note.

d   Site diary.

2   Which scale should be used for a detail drawing?

a   1:5.

b   1:75.

c   1:500.

d   1:7500.

3   What is the hatching symbol shown below?

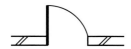

a   Door.

b   Roof light.

c   Window.

d   Hallway.

4   What is the hatching symbol shown below?

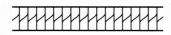

a   Plastic.

b   Insulation.

c   Timber.

d   Blockwork.

5   What is the point shown below?

a   A point of a known height used for setting out.

b   A point of unknown height used for setting out.

c   A point of known position used to determine the building line.

d   A point of unknown position used to determine the building line.

6   What type of brick is shown below?

a   Flemish.

b   Concrete.

c   Trench.

d   Air.

7   What foundation type covers the footprint of the building?

a   Strip.

b   Raft.

c   Pile.

d   Pad.

8   In a concrete mix ratio of 1:2:3, the 3
    represents

    a   Retardant

    b   Fine aggregate

    c   Coarse aggregate

    d   Cement

9   What part of a roof retains heat within the
    building?

    a   Insulation.

    b   Restraint strap.

    c   DPC.

    d   Concrete tiles.

10 What brick bond is shown below?

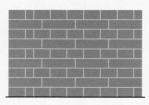

    a   German.

    b   English.

    c   French.

    d   Flemish.

Chapter 3
Unit 221: Apply plastering materials to interiors

This chapter covers preparing backgrounds and selecting suitable and compatible plasters to form and finish one, two and three coat plastering to interior surfaces. This provides a finish that can then be decorated to fulfil the customer's needs.

Learning about different types of plaster and their properties will help you understand how the performance of modern buildings has evolved over the years, to meet greater demands for thermal, sound, fire, heat and moisture resistance.

You will also learn why there is still a need to use traditional sustainable plastering materials and methods in order to preserve our heritage within historic buildings.

By reading this chapter you will know how to:

1   Interpret information for interior work.

2   Select and prepare equipment and materials for interior work.

3   Apply one, two and three coat plastering to interior backgrounds.

INTERPRETING INFORMATION

DRAWINGS

Before you carry out plastering work, you need to study the relevant working drawings as these provide valuable information that will help you successfully complete the work to the standards required in the contract agreement. Refer back to Chapter 2, pages 49–51, for examples of these types of drawings.

■ Block plans show the property in relation to its surroundings.

■ Site plans show the plot in more detail.

■ Floor plans contain the specific and precise dimensions of each room in order to calculate quantities of plastering materials needed for the job. They also show the layout of each room, allowing you to form a clear idea of how you can complete the scheduled work.

■ Elevation drawings show how each individual wall is seen, whether they are plain walls or have windows and/or door openings. You can refer to these drawings when measuring openings for doorways and windows, or when checking whether the background walls contain different properties, such as **lintels** or **wall plates**.

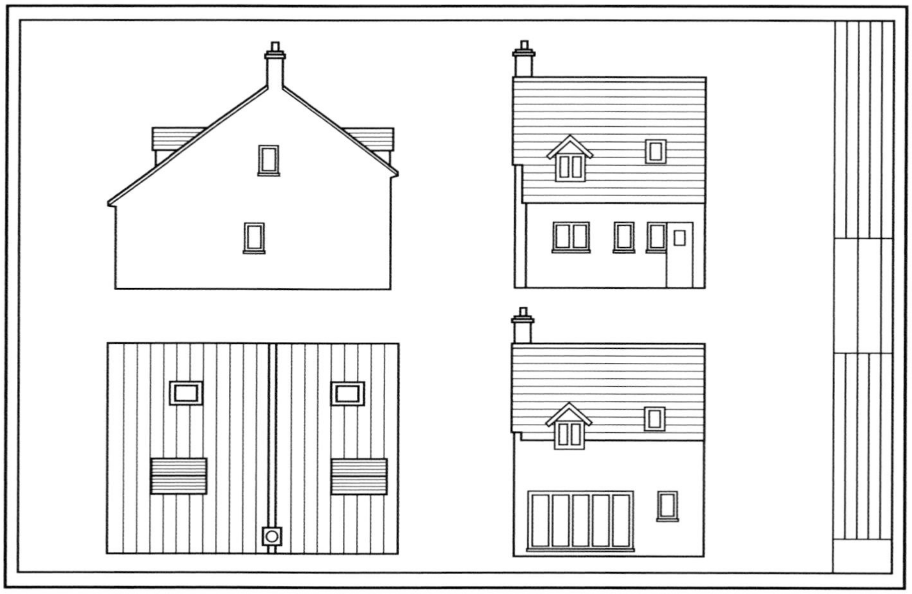

Elevation drawing

■ A reflective ceiling plan shows the ceiling dimensions of each floor. This allows you to measure and calculate the amount of plasterboard, fixings and setting plaster needed to complete the ceiling surface areas.

Lintel

A horizontal member for spanning an opening, such as a door, to support the structure above, usually made from steel or concrete

Wall plates

Timber that runs along the top of a wall, to which the roof is fixed

FUNCTIONAL SKILLS

From a floor plan, work out the area of an interior wall's plaster.

Work on this activity can support FM2 (C2.7).

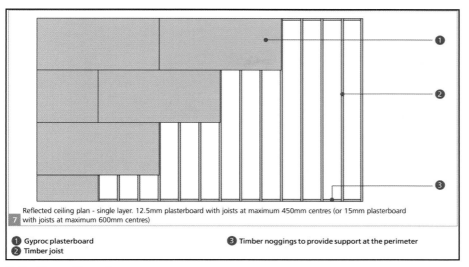

Reflected ceiling plan - single layer. 12.5mm plasterboard with joists at maximum 450mm centres (or 15mm plasterboard
7 with joists at maximum 600mm centres)

1 Gyproc plasterboard   **3** Timber noggings to provide support at the perimeter
2 Timber joist

Reflective ceiling plan

- A detailed drawing or assembly drawing provides clear, accurate information, for example, showing how the standard angle beads meet at returns and **soffits**, and details where movement beads are fixed to expansion joints.

Soffit

The underside of a window, door head or beam

EML   Wall plate   Plaster dabs

Standard angle bead

Brickwork

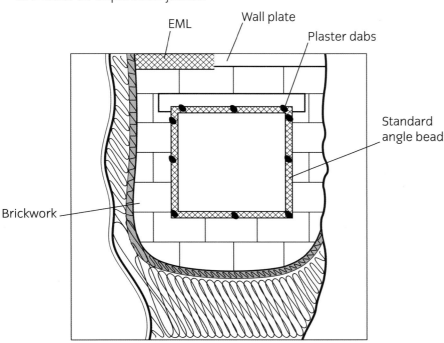

Detailed drawing

When reading drawings, it is important to report as soon as possible anything on them that you think is a mistake in case it causes more problems at a later stage. The mistake must be reported to someone in higher authority, who will then contact the architect and ask them to correct the problem.

DOCUMENTATION

PLASTERING SPECIFICATIONS

Plastering specifications provide information on the type of materials to be used for the internal solid plastering contract. The specification may also state the methods to be used for preparing backgrounds and the type of application (see Chapter 2, pages 52–53).

When working to a specification, you must use only the specified materials to carry out the work. For example, if the architect has specified a special type of plaster that contains gypsum, then you must purchase that type of plaster to carry out the work. You don't need to use a certain manufacturer, even if the architect names one, but the material you buy from another manufacturer must be the same type and of the same quality.

The specification document also states the expected standard of workmanship for the completed work.

You will need to refer to the specification when estimating for quantities and costs of materials for the plastering work.

DATA SHEETS

Data sheets are useful documents that provide valuable health and safety information on construction materials, such as undercoat and top coat plasters, cement, limes and additives used for plastering. Data sheets list a range of safety points that need to be complied with when using the product. Being aware of the health and safety issues will help you understand the possible dangers that may affect you and other operatives when handling, storing, mixing, applying and disposing of plastering products.

Data sheets should be referred to when planning and producing documents such as risk assessments and method statements. Typical headings found on plaster manufacturers' data sheets cover:

- the name of the substance
- the hazards
- any specific first-aid measures
- any relevant firefighting measures
- accidental release measures
- handling and storage procedures
- exposure control/personal protection
- the physical and chemical properties of the substance
- toxicology information (about the chemicals and any poisons in the substance)
- disposal considerations.

> **INDUSTRY TIP**
>
> The specification is sometimes simply referred to as the 'spec'.

> **ACTIVITY**
>
> Search online to find some different top coat and undercoat data sheets. Discuss your findings as a group. Your tutor can help you with this activity.

SCHEDULES

There are two types of schedules that are referred to in the construction industry.

- A materials schedule lists the correct amount of different materials and components that are required to complete the build. When applying plaster to interiors, the schedule document will not only list the different types of undercoat and finishing plaster but also the number of different beads to be used to form returns and stops.

- The other type of schedule is sometimes referred to as a 'labour schedule', 'programme of work' or 'work schedule'. This lists the different craftsmen and trades required to complete set work activities at different stages of the construction process. This is identified on a progress chart, such as a Gantt chart. (See Chapter 2, page 57.)

OUR HOUSE

Design your own specification and schedule for plastering 'Our House' using two coat undercoat and top coat setting plasters.

Planning the work beforehand is an important part of the plastering process. Risk assessments and method statements need to be produced before the work starts. Completing these documents beforehand will provide a safe method of work, outlining the dangers and risks involved with this type of plastering work. Refer back to Chapter 1, pages 5–6, to refresh your memory about these.

CALCULATING QUANTITIES

Before ordering materials you need to calculate the required quantities of undercoat and top coat plasters that are to be used on the internal walls. You also need to calculate lengths of different types of beads for openings and how much expanded metal lathing (EML) you will need for the wall plates.

Poor planning can be costly: being organised in advance with the correct labour, quantities of materials and resources needed to carry out the work efficiently will mean there is less opportunity for problems to occur and less rushing around and being disorganised. Poor planning may result in a poor standard of work, which may also have a knock-on effect on the work schedule.

Refer back to Chapter 2, pages 57–72, to refresh your memory about how to calculate quantities.

ACTIVITY

In groups, discuss and list some examples of the effects of inaccurate measuring.

INDUSTRY TIP

When working with others, always make sure that you are all using the same unit of measurement. For example, make sure that you are all using millimetres and metres rather than feet and inches.

SELECT AND PREPARE EQUIPMENT AND MATERIALS

Selecting suitable plasters for the work should be done with careful consideration and planning as there are many implications that may cause issues at a later stage.

- The plaster must be **compatible** with the background.

- Some specifications may state that you have to use a certain type of plaster. For example, it may be specified that you have to use traditional lime-based plasters because the site is in a conservation area, or you have to use modern pre-mixed plaster on a new development where the thermal values, acoustic levels or fire protection are taken into account.

- The client or architect might have their own preference for the type of plaster used.

Compatible

In a plastering context, this is when the plaster materials used are the right strength for the background they are applied to

PLASTERING MATERIALS

Plastering materials have changed a lot during the last century. Modern materials have been developed, replacing traditional materials that may not be suitable today due to the greater performance requirements for modern buildings. However, the skills used to apply the plaster and finish the interior surfaces have stayed virtually the same. Let us look at how materials used for plastering mixes have evolved over the last century.

LIME-BASED PLASTER MIXES

Aggregate

A 'filler', aggregate makes up the bulk of a mix

Traditional undercoat mixes used for applying pricking up, scratch and floating coats were referred to as 'lime mortar', a mix made of hydraulic lime putty as the binder, coarse sand as the **aggregate** and the addition of horse hair for reinforcement. This helped bind and strengthen the mortar and reduced **shrinkage**, which was a constant problem with this type of mix.

Shrinkage

When plaster shrinks once it has been applied to a background. Caused by poorly graded sand in the undercoat mix, high suction in the background or excessive thickness of plaster being applied

The setting coat was a mixture of lime putty with fine silica sand as filler or fine aggregate to bulk up the consistency.

Lime mixes were deemed weak and slow setting; they could take several days, weeks or even months to set between each application, depending on the temperature. The use of lime could be a constant strain on plastering contracts that needed to be completed by a deadline, which might not be met due to the slow set.

Restoration work

Restoring work back to its original state using traditional materials and methods

Lime-based plaster mixes are still commonly used today in conservation or **restoration work**. One advantage of lime plastering mixes is that they allow the walls to breathe, which reduces condensation.

Conservation plastering using lime-based plaster

There are two types of lime-based plaster mixes.

Lime-based plaster

- *Non-hydraulic lime* sets by re-absorbing carbon dioxide (CO_2) from the air, a process known as carbonation. It is set only once dry.

- *Hydraulic lime* comes in powder form and has similar setting characteristics as cement. Using hydraulic lime in mixes is less labour intensive than using non-hydraulic lime as its setting time is not dependent on the temperature.

CEMENT-BASED PLASTER MIXES

Renovation plastering using cement-based plaster

Cement

Cement was introduced into the industry just after World War II. Made of 75% limestone and 25% clay, cement is a **binder** that provides a faster set but also provides strength in the mix. The introduction of cement in undercoat mixes meant that building and plastering work would have faster setting times. Work could be produced at speed, which suited the high demand for new housing after the war.

Cement mixed with sand and water will begin to set after 45 minutes and is normally completely set by the next day. But the mixture can take several days to reach its final strength. This process is known as 'curing'.

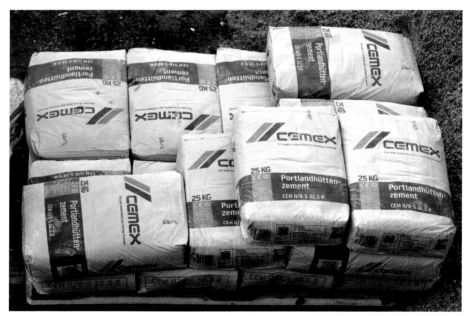

Ordinary Portland Cement (OPC) is a common cement used in the industry

Although cement had advantages over lime mortar, it also had its own problems, such as shrinkage, mixes being too dense or brittle, and having irregular strengths resulting in cracking. These days, cement-based mixes are commonly used on **renovation work** or when harder background surfaces are required.

Cement- and lime-based plaster mixes should only be applied to solid backgrounds. The mix **ratio** commonly used is 5:1 sand and cement or 6:1:1 sand, cement and lime. However, mix ratios can vary to take into account the strength and compatibility of the background.

Sand

Sand is used as the aggregate in cement-based mixes to bulk the mix. Well-graded sand will have a uniform mix of small, medium and large grains and be angular in shape. Too much **silt** will prevent the cement from binding with the sand and cause the mix to be weak.

Binder
The active ingredient in a mix. It sets and holds the aggregate and other materials together

ACTIVITY
Research how cement and lime are manufactured. Discuss your findings in a group.

Renovation work
Repairing work that has deteriorated or been damaged over time. The work will require updating to conform to modern building regulations using either modern or traditional plastering materials and methods

Ratio
The proportion of materials that are mixed together, eg six parts sand to one part cement

Silt
Fine grains of sand

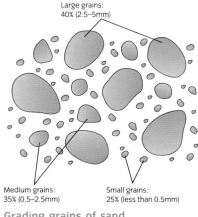

Large grains:
40% (2.5–5mm)

Medium grains:
35% (0.5–2.5mm)

Small grains:
25% (less than 0.5mm)

Grading grains of sand

There are several types of sand, the following are just some of the types you may come across.

- *Dredged sand* is most commonly used today in plaster mixes. It is brown or yellow in colour and has been dredged up from the bottom of an **estuary**.

- *Pit sand* is quarried from the ground. Red in colour, this sand is generally classed as being too round and fine in grain. However, other types of pit sand, such as Leighton Buzzard sand which is a well-graded coarse sand, are considered suitable for plaster mixes.

- *Coarse sand/crushed aggregate* have large voids of air between grains. However, they can be mixed with finer sand when used in plastering mixes.

- *Sea sand* is not recommended for plastering as it contains salt which can penetrate plastered surfaces in the form of a white powder, known as efflorescence. It can also contain impurities such as shells, and is badly graded.

Lime

Hydrated lime can be added to sand and cement undercoats. This improves the workability and adhesion of the mix. Adding lime can also reduce the plaster's tendency to crack because it allows for slight movement in the masonry.

Additives

Plastering materials can also contain **additives** designed to give the plaster a different characteristic and improve its performance. These additives can be added either during manufacture or in either liquid or powder form when mixing.

Plasticisers are mixed into the gauging water. They improve the workability of a sand/cement mix. When using a plasticiser, always follow the manufacturer's instructions carefully.

Estuary

Where the mouth of a river or stream meets the sea's tides

Hydrated lime

Additive

A substance that is added to plaster mixes to change their natural properties

Plasticiser

GYPSUM PRE-MIXED LIGHTWEIGHT UNDERCOAT AND SETTING PLASTERS

Pre-mixed

Plaster materials that have been mixed in a processing plant and are sold bagged, needing only clean water added for mixing

Sag

To slide down the wall because the plaster has been applied too thickly

A range of gypsum **pre-mixed** undercoat and top coat plasters have been specifically manufactured for use on different types of background surfaces. Gypsum is a binder that is mixed with lightweight aggregates, such as expanded perlite and/or exfoliated vermiculite, to bulk the plaster to the required consistency and thickness. The plaster can be applied between 8mm to 12mm thick without causing the plaster to **sag**. It is used in modern internal plastering work.

Modern internal plastering work

Gypsum pre-mixed plaster

Suction

The rate at which a background absorbs moisture

Gypsum pre-mixed plasters have many advantages over traditional plastering materials because they have been designed with specific application in mind. During the manufacturing process the plasters are tested in laboratories to ensure that they satisfy their intended use. The range of plaster produced today can be used on low- and high-**suction** backgrounds.

There are several different types of plasters available.

- *Bonding grade plaster* is a pre-mixed undercoat plaster that contains vermiculite and perlite aggregate. Vermiculite is sharp and angular in shape, giving the plaster excellent bonding abilities compared with other types of plaster. This type of plaster is suitable for use on low-suction and poorly keyed backgrounds.

- *Undercoat plaster* that contains perlite as the aggregate will have to rely on the background having the necessary key to ensure that the plaster bonds sufficiently; this is because the perlite aggregate is round in shape and does not bond well to backgrounds that have a poor key.

Vermiculite

Perlite

- *Multi-finish plaster* can be applied to a range of gypsum undercoats and to sand and cement backgrounds.

- *Board finish plaster* is made to be applied to plasterboard.

- *Hard grade finishing plasters* have been developed to be used in areas that are prone to greater impact than normal, such as high traffic areas where people walking past may frequently knock into the plaster.

- *Other pre-mixed undercoats* may contain additives that improve adhesion or cope better when there are high-suction levels. Thistle Hardwall is one example; it can be applied on various types of masonry surface such as solid block, lightweight aerated block and common brick.

Although gypsum plasters have advantages over traditional plaster mixes with regards to thermal values and heat resistance, gypsum undercoat plasters are not suited to older buildings. Older buildings may contain areas that have been in contact with or affected by rising or penetrating damp; this means that the background may still contain some moisture. Gypsum plasters have high absorption rates so this could result in problems if the dampness has not been treated and completely removed from the background. Gypsum plasters can become mouldy and eventually perish in persistently damp conditions.

Plastering manufacturers British Gypsum and Knauf have developed plasters that can be sprayed directly onto the background, saving time and labour by improving efficiency. Spray machines can be impractical on small residential properties due to the challenge of setting up the equipment in small, tight spaces. If you look at the British Gypsum and Knauf websites you will see case studies and videos of plasterers using spray machines to apply and finish different types of plasters.

Spray finish plastering

OUR HOUSE

Work out the amount of undercoat and setting coat plaster required to plaster the living room walls in 'Our House' by working through the tasks below. Note that you can choose the type of pre-mixed undercoat and setting coat plaster for these tasks.

1 Measure the perimeter of the room and multiply by the height. This will give you the overall surface area to be plastered in m².

2 Measure all window and door openings by multiplying their length by the breadth. Deduct this measurement from the surface area calculated in Task 1.

INDUSTRY TIP

The undercoat plaster manufacturer's guidelines will provide specific instructions on use, including the types of background that are suitable.

ACTIVITY

In groups, list five advantages and five disadvantages of using pre-mixed gypsum-based plasters instead of traditional mixing.

ACTIVITY

Search the internet for the websites of plaster manufacturers such as British Gypsum and Knauf. Note the range of undercoat and setting coat plasters that are available.

3 Now that you have the total measurement in m², work out how much pre-mixed undercoat you require to float the walls. You can do this by dividing the amount of bag coverage by the surface area calculated in Task 2, working to the nearest full bag.

4 Repeat this process for calculating the setting coat plaster.

5 When you have calculated the amount of bagged undercoat and setting coat plaster required, work out the cost. Don't forget to add 10% to allow for waste.

CEMENT PRE-MIXED LIGHTWEIGHT PLASTER

This undercoat plaster is a mixture of cement, lime, perlite and synthetic fibres that are added during manufacture to improve its strength and binding ability, and to help reduce shrinkage. This type of plaster is used on renovation work after a chemical damp course has been installed or if moisture has been a persistent presence in the background. Like lime mortar mixes, this plaster allows walls to naturally breathe, allowing trapped moisture to dry out from within the masonry.

ACTIVITY

Search the Pozament website (www.pozament.co.uk) for their full range of pre-mixed plasters and discuss the benefits of using these types of plaster.

COMPATIBLE PLASTERS

Using a type of plaster that is compatible with the background

Different plasters are compatible with different types of background surfaces. As a plasterer learning the trade you need to understand how the plaster is applied and how it bonds with the background. If the background is dry, solid and has a good key then this will form a good basis for your plaster effectively bonding to the surface.

The plaster applied needs to be weaker in strength than the background material. If the plaster is stronger than the background material this may cause stress between the background and the plaster, resulting in bond failure.

Backgrounds can be treated to improve compatibility, for example by pre-keying them or treating them with adhesives.

STORAGE

Storing plastering materials

Bagged materials such as plasters, cement and lime are bagged when manufactured and contain a 'use-by' date stamp. Modern bagged products contain a lot more information than in previous years; manufacturers also provide information on mixing, storage and safety.

Storage of materials for plastering is very important. A clear, flat surface needs to be set out for pallet storage of the plastering materials. The storage area must provide shelter away from moisture and frost as these can affect the shelf life of the materials.

A form of stock rotation called 'first in, first out' (FIFO) should be used. This is where any old stock that is still within date is placed on the top of the stack, with the newest stock at the bottom. This ensures that the older plaster is used first and is not left at the bottom of the pile to go out of date.

- Plaster should be stored under cover and off the floor in a dry and well ventilated storage area. When stacking bags of plaster, they should be **bonded** – this will make the stack more stable. The stacks should be no more than 1m high. A well-kept store is essential to help minimise damage and waste.

- Sand can be purchased loose, in bags or in sacks. Sand used in plastering mixes should be protected from leaves or animal contamination as these can affect the binding and quality of the surface finish. A good cover or tarpaulin should also be used to protect it from rain water as this can cause sand bulking.

INDUSTRY TIP

Always use protective clothing and follow manual handling rules when moving bagged materials. Plaster, cement and lime can cause skin burns and breathing problems. Always read the manufacturer's information for guidance on safe use. Refer to Chapter 1, pages 9–11 for information on the Control of Substances Hazardous to Health (COSHH) Regulations 2002.

Bonded

Overlapping the bags on each layer with those on the layer below

- Depending on the storage area available, materials such as aggregates can be bought loose, in sacks or in sealed bags.

You should avoid using damaged materials as they may have irregular setting times, **flash set** or have poor strength. Using materials and additives that have passed their use-by date can affect the quality of strength causing poor surface finish. Damaged or out-of-date materials need to be placed to one side and reported to your supervisor.

Flash set

Where gypsum plaster sets far more quickly than expected. Can be caused by using dirty or contaminated water, tools and equipment, or out-of-date or poorly stored plaster

BEADS AND TRIMS

There is a range of different beads used for floating interior surfaces that have angles and returns. They are used to provide strength to corners, and to provide plumb and level edges or arrises to the external angles of walls. Beads and trims are made from galvanised steel or plastic and come in standard lengths of 2.4mm.

TYPES OF BEADS

Angle beads

Standard two coat angle beads are made to be used on two coat work. When fixed they allow for a suitable plaster thickness, including the floating and setting coat. They can be fixed using several methods; however, the majority of standard angle beads are fixed with dabs of stiff setting plaster. Setting plaster is preferred because it is a fine material that allows the mesh wing of the bead to bed into the plaster with ease. You may also use undercoat plaster to bed beads, but if you do this it is best to apply a continuous dab along the full length of the bead.

Thin coat angle beads can be fixed to solid or plasterboard corners. They are a smaller type of angle bead that allows for the thickness of setting plasters. There are two types of thin coat bead on the market: mini mesh beads and solid beads. Thin coat beads can be fixed with galvanised nails, drywall screws, dabs of plaster or staples.

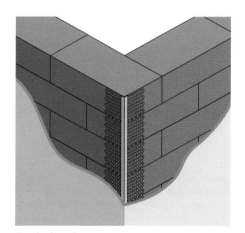

Angle beads

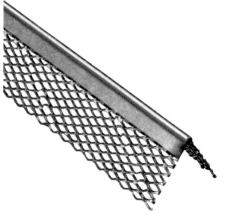

Mini mesh beads

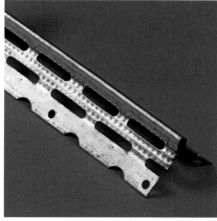

Solid beads

Stop beads

Stop beads are used when the plasterwork needs to stop at a different surface. This could be when it goes up to timber or decorative masonry. Stop beads can be fixed with galvanised nails or bedded into position, depending on how **true** the background is.

Thin coat stop beads are used in the same way as a standard stop bead. These beads are very popular when forming splayed angles that are not at right angles

True

Accurate to plumb, level and/or line

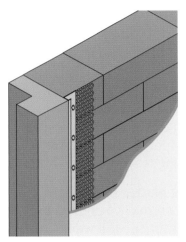

Stop beads

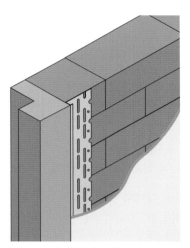

Thin coat stop beads

Expansion beads

Expansion beads are used on walls that have expansion joints that allow slight movement in both sides of the wall to prevent cracking. These areas are considered weak so expansion beads are fixed in line with the edge of the joint, allowing the plastered wall to move freely without cracking.

STORING BEADS

Galvanised beads should be stored on a flat surface or upright in racks, away from impact or pedestrian traffic routes, to avoid any possibility of damage. Beads are protected with a galvanised coating to prevent rusting when they come in contact with the wet plaster, but if left outside in wet conditions for long periods they may corrode and become unusable. Corroded beads should be placed aside: if used they will rust and cause a pattern stain along the length of the bead that will penetrate through to the plaster surface. This can be difficult to remove.

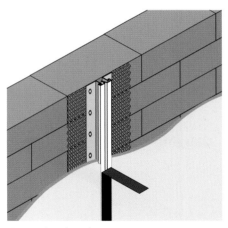

Expansion beads

ACTIVITY

Search online for beads and trims. In particular research Expamet and Catnic, two manufacturers of galvanised beads. Share your findings.

TOOLS AND EQUIPMENT

When you carry out internal plastering you will need a range of tools and equipment, some specific to carry out certain aspects of the work.

Tool	Use
Hawk	The plasterer's hawk is used to hold and transfer a workable amount of plaster from the spot board to the wall. The hawk is used in conjunction with the trowel to manipulate and apply the plaster directly on to the background surface. Some plasterers prefer hawks with detachable handles as they are easier to store.
	Hawks were traditionally made from timber, but today modern hawks are made from polyurethane or aluminium.
Finishing trowel	A good plasterer will have two types of laying trowel: one for applying undercoats and another, which may be mild steel or stainless, for applying the setting coat, known as the finishing trowel.
	The best type of trowel used for laying setting plaster has been 'broken in' as a result of constant use. This is normally achieved by using a new trowel to apply undercoat plaster for several weeks or months until the edges become sharp and the corners slightly rounded. Some laying trowels can be purchased pre-worn and take less time to wear down.
	In contrast, the blade of the finishing trowel should be kept firm and straight. This is best done by purchasing a trowel with a long shank on its rear; this will provide stability for the blade preventing it from going out of shape.
Gauging trowel	This tool has many purposes and uses within the plastering craft. Its main purpose used to be to gauge small quantities of plastering materials. Today, this trowel is used for reaching into awkward areas where a normal trowel won't reach. Another is for cleaning and removing excess material off the straight edge and to clean plaster droppings by scraping the floor.
Comb scratcher	A comb scratcher can be used to key the surface when you apply a scratch coat.

Tool	Use
Straight/feather edge 	A straight edge is used for ruling surfaces, checking for straightness, or forming the hard angle of a return. It is also known as a feather edge rule because it has a taper on one side allowing you to rule from the tight angles on a wall. Some straight edges can be square on both sides and are generally used for floor screeding or when dry lining.
Darby 	Another tool used for ruling and flattening walls to a smooth surface. You can also use this tool to form returns when applying a scratch coat.
Finishing blade 	Speedskim manufactures plastering tools and has designed specific straight edges and finishing blades for ruling undercoats and finishing setting plaster surfaces. A finishing blade is one of them. Finishing blades are being used more and more because they speed up some aspects of plastering and help achieve a consistently flat and smooth finish.
Tin snips 	Snips are used for cutting various types of trims such as angle beads, stops and rolled EML before it is fixed onto the wall plate. Always wear protective gloves when cutting EML because it is very sharp.
Spirit level 	A spirit level can be used on its own or with a straight edge, which extends its length. It is used for plumbing and levelling surfaces such as standard angle beads to window openings and returns, or for plumbing dots to form accurate screeds when floating.
Float 	Used for consolidating undercoat surfaces to form either a plain smooth finish or a key, preparing for the setting coat. These floats are generally made from polyurethane.

Tool	Use
Devil float 	A devil float is made by nailing tin tacks to one end of a float edge. It is used for devilling or keying a surface. When making a devil float, space the tin tacks equally and start from the middle, fixing every 15mm. Use fixings such as galvanised nails: screws will cause damage and split the edge of the float.
Small tool 	Used in tight, difficult angles. The types shown here are leaf and square.
Mechanical drum mixer 	A mechanical mixer that is best used for mixing cement-based plasters. This type of mixing is carried out outdoors, as it can be noisy and the materials used will cause high dust levels.
Plasterer's wheel 	A hand mixing tool used for mixing setting plaster. Also known as a plunger. During and after the mixing process it should be kept off the floor to prevent any bits of debris from sticking to the bottom of the tool, which could contaminate the next mix.
Drill and whisk 	A mechanical mixing tool used for mixing lightweight undercoat and setting plasters. It is a fast and efficient way of mixing lightweight plasters.
Flat brush 	Used to apply water when finishing setting plaster.

Tool	Use
Small brushes 	Used to clean internal angles and frames.
External corner trowel 	Used to form rounded hard angles, eg in walls with window openings.

ACCESS EQUIPMENT

Plasterers use various types of access equipment to carry out their work when fixing plasterboard and applying plaster to ceilings or high walls. Access equipment is used to provide a safe means of working at height, reducing the risks of falls which can cause serious injury.

Hop-ups are the most common type of **low level** platform used when plastering walls. They allow you to step on and off, applying plaster at a steady pace to a standard ceiling height of 2.5m.

Low level
All work undertaken below 2.5m is classed as low level

Hop-up

When applying plaster to ceilings, fully boarded platform staging is preferred. This gives you a continuous platform allowing you to apply and finish the setting plaster at regular intervals as the plaster sets without causing strain.

Fully boarded platform staging

ACTIVITY

Make a list of the hazards associated with working from access equipment while hacking backgrounds.

MEWP

This is the abbreviation for mobile elevating work platforms. These are a mechanical device used when temporary access at height is needed

Building out

Applying plaster to a very uneven background surface until it has an even surface

Adhere/adhesion

How well plaster sticks or grips to the background

Key

How rough or smooth the background surface is. Creating a rough surface on a background helps the plaster adhere to it

Access equipment used for construction is governed by the Work at Height Regulations 2005 (as amended). Any type of access that does not conform to these regulations is deemed not safe and unfit for use. You will have to carry out training and carry an approved card to be able to use many of the different types of access equipment used on site, such as towers, **MEWPs** and scissor lifts. For more information on safe use of access equipment refer back to Chapter 1.

PREPARE BACKGROUND SURFACES

The key to creating a good plaster surface is identifying and preparing the background correctly before starting work. It is important to understand that not all backgrounds have the same properties. Some will be soft and weak, some will be hard or dense, and some will be uneven and require '**building out**'.

Different backgrounds need to be prepared for plastering in different ways. There are several steps that you need to follow to make sure the plaster **adheres** well to the surface. These steps include controlling the suction and ensuring that the background has a good **key**. Only then can you apply the plaster.

Checking the suction will tell you if the background is dry and porous. You can do this by splashing water onto the background with a brush. The quicker the water is absorbed, the higher the background's suction.

Testing a background's suction by splashing it with water

- No suction or low suction (when the splashed water stays on the background's surface) will indicate that the background is hard or dense.

- High-suction backgrounds (when the splashed water soaks in quickly) will absorb moisture from the plaster mix and may cause it to dry too quickly when applied.

TYPES OF BACKGROUND SURFACES

Let's examine the surface characteristics of different backgrounds in more detail.

Type of background	Comment
Hollow and solid blocks 	Newly constructed buildings that have block walling will need very little preparation before you apply plaster to their surface because they have medium to adequate key. This surface is flat and can be plastered using traditional or modern pre-mixed plasters. Block walling built to today's specification and standard will require only a base coat and finish, known as float and set.
Lightweight aerated blocks 	These blocks are lightweight and weak with an adequate key, but have high-suction levels. Cement-based mixes are not compatible with these backgrounds because they are too strong for this surface. This type of block is best suited for pre-mixed plasters that are weaker than the background. Applying a solution of PVA (polyvinyl acetate) diluted with water (to the manufacturer's instructions) will seal the surface and control the suction.
Plasterboard and fixings 	There are several different types of plasterboard used in our industry, but they are all made with a plaster core within an outer skin of paper. Plasterboard may have square or tapered edges. Both types need to be reinforced at their joints in order to prevent cracking before applying the plaster finish. Plasterboard has a flat surface with low suction and only requires a finish coat that can be applied in one application. Plasterboard can be fixed with galvanised nails or drywall screws. The fixings should be flush otherwise they could penetrate the paper skin surface of the board. Fixing plasterboard over uneven studwork may require **filling out**; this should be done with a bonding grade plaster. Avoid using plasterboard in damp areas as this will cause the core of the board to perish and become weak. You will learn more about plasterboard in Chapter 4.

Filling out

Applying plaster to uneven areas to form a straight background

Type of background	Comment
Lath background 	Laths were traditionally used on timber backgrounds. They consist of thin strips of wood over which plaster can be spread. It can be a time-consuming process to prepare, fix and plaster this surface. This type of background is still used in the restoration of listed buildings.
Existing solid plaster 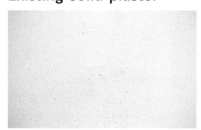	This type of surface is common with solid walls that require a makeover due to poor surface condition that has developed over the years. Over skim makeovers enhance the appearance of a wall by re-skimming the surface without removing the old plaster from the background. When applying plaster to this type of surface, remember that it can only be as good as the background you plaster over. The surface needs to be solid and sound with no hollowness. Any flaking paint and surface grime or grease that could prevent the new plaster from **bonding** should be removed. This background has no key and, if it is painted, usually no suction, unless the background has different properties that are hidden behind the decorated wall surface. For example, if the wall has been re-plastered after having electrical services installed, it may contain different plasters on the background, creating different suction rates. This background will need a bonding adhesive on its surface before it can be re-plastered.
Existing plaster surface that has decayed over time 	There are many different types of plaster surface that may need to be replaced or restored, whether due to poor workmanship or deterioration over time. This type of surface may show signs of cracking, **hollowness** or a crumbling surface that cannot be decorated due to its condition. You will have to remove any existing surface finish before you are able to identify its background properties.

Bonding

When the plaster sufficiently adheres to the background surface

Hollowness

A result of loose plaster that has blown from the background surface

Type of background	Comment
Clay bricks 	Clay bricks were very popular at one time and can be found in all types of buildings. A common fault with clay bricks is that they would shell their face, causing the plaster to 'blow' (come away from the background). This type of background is often uneven due to the fact that the bricks were manufactured in kilns at great heat which made them all a slightly different shape. They were then laid on a lime mortar bed, which is very weak. Clay bricks and lime mortar joints have a high absorption rate that will cause high suction levels. This surface will need to be treated with a bonding adhesive before plastering. Raking out the joints will also improve the key.
Concrete bricks 	These bricks are made from coarse aggregate mixed with cement. This surface is smooth and hard which means the key is poor and the suction is minimal. A bonding slurry is best suited for this surface. You can read about bonding slurry mixes further on in the chapter (see pages 133–134). A traditional method for bonding surfaces was to use a spatterdash slurry. This is a mixture of cement and sharp sand made into a slurry and then thrown on to the background with a paddle or small shovel. Glue additives were added as they were developed to increase and improve the bond.
Engineering bricks 	This is a hard, dense surface with poor key and no absorption rate. The face of the brick has a glossy surface that makes it difficult to prepare for plastering. It has an enamel look and is closed as a low-suction background. This surface needs to be **scabbled** or roughened to remove the sheen. You can then slurry the surface with a bonding adhesive (see pages 133–134). Alternatively, you can fix sheets of EML to its surface with mechanical fixings – this is a good way to reinforce and form a key on the background.

INDUSTRY TIP

You can check the background for hollowness by tapping the surface to see if it is loose or solid.

Scabbling

Creating a rough surface on a smooth background to improve the key

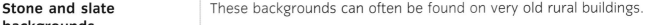

Type of background	Comment
Stone and slate backgrounds 	These backgrounds can often be found on very old rural buildings. Stone can have rough or smooth surfaces. Due to their irregular shape and size, this background is very uneven and will require additional layers in order to build out the surface, the first layer being the **dubbing out** coat. Slate is similar to stone in that it can have uneven surfaces with a smooth face and no suction. The mortar joints between the slate and stone can be very thick and wide, causing large voids. The old mortar joints will need to be filled in with a suitable plaster mix after being raked out, then keyed with a comb scratcher. Any large stone or slate that has a smooth surface will need to be prepared with a bonding slurry to improve the bond.
Concrete lintels and pad stones 	This surface is generally flat and hard with minimal suction. Concrete is used to make lintels and pad stones, which provide load-bearing surfaces above openings such as windows. If using cement-based plaster, concrete should be prepared by applying a bonding agent to the surface. If using lightweight plaster then a bonding-grade plaster should be used on this type of low-suction background.
Timber wall plates covered with EML 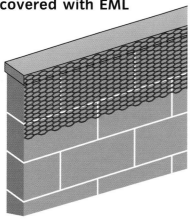	This background generally has low suction and no key. Timber can move and twist with moisture contact. Wall plates are used on top of walls as a fixing for the roof trusses. EML is a good way of reinforcing the timber and providing a key.

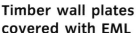

Dubbing out

Filling out between uneven surfaces such as stone joints, building up the uneven surface until it is smooth

ACTIVITY

When you're next in the workshop or your workplace, carry out a suction test on various backgrounds to see how fast they absorb moisture. You can do this by splashing them with water using a small brush and seeing how fast the water absorbs into the background.

REMOVING EXISTING PLASTER AND CLEANING DOWN SURFACES

Removing old plaster from backgrounds is a process known as 'hacking'. It is important to remove all loose plaster from the surface. This can be carried out by hand or mechanically using various different tools and equipment, but before you start you need to protect certain areas to prevent damage that can be caused by this type of work.

Hacking a surface

Plywood sheeting can be used to protect floors and openings such as windows and doors. Dust sheets and tarpaulins are good for protecting furniture that might be too heavy to move out of the building. Causing damage to the client's property is unprofessional and can be costly to replace!

Once the hacking process has been completed and all the loose rubble and debris has been safely cleared, the next stage is to remove any high spots or loose debris that may still exist on the background. This can be done by chipping the surface with a scutch hammer. This is a good tool for this job as it is light to use and has teeth designed to remove small areas of plaster. The remaining dust on the surfaces should be brushed off to leave a clean background.

Brushing down a background

FORMING A KEY AND USING BONDING AGENTS

Harder surfaces with poor key need to be prepared using different techniques and materials.

FORMING A KEY

Mechanical key

Mechanical scabbling tools are used on dense smooth surfaces to create a rough area that will result in a good key, increasing its bonding properties. This tool has teeth or pins that are made from strong steel that vibrate on the background surface.

Preparing a concrete background with a scabbler

Expanded metal lathing (EML)

Another good way of providing a background with reinforcement and key is to fix EML to its surface, especially if the surface contains large cracks or different composite (materials). EML is also used on timber backgrounds, such as old timber lintels and wall plates.

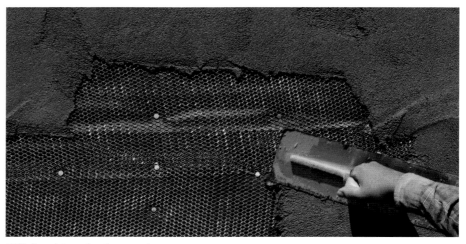

EML fixed to a background

USING BONDING AGENTS

PVA

PVA is the abbreviation for polyvinyl acetate, a water-based glue that is used for preparing background surfaces by improving adhesion.

PVA is mainly used when mixed with water for sealing suction. However, if it is used neat it can be used to bond finishing plaster to low-suction backgrounds.

When using undercoat plasters, it is advisable to mix the PVA with Ordinary Portland Cement (OPC) – this will then become a slurry and a strong bonding agent for cement-based plasters.

PVA

Applying slurry coats

There are two main methods used to apply a slurry coat for bonding cement-based undercoat plasters.

- *Method 1:* Mix and apply the slurry to the background with a brush and then apply plaster directly to the slurry while it is still wet and tacky. This method will bond both surfaces at the same time.

Wet slurry method

- *Method 2:* Mix the dry slurry with water and apply directly to the surface with a brush, then stipple the surface to create a textured finish that forms a good key. This type of slurry is left for 24 hours to go hard before cement-based plaster is applied.

Dry slurry method

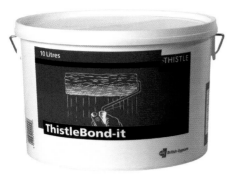

Thistle Bond-it

Febond Blue Grit

There are many new products for bonding plasters on the market today that have been developed in laboratories. For example, Thistle Bond-it and Febond Blue Grit have been developed for over skimming solid surfaces. You can apply these adhesives with a soft brush or roller.

A traditional method for bonding surfaces is using a spatterdash slurry. This is a mixture of cement and sharp sand made into a slurry and then thrown onto the background with a paddle or small shovel. Some commercial types of this slurry have glues added to increase and improve the bond.

The spatterdash method

COMMON PLASTERING FAULTS

Faults occur in plastering work for a number of reasons, including the following.

- Applying plaster onto poorly prepared backgrounds can cause defects in the finished work. Backgrounds that have poor key and low suction will not bond and will become loose over time.

- Plaster applied to background surfaces should be slightly weaker than the background; applying plaster that is stronger than the background will cause stress, causing the plaster to crack and blow.

- Hot and cold climate conditions can affect the set of plasters in different ways. Mixing in freezing conditions will affect the strength of the mix and cause the plaster to crumble when set. Hot conditions can remove the moisture content from the mix; this will affect the curing process and can weaken the mix.

- Using pre-mixed plaster on persistently damp backgrounds should be avoided. Gypsum is a product that absorbs moisture when set and will perish in these conditions.

- Applying plaster onto backgrounds that have high suction levels can cause the plaster to lose its moisture content, reducing its initial strength.

- Plaster applied over high-suction backgrounds will lose its moisture content too quickly and produce a fine crazing surface. This is also known as fire cracking.

A fine crazing plaster surface

PREPARE FOR MIXING PLASTERING MATERIALS

Before setting up the mixing area you need to protect the floor area by placing tarpaulin or timber sheets on it to protect it from splashes and spillages that may occur when mixing. Dust sheets and cling film can be used to protect walkways and furniture.

It is extremely important to follow the specification when gauging plastering mixes and to **gauge** the materials accurately. Inaccurate mixing or gauging can lead to weakened mixes or mixes that are too strong.

Gauge

The term used for measuring materials

Gauging boxes were traditionally used to measure quantities of materials. Today, plastic buckets are preferred as they are lighter and have handles, which makes the job easier. To measure quantities and volumes of materials accurately, fill the bucket or box to the top and then 'flatten off' with a piece of timber. This will ensure that the correct **proportion** of each material is added to make your mix.

Proportion

A part of a whole

Gauging materials with buckets

Damp affecting plaster

MIX RATIOS

Cement-based **ratios** for dubbing out and scratch coats can vary depending on the characteristics of the background. In some cases, the background may have penetrating or rising damp, which is quite common in old housing. This will mean that the ratio of the mix will be different compared with walls that have no damp issues but may have poor adhesion and key. The following table shows the ratio of mixes for scratch coats and dubbing out.

Ratio of mixes	Use
Ratio (written as 6:1:1) of: 6 sand 1 cement 1 lime plus plasticiser. **Ratio (7:1:1) of:** 7 sand 1 cement 1 lime plus plasticiser.	These ratios of mix would be preferred on severe uneven backgrounds, such as stone or old brickwork. In some cases, less lime is added; however, this will depend on the specification.
Ratio (3:1) of: 3 sand 1 cement plus waterproofer. **Ratio (4:1) of:** 4 sand 1 cement plus waterproofer.	These ratios of mix would be preferred when dubbing out and applying scratch coats to backgrounds that have been treated for rising or penetrating damp.
Ratio (4:1) of: 4 sand 1 cement.	This ratio is preferred when applying scratch coats on to slurry surfaces.
Ratio (5:1) of: 5 sand 1 cement.	This mix would be used on uneven surfaces that have good key, and only requires preparing with water or PVA.
Ratio (5:2) of: 5 sand 2 lime.	Used for training purposes in colleges.

Mixing cement-based plaster

Mixes can vary depending on the background and area to be covered. Always follow the specification when mixing materials.

MIXING TRADITIONAL CEMENT-BASED PLASTERING MATERIALS

MIXING USING MACHINERY

Traditional sand, lime and cement materials are best mixed with a mechanical drum mixer which will thoroughly mix the different materials that make the plaster mix.

- Clean water and any specified additive such as plasticiser should first be added to the mixer. This will prevent materials sticking to the back of the drum.

- The consistency of the mixed material should be drier rather than wet when mixing is in progress. This will allow the additive time to make the mix workable and easier to use when applying the plaster.

- Mixing should be carried out for at least five minutes, allowing the materials to fully mix together.

- Don't forget to wear gloves/barrier cream, goggles/glasses and boots to protect from splashes from the turning drum of the mixer.

Mixing with a drum mixer

> **INDUSTRY TIP**
>
> Adding too much water will make the plaster slide down the wall, while not enough water will make it difficult to spread.

MIXING BY HAND

There are some instances where smaller amounts of mix are required. This can be mixed loose on a flat surface or in a bucket. The following steps show how to mix cement-based plasters by hand.

STEP 1 First, gauge the materials.

STEP 2 Then, place the materials into a single pile.

STEP 3 Mix the materials dry (without adding water).

STEP 4 Once the materials are mixed, make a dip in the middle of the pile.

STEP 5 Measure the correct amount of plasticiser needed. To improve work-ability, add the plasticiser to the water.

STEP 6 Mix the plasticiser into the water.

STEP 7 Pour the water into the middle of the pile of material.

STEP 8 Using a shovel, pull the dry material slowly towards the centre, into the water.

INDUSTRY TIP

Don't add too much water or the mix will become too heavy, unworkable and difficult to use.

ACTIVITY

In groups of two or three, follow the procedure for mixing lime and sand mortar to a ratio of 3:1, plus plasticiser.

STEP 9 Mix and turn the material. The longer you turn, the better the mix.

STEP 10 The finished mix.

PRE-MIXED PLASTERS

Pre-mixed gypsum-based plasters can be mixed either by hand with a plunger or mechanically with a drill and whisk. When mixing it is important to follow the manufacturer's technical instructions; these are normally printed on the back of the bag. Irregular setting can occur if you do not follow the rules of using clean water, tools and equipment when mixing this type of plaster.

Pre-mixed plasters used to be mixed in baths with a rake or shovel, until a modern powerful motorised drill was developed with a whisk attachment. This tool can mix pre-mixed plaster with ease.

Mixing with a plunger

Mixing with a drill and whisk

APPLYING ONE, TWO AND THREE COAT PLASTERING TO INTERIOR BACKGROUNDS

The type of plastering carried out on internal walls within buildings will be restricted by the background's surface. Internal solid plastering can be classed as one, two or three coat work; this is known as scratch, float and set.

THREE COAT WORK

Three coat work is generally applied on uneven backgrounds, building up the surface in three layers of plastering material to obtain the desired finish. However, some severely uneven backgrounds may need more than one scratch coat to build the surface out.

Plastering an uneven background

Floating coat

TWO COAT WORK

Two coat work is applied on flatter backgrounds such as block and brick surfaces which can be completed using a floating and setting coat. This has an approximate overall thickness of 13mm; however, this may vary on uneven backgrounds. This surface does not require a scratch coat.

ONE COAT WORK

Although one coat work is generally related to the application of the setting coat, there are pre-mixed plasters that can be applied approximately 10mm thick and finished in one process, which replaces the two coat process of float and set. This plaster is known as one coat plaster and it can also be applied by a spray machine.

Applying setting plaster to plasterboard

Thistle one coat plaster

Hanson one coat plaster

PLASTERING A TYPICAL TWO OR THREE BEDROOM HOUSE

Before starting any plastering work on a house, you need to plan carefully each aspect of the work, allowing you to complete one stage at a time. By making sure you have the necessary tools and resources to hand, this will help you complete the work to the schedule.

A standard order of work is shown in the list below.

Plastering a typical bedroom

1 Fix plasterboards to the ceiling and partition. You will need access equipment to carry out this job safely.

2 Prepare background surfaces by fixing EML to the timber wall plates. You may also need to dub out recessed lintels above openings.

3 Fix standard angle beads to window and door reveals, heads and wall returns.

4 Apply your floating coat plaster to all solid walls including returns, reveals and soffits.

5 Apply setting coats to ceilings.

6 Fit thin coat angle beads to plasterboard external angles.

7 Apply setting plaster to walls and partitions, including returns, reveals and soffits.

APPLYING THE SCRATCH COAT

Uneven surfaces need to be prepared by applying a scratch coat to the surface. This will build up and straighten its uneven surfaces, forming a base for the floating coat, and controlling the suction. Once applied, the scratch coat is keyed with a comb scratcher to allow the next coat to bond. The scratch coat makes it simpler to apply and rule the next layer with an even thickness of plaster; the next layer is called the floating coat.

The following steps show you how to apply a scratch coat. Before you begin, mix the different materials and include the plasticiser, which will give the mix its workability.

STEP 1 Load the spot board. Next, set up your hop-up. This will give you a platform that allows you to reach the ceiling height of the wall.

STEP 2 Wet the background surface using a brush to reduce the suction.

STEP 3 Transfer the plastering material from the spot board to the wall using your hawk and trowel.

STEP 4 Apply the scratch coat, starting at the top-right corner (if you are right-handed) or the top-left corner (if you are left-handed), laying four trowel widths apart and in lengths of 300mm long. The plaster should then be flattened using the trowel at a shallow angle to help spread the material. The applied scratch coat needs to be about 10mm thick.

STEP 5 Working downwards and across, follow the same procedure until you have applied an area of 1m². It is best to break the wall surface into sections as this is more efficient and will help you complete the work in a methodical order.

STEP 6 This section of the surface is now ready to be keyed using a comb scratcher. The surface should be keyed horizontally, deep enough to allow the next coat to grip but not so deep as to penetrate through the scratch coat to the background.

STEP 7 Apply the scratch coat to the rest of the wall and key it, using the same procedure.

STEP 8 Once the wall has been plastered, check its surface with a straight edge. Fill in any hollows or remove excessive thickness, preparing the surface to receive the next layer once the scratch coat has set.

STEP 9 Once the wall is complete, the next stage is to clean the work area: wet or messy surfaces are a slip hazard.

APPLYING THE FLOATING COAT

Depending on the background and the specified plaster, the floating coat will provide a flat and lightly keyed base for the setting coat. It will be ruled with a straight edge, hollows filled in and any high spots in its surface removed that would cause unevenness after application. The plaster surface is then left to **pull in** before it is consolidated and keyed with a devil float, preparing it for the final application known as the setting or finish coat.

Pulled in

When material has stiffened up or started to set

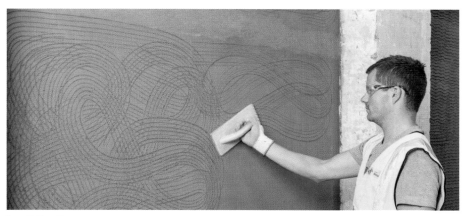

Devil floating

Lime and cement plaster mixes must be left to dry for several days before they can be finished with a setting plaster. Gypsum undercoat plasters set within two hours and will need to be finished with a setting plaster as soon as possible. If left for more than a day, gypsum undercoats can develop excessive and irregular suction rates that would need to be treated with diluted PVA to prevent the surface from drawing too much moisture from the setting plaster and causing it to craze crack.

Once set, all floated surfaces need to be prepared by scraping the surface with the edge of the trowel prior to applying the finishing coat. This will remove any **snots** or nodules which could protrude when applying the setting plaster. All internal floated angles and ceiling lines must be cut back to leave the surface flat.

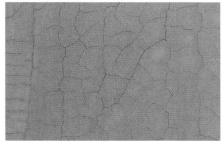

Craze crack

Snots

Residue left on the surface of the floating coat after consolidation. This needs to be removed to prevent it penetrating the surface of the setting coat

Removing snots from the floating coat

Cutting angles

Floating coats can be applied using the following three methods, each method having its own individual purpose with regards to accuracy and speed of application:

- the plumb dot and screed method
- the broad screed method
- the free hand method.

PLUMB DOT AND SCREED METHOD

The plumb dot and screed process is the most accurate method of applying a floating coat and also the more time-consuming way. If the client is prepared to pay for this method then he or she will benefit from having accurate, plumb plastered walls.

Timber dots are used to set out accurate plumb walls and also used to form horizontal or vertical screeds (strips of plaster). The screeds are left to set before being used as guides, allowing the plasterer to fill in between and accurately rule the surface to obtain a flat plumb wall. The surface is later consolidated and lightly keyed using a devil float once the material has pulled in.

This system may well be used today in areas such as bathrooms or kitchens due to the accuracy required to fit and fix units and sanitary tiles or where fibrous plaster is to be installed.

INDUSTRY TIP

The plumb dot and screed method was used a lot in early industry and was classed as high standard or high class work.

STEP 1 Apply a dab of plaster approximately 150–300mm from the ceiling and adjacent wall.

STEP 2 Set the dot into it. The distance from the wall surface to the face of the dot will be the thickness of the floating coat.

STEP 3 Directly below the top dot, set another dot approximately 300mm from the floor.

STEP 4 Check that the dots are plumb.

STEP 5 When the dots have stiffened, apply plaster material between them to form the screeds.

STEP 6 Using the floating rule or feather edge, rule off the excess plaster between the dots. Remember to wear a hard hat when using a hop-up.

STEP 7 Fill any hollows. Repeat Steps 6 and 7 until the screed is flush with the dots and free from hollows.

STEP 8 When the screeds have stiffened sufficiently, consolidate the surface with a float and form key with a devil float. Remember to remove the dots and fill in with stiffening floating material.

STEP 9 Apply plaster between the screeds, starting at the top of the wall and working heel to toe.

STEP 10 Repeat until you reach the bottom screed.

STEP 11 Place the thinner edge of the rule across both screeds and, using a side-to-side motion, draw the edge up the screeds, ensuring that the edge remains in contact with both screeds at all times.

STEP 12 Any excess plaster will gather on the edge of the rule. This should be cleaned off the edge and returned to the spot board.

STEP 13 Fill any hollows until the plaster is flush with the screeds and all hollows are filled.

STEP 14 Repeat Steps 9 to 13 until the area between the screeds is completely covered and ruled off.

STEP 15 The finished floating coat.

BROAD SCREED METHOD

The broad screed method is also known as the box screed method. It also uses screeds as guides to help float the wall but is different from dot and screed.

Wet screeds are applied around the perimeter and ruled. Once the screeds have been laid on and ruled accurately you must also check that they are flush where each screed meets at its ends. The next stage is to fill in between the perimeter screeds and rule the surface either horizontally or vertically against the screeds. Although this method of floating coats produces straight walls and is more commonly used in the industry compared with dot and screed, the finished surface may be straight but not plumb.

When using this method, particular attention should be paid to all the internal angles. If these are not correct, it will be an obvious defect that will need correcting.

Wet screed

A band of undercoat plaster screed being used as a floating guide while it is still wet

STEP 1 Form the first screed up to 500mm wide, applying plaster to the right-hand side of the wall from the ceiling to 25mm short of the floor/DPC and approximately at the required thickness.

STEP 2 Rule this off, checking it is plumb and filling hollows, etc.

STEP 3 Apply a second screed along the ceiling line.

STEP 4 Rule in the ceiling line.

STEP 5 Apply another screed 25mm short of the floor/DPC.

STEP 6 Apply the floating coat between the screeds and rule off. Take care not to scoop out the screeds as they will still be soft.

STEP 7 Ruling in.

FREE HAND METHOD

The free hand method of producing floating coats is seen as a way of completing the work efficiently and at speed, which is why it is best suited to large commercial sites where work is being done by **sub-contractors** who have tighter work schedules than plasterers carrying out private work. However, due to the speed and the way it is produced this method can also be less accurate in terms of straightness. To help reduce this problem, this type of work is carried out on new block or brick backgrounds which are much straighter than older uneven walls.

Sub-contractor

A tradesperson that is not directly employed by a company but is employed for short periods to complete some aspects of the work. They are paid by the work completed at a set price

INDUSTRY TIP

The industry standard for a plastered wall is ± 3mm tolerance in a length of 1.800mm in any direction of the surface.

Free hand method

Filling hollows

Checking free hand plaster with a straight edge

To carry out this work you need to be highly skilled and experienced, as there will be no guide such as screeds to help you rule your work. The plasterer will lay on plaster to cover a certain area of the wall before it is ruled using either a darby or a straight edge, filling in any hollows as the work proceeds. When ruling the surface this is done horizontally and vertically to the applied surface to eliminate as much unevenness and to fill in as much as possible. Once the wall has been completely laid on and ruled, the surface will be checked at wall angles, ceiling lines, skirting lines and diagonally for straightness before consolidating with a devil float.

FLOATING CEILINGS AND BEAMS

Floating ceilings and beams involves a different technique from floating walls. Your tutor should be able to show you the methods below.

FLOATING A CEILING

Set out for floating ceilings using a bonding-grade undercoat plaster and then follow this method.

1 Mark a datum line around the room about 400mm from the ceiling line.

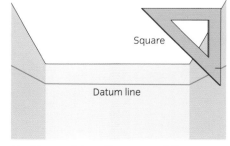

Marking a datum line around the room

2 Using a tape measure, find the lowest point from the ceiling to the datum line; this will indicate the minimum thickness of your floating coat. At the lowest point close to the corner, you can start to set out your dots and apply your undercoat plaster to form a perimeter screed to the ceiling.

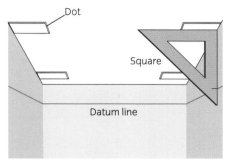

Setting out the dots

3 Once the screeds have set and been keyed, proceed to fill between with plaster, ruling off the screeds to form a level ceiling.

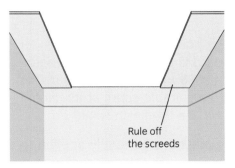

Filled screeds and ruling off

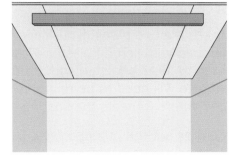

Checking ceiling is level with a straight edge

If you have an uneven plasterboard ceiling with hollows, you will need to prepare and build this out by applying bonding plaster first, allowing it to set before applying the setting coat. Bonding plaster can be used to float plasterboard or EML that has been fixed to the ceilings.

FLOATING A BEAM

Set out a beam from the ceiling, making sure that both ends are equal distances and that the soffits are set out level, then follow this method.

1 Angle beads should be fixed and checked for level and equal margin along the soffit of the beam.

2 Apply the undercoat to the sides of the beam and then rule the surface with a square, ensuring it is 90° to the ceiling.

3 Apply the undercoat plaster to the soffit of the beam and rule the surface of the plaster against the beads.

INDUSTRY TIP

Make sure that the angle beads are fixed level and the correct width gauge along their length. Use a piece of timber to mark the gauge to make sure they are of equal length.

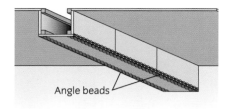

Angle beads fixed to the beam

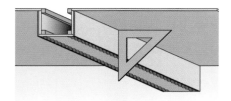

Undercoat plaster applied and ruled on the sides of the beam with a square

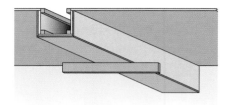

Ruling the surface of the plaster against the beads

SETTING COAT

Skim

The term used by some plasterers when applying the setting coat

The final coat will be applied in two thin layers of setting plaster using two different gauges. This coat is also known as the '**skim**', which refers to skimming a surface with setting plaster. When this finish is completed it will have an approximate thickness of 2–3mm on walls and 3–5mm on ceilings.

There are two types of surfaces in new housing that need to be finished with setting plaster. Plasterboard is one, a sheet material fixed to joists and studwork forming a base for the setting coat. This surface will need to be reinforced with a suitable scrim at its joints and where it meets the floating coat before the finish is laid on.

Ceilings are the other surface. Setting plaster is generally applied to ceilings before it is applied to adjacent walls, as this will reduce dirty water and plaster splashes from affecting the surrounding surfaces.

METHOD FOR APPLYING FINISHING PLASTER TO PLASTERBOARD CEILING (FOR A RIGHT-HANDED PLASTERER)

Make sure you have the necessary PPE to carry out this task. Before you carry out this task make sure you have erected a fully boarded staging, this will allow you to apply your plaster in long strokes making the job simpler to complete. A fully boarded staging will allow the work to be completed efficiently and safely.

Plasterboarded wall

Grinning

When the plaster surface reveals imperfections caused by deeply keyed devil floating or variation of suction in backgrounds

On some commercial sites plasterers apply two applications of setting plaster using the same gauge. This can lead to imperfections such as sagging and **grinning** occurring in the work. This can be avoided by using two different gauges.

STEP 1 Apply scrim to reinforce the joints of the plasterboard including the wall and ceiling line.

STEP 2 Apply plaster to cover the scrim. This will help keep it in place and prevent it folding when applying the first coat.

STEP 3 Apply the first coat of plaster to the ceiling working from left to right, laying the plaster in line with your right shoulder. This will help protect your face from any plaster droppings.

STEP 4 Make sure that while plastering you stand in the correct position: put your right foot forward and your left back. This will allow you a longer reach when applying the plaster.

STEP 5 Continue to work around the perimeter of the ceiling and then start at the opposite end.

STEP 6 The ceiling has now been completely covered with approximately 3mm of plaster.

STEP 7 The next stage before applying the second coat is to flatten the ceiling surface with your trowel or finishing blade. Normally the surface of the first coat will become matt in appearance ready for the second coat.

STEP 8 Use a second gauge to apply your second coat in the same sequence as the first coat; this should only be applied if your first coat has started to pull in.

STEP 9 Once the ceiling has been applied with a second coat, flatten the surface working in the same sequence. Make sure there are no blemishes or gauls and that you have a good ceiling line along the wall.

STEP 10 Always lay and finish the plaster along the length of the bead to prevent any unforeseen steps or blemishes, which can be difficult to overcome at a later stage.

STEP 11 When the second coat begins to pull in apply some water to the face of the plaster using a splash brush and trowel the ceiling, continuing to work from left to right in line with your right shoulder. This should be repeated every 15–20 minutes at least two times.

STEP 12 A final cross trowel should then be applied to finish the ceiling to a flat smooth surface, as it will eliminate any fat marks.

Timber rule

A straight plane timber used as a guide to form the edge of a return. Before the introduction of aluminium feather edges, they were also used as straight edges

INDUSTRY TIP

When you lay on setting plaster to beads you should always work your trowel along the length of the bead. Laying across the bead can cause a recess in the plaster surface as it meets up to the edge of the bead.

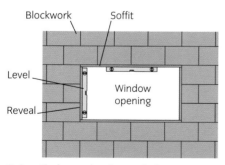

Using timber rules in a window

FORMING EXTERNAL ANGLES

Walls with window openings

Before you plaster a window wall you need to prepare your angles. There are two methods used to do this. One method is to use **timber rules** as guides, fixed or wedged to the reveals and soffit, and positioned to allow for the appropriate thickness of plaster. This method is known as forming hard angles. The other is to use angle beads.

Forming hard angles

Hard angles are commonly used in conservation work which specifies using this traditional method of forming corners. This method can be time consuming: you can only apply plaster to one surface at a time and it needs to set hard before the timber rules are removed and fixed onto the face of the wall, allowing you to plaster the reveals and heads. If you have to apply three coats this will mean you will have to fit and fix the timber rules three times, adjusting for each thickness of plaster application.

There are other types of external angle used to form hard angles. You should become familiar with the following:

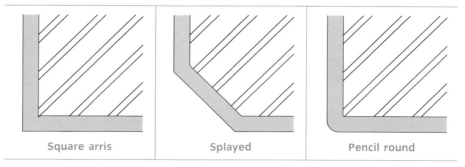

| Square arris | Splayed | Pencil round |

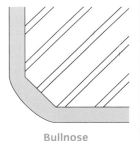

Bullnose

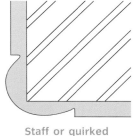

Staff or quirked

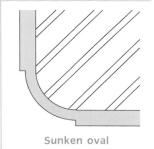

Sunken oval

The timber rule method is also used when applying the setting coat when you need to form rounded hard angles using an external corner trowel. The setting plaster would be applied to the external corner of the floating coat in 50mm-wide strips each side. This would then be trowelled with the corner trowel several times to form and finish the corner until it has set. Setting plaster would then be laid and finished to the corner's edge.

Reveal gauges are used to rule the floating coat on the reveal and soffit, providing a square return surface with equal margins along the frame.

Fixing angle beads

Standard angle beads are used not only to speed up the work but also because they provide accurate sharp corners that are reinforced to protect against impact damage, helping prevent chipping of the external angle.

Reveal gauge

Window fitted with angle beads

If severely uneven walls are to receive three coat work then timber rules or a straight edge might be used on the reveals to build out the unevenness first, before applying the angle beads. The procedure for setting out and fixing angle beads will be similar as for a wall with doorways and returns. Standard angle beads can be fixed with plaster dabs or galvanised nails. The preferred method is to use plaster dabs when fixing as this is simpler when plumbing or levelling the bead. Positioning beads with nails and plumbing at the same time can be a difficult process to master.

INDUSTRY TIP

When you fix beads with plaster dabs don't forget before it sets to cut back any excessive dabs that may stick out past the nosing.

Using plaster dabs to fix angle beads

The following step-by-step instructions show you how to fix angle beads to a window wall. This method will allow you to set out your beads to the required depth and dimensions.

STEP 1 Place the straight edge on the window sill and place a mark on its edge between the wall. This mark on the sill indicates the thickness of the undercoat plaster that will be applied to the wall. If there is more than one window then a chalk line can be snapped from the outer side of each opening to indicate the line of the horizontal beads.

STEP 2 Use a square to mark a right angle from the window frame to the left and right reveal, making sure that this is a similar thickness. Check that you have an equal margin along the frame's edge as this will be the finished edge of the plaster at the reveals.

STEP 3 The marks have now crossed on the sill, indicating the fixing points for the two angle beads.

STEP 4 The next stage is to cut both angle beads just short (by about 10mm) of the head soffit. This is to allow for the remaining bead that fits to the head; this can be cut after both sides have been fitted with beads.

STEP 5 Mix your plaster stiffer than normal and apply the plaster dabs to the reveal, pinching your plaster away from the corner leaving a dab. Apply dabs every 400mm (this can be less if the window is small).

STEP 6 Place the angle bead to your crossed lines at the sill and bed the angle beads in position, checking to see if it lines with the edge of the window. Remove excess plaster from the dab once the bead is in position.

INDUSTRY TIP

Experienced plasterers may choose to set out the head bead first on single window walls.

INDUSTRY TIP

Always double check that standard angle beads are plumb and level after fixing – once the surface has been plastered, they cannot be moved or adjusted.

STEP 7 Use a level to check that both sides of the bead are plumb in line with the face of the wall and reveal.

STEP 8 Cut your head bead and repeat the process for setting out and fixing. However, this time make sure the bead is level along the head and that it does not have steps at both sides to the reveal beads.

STEP 9 Leave the plaster to set before applying the undercoat, as the angle bead will be used as a guide to rule the surface.

Use a square or gauge to form the reveals and head. The undercoat will require **cutting back** at the edge of the bead, allowing the setting plaster to finish flush with the arris.

Cutting back

Removing undercoat plaster from around door frames or beads allowing you to apply setting plaster flush, preventing plaster from gathering and building up over beads

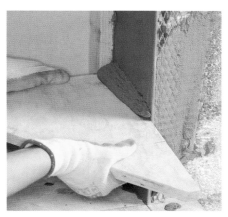

Using a square or gauge to form the reveals and head

Cutting back the undercoat at the edge of the bead

There are other surfaces that have returns and angles. These will also require setting out before the angles are formed, using the hard angle method with timber rules or fixing angle beads in plaster dabs.

Walls with door openings

Walls that contain timber door casings or **linings** are very helpful to the plasterer as the lining can be used as a guide to rule the surface. However, if the lining is not fixed plumb and true and is used to rule the surface, this will cause the floating coat to be a similar shape as the frame. Always check the door linings to make sure they are plumb and that they are fixed to allow a **nominal** thickness of plaster to the wall surface. If you find linings or frames to be out of line or not level or plumb, you will need to report the discrepancy to your foreman or supervisor as soon as possible in order for the defective work to be rectified.

Linings

Timber surround for internal doors, forming a lining to the masonry or studded opening

Nominal

The standard thickness of plaster application

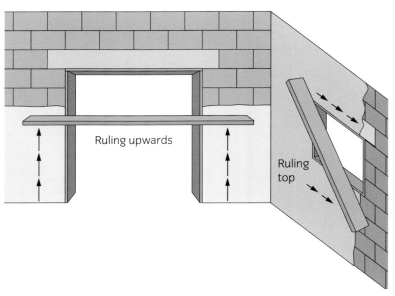

Ruling upwards

Ruling top

Ruling a door and window lining

If the wall contains a return at its end then a standard angle bead will need to be fixed to the return. This should be lined through from the door lining to the corner, making a mark on the floor to indicate the thickness of the floating coat and the position of the bead. Another method is to fix a timber ledge or rule to the face of the return to the same line as the door lining; this is later removed and reversed to complete the other side of the return.

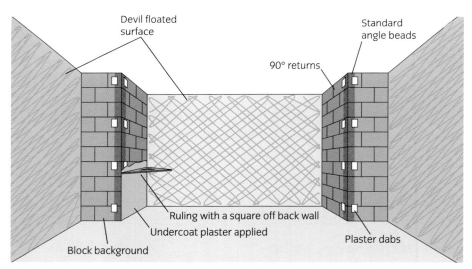

Standard angle bead fixed to a wall with a return and forming returns with a square

After consolidating the plaster surface you will need to cut back to the edge of the frame; this will allow you to apply a setting coat of plaster flush against the frame. Failure to do this can cause excessive build-up on the frame.

Walls with attached piers

For walls with attached piers, such as pillars, you need to set out snapping chalk lines at each end of the pier at floor level to the thickness of the undercoat. Once you have snapped your line you should use this as a plumbing point for fixing the angle beads or timber rule. If you fix to the snapped lines this should ensure that all beads or timber rules will line in.

You can also use this method when setting out independent piers that are in line with each other. The internal right angle to the face and rear of the pier can be set out using a square from the snapped chalk line which runs along the length of the pier.

A wall with attached piers

Snapped chalk line

Walls with a return

Walls with a return can be set out using a square similar to a reveal; the square must be positioned to 90° from the line of the main wall. The image in the margin shows the floor marked out so that a wall with a return can receive standard angle beads.

Wall with a return

Walls with a chimney

Walls with a chimney will have two returns at each end similar to a pillar. Once the beads are set out you can check the margin from each side of the bead to the other at the top, middle and bottom for accuracy.

Wall with a chimney

Walls with an independent pier

When setting out an independent pier with equal sides for fixing beads, a parallel line needs to be set out to the front and rear of the pier to the required thickness (approximately 10–20mm). The next step is to use a square and set it to the parallel lines and mark the same thickness to both sides, making sure the sides are at 90°. Once you have set out your marks you can proceed with fixing your beads plumb to form the external corners. For accuracy, check the beads for equal margins at the top, middle and bottom.

Setting out an independent pier with equal sides

MAKING GOOD A CHASE

Making good a **chase** may have to be done if plasterwork has become defective and been replaced, or if new services need to be installed behind the original plasterwork. Once the work has been carried out, the chase has to be made good to bring the plasterwork back to its original state.

The following steps show you how to make good a chase. Firstly, you must mark out the chase on a plastered wall. Using a lump hammer and bolster, remove the plaster to leave a chase in the plastered wall. Now follow the steps below.

Chase

A void for installing services which will require making good with plaster

INDUSTRY TIP

It's important to wear safety clothing and glasses to avoid flying debris when cutting out a chase.

STEP 1 Remove the dust and dampen the background to control the suction.

STEP 2 Mix the undercoat plaster and apply directly into the chase.

STEP 3 Remove excess plaster with your trowel in line with the existing surface, filling out any hollows.

STEP 4 Clean off the previously plastered face using a trowel and a water brush.

STEP 5 As the undercoat plaster starts to pull in, cut back the surface with a gauging trowel or small tool to form a recess of approximately 2–3mm in the chase surface to allow for the setting coat.

STEP 6 Key the undercoat with a devil float.

STEP 7 Soak the edge around the chase several times to control the suction at its edge before you apply your setting coat.

STEP 8 Mix your plaster and apply it to the chase, removing any surplus plaster that is applied beyond the edge of the chase.

STEP 9 Remove any surplus plaster away from the edge and clean the surface with a splash brush.

STEP 10 Repeat the process and apply the second coat.

STEP 11 Trowel the face of the plaster chase, making sure that the surface is flush with the edge.

When you have completed this task, run the palm of your hand along the surface to feel if there are any recesses or bumps between the chase and the previously plastered face.

ACTIVITY

Mark out a chase in a plastered wall and follow the steps for making good a chase.

Case Study: Ellie

Shortly after buying a property, Carolyn realised that there was a problem with the plasterwork which could be seen running just below the ceiling line of the upstairs bedrooms. The plaster in this area contained cracks and when Carolyn tapped the surface it sounded loose and hollow in certain areas. It was strange to see that the cracks were only along the top part of the wall to the external perimeter walls.

As Carolyn was unsure what had caused the cracks and what remedial action to take; she asked a friend of hers who happened to be a plasterer to come and have a look and assess the situation.

Her friend Ellie recommended that they remove some of the plaster to get a clear look at what was behind. It then became clear to Ellie that in places the timber wall plate had not been adequately covered with EML to reinforce and key the surface.

Ellie told Carolyn that she would need to remove the loose plaster below the wall plate line and fix new strips of EML to cover the timber surface, making sure it overlapped down the wall a minimum of 50mm to strengthen and prevent further cracking to the weak, straight join between the top of the wall and the timber wall plate. Only then could the surface be made good using a bonding grade undercoat and a multi-finish plaster.

Ellie gave Carolyn a quotation for the work which included labour and material costs to carry out the work. Before she started the work, Ellie removed the furniture and protected the floors with polythene sheets and hardboard. She then hacked off an area about 150mm down the wall along the perimeter of the external walls.

After fixing new EML to the wall plate, Ellie applied a solution of PVA diluted with water to eliminate the suction in the background below the wall plate along the existing wall. She then mixed and applied a pre-mixed bonding grade plaster to prick up the EML surface. She let it set before applying the floating coat. To get the surface flat and straight she applied the floating coat and ruled the plaster with a straight edge from the existing plasterwork. After devil floating, Ellie then cut back to the existing surface which made it simpler for her to finish setting the plaster flush, making good the work.

Work through the following questions to check your learning.

1   Which one of the following types of sand would be used for a traditional lime mortar mix?

   a   Sharp.

   b   Dredged.

   c   Silica.

   d   Silver.

2   Which one of the following types of aggregate is used in a pre-mixed lightweight plaster to improve the adhesion properties of the plaster?

   a   Perlite.

   b   Sand.

   c   Quartz.

   d   Vermiculite.

3   Floating coats are keyed using a

   a   devil float

   b   cross grain float

   c   plastic float

   d   long grain float.

4   To avoid pre-mixed lightweight plaster setting too quickly, it is important to mix the plaster with

   a   clean water

   b   warm water

   c   retarders

   d   accelerators.

5   'Flash set' occurs in setting plaster as a result of using

   a   clean water

   b   tap water

   c   bottled water

   d   dirty water.

6   Undercoat plaster that adheres to the background is termed

   a   suitable

   b   compatible

   c   desirable

   d   pliable.

7   Backgrounds that have high absorption rates are classed as

   a   low suction

   b   no suction

   c   high suction

   d   even suction.

8   Which one of the following backgrounds is one coat setting plaster applied to?

   a   Plasterboard ceilings.

   b   Timber wall plate.

   c   Expanded metal lath.

   d   Uneven brickwork.

9   Which one of the following backgrounds will require three coat plasterwork to form an even surface?

   a   Stone.

   b   Plasterboard.

   c   Solid block.

   d   Hollow block.

10   Which one of the following results would occur when applying an excessive thickness of undercoat plaster?

   a   Drying.

   b   Sagging.

   c   Blistering.

   d   Sweating.

11 Setting coat plaster is best applied and finished using how many layers of plaster?

a One.

b Two.

c Three.

d Four.

12 Which one of the following backgrounds would thin coat angle beads be fixed to using nails?

a Blockwork.

b Stonework.

c Plasterboard.

d Brickwork.

13 At what intervals should dabs be spaced when fixing standard angle beads?

a 400–600mm.

b 700–800mm.

c 900–1000mm.

d 1100–1200mm.

14 Which one of the following trowels would be used to form a bullnose hard angle in setting plaster?

a Internal corner.

b Gauging.

c External corner.

d Floating.

15 Which one of the following is an example of information found in a specification relating to plastering?

a Thickness of plaster.

b Coverage of plaster.

c Cost of plaster.

d Use-by date of plaster.

16 Which one of the following methods is used to form an accurate floating coat to block walls?

a Dot and screed.

b Wet screeds.

c Broad screeds.

d Wall screeds.

17 The process of cutting back the floating coat is carried out at

a window frames

b door frames

c door thresholds

d window sills.

18 How thick should setting coat plaster be applied?

a 1mm.

b 3mm.

c 6mm.

d 9mm.

19 How thick should floating coats be applied to a block?

a 2mm.

b 4mm.

c 6mm.

d 10mm.

20 Before applying the setting coat, the undercoat surface wall should be prepared by

a cutting back

b checking for plumb

c keying with a comb scratcher

d scraping to remove snots.

Chapter 4
Unit 222: Fix dry lining and plasterboards to interiors

This chapter explains the process and techniques for fixing and finishing different types of plasterboard surfaces.

The term 'dry lining' refers to fixing plasterboard to backgrounds that are solid (brick or block walls), timber or metal to create a lining surface that can be finished with either a setting plaster or 'tape and jointed'. Plasterboard is used as a quick, dry method of covering the wall to provide a background surface. It has replaced the use of undercoat plasters which contain high moisture levels when mixed with water and applied to background surfaces.

By reading this chapter you will know how to:

1 Interpret information from drawings and specifications for fixing dry lining and plasterboards.

2 Select materials and components for fixing dry lining and plasterboards.

3 Fix dry lining and plasterboards.

WHAT ARE PLASTERBOARD AND DRY LINING?

Plasterboards are rectangular sheets manufactured from gypsum that are sandwiched between lining paper on both sides. They are used as a background surface in new and traditional buildings to form a dry construction background known as 'dry lining'. Plasterboards fixed to the background can be finished flat and smooth, providing an excellent surface for decoration.

Plasterboard has been used as a replacement for lath and plastering since the Second World War as lath and plastering was a problematic and a slow process of lining timber backgrounds. Today over 200 million square metres of plasterboard are used each year. Plasterboards have been developed to meet evolving changes in industry demands, and modern varieties include ones that reduce the transmission of sound, the passage of moisture and the spread of fire, and others that improve the thermal qualities of walls and ceilings within buildings. These characteristics would not be achievable using traditional plastering on walls and ceilings.

ACTIVITY

Find out about the first forms of plasterboard developed in the late 19th century by Augustine Sackett and Fred L Kane.

Plasterboard being manufactured

Fixing centres

The distance between fixings when installing plasterboard

PLASTERBOARD PRODUCTION

Plasterboard is produced by sandwiching wet recycled plaster between two sheets of building paper. This is then pressed between rollers to form a flat surface. The board runs along a conveyor and is cut to length. Plasterboard comes in standard thicknesses of 9.5mm, 12.5mm and 15mm. It is fit for purpose so long as it is supported by fixings or adhesives at certain **fixing centres** or intervals, which add to its surface strength.

ADVANTAGES OF PLASTERBOARD AND DRY LINING

Unlike plaster undercoats that have been mixed with water and therefore contain moisture, plasterboard is a pre-made dry product that only requires finishing by applying a setting coat, or it can be finished with a paper tape and jointing system (see pages 193–195 later in this chapter). Compared with traditional or pre-mixed undercoats, dry lining surfaces contain less moisture and therefore require less drying time. This can speed up the plastering process, helping to meet the high demand and tight deadlines that are set by industry demands for new housing.

Because dry lining contains less moisture, less drying time is required before the surface is ready to be decorated. And using plasterboard is also less likely to show cracking, unless there is movement or shrinkage along its **joints** or if the **core** has been damaged, which may cause the plaster to blow from its surface.

INTERPRETING INFORMATION

PLASTERBOARD TYPES

There are different manufacturing companies that make plasterboard but they all have one thing in common: they produce a range of plasterboard designed to meet and cope with the various requirements and demands of new homes built today. They also comply with building regulations and industry changes that often govern which type of plasterboard is used.

Plasterboard is manufactured in a range of sizes and thicknesses, each type with a specific design and use. The most common types used in the plastering industry come in two standard sizes.

- One is 2400mm long × 1200mm wide and is designed to be used in new buildings that have walls of the same height, or studwork or joists at adequate centres, reducing waste from offcuts.

- The other plasterboard is slightly smaller and lighter, being 1800mm long × 900mm wide. This makes it easy to handle and fix if you are working on your own or if the joist centres are uneven and vary in width.

A third type called base boards are much smaller in size but are used mainly for DIY work rather than by professional plasterers.

Plasterboard is also available with two different types of edge. The plasterboard's edge type determines the type of finish surface it will receive.

1 Square edge plasterboards are manufactured to be finished with setting coat plasterboard finish or multi-finish.

2 Tapered edge plasterboards are manufactured to be finished with a tape and jointing compound, which is sanded and sealed with a primer to protect the board's surface and prepare it for decorating.

Square and tapered edges are often abbreviated to 'SE' and 'TE'. This is useful to remember when selecting the necessary plasterboard from catalogues.

Joints

Where one sheet of plasterboard is butted against another sheet. Joints that need to be reinforced when finishing the surface

Core

The term for the plaster that is sandwiched between both sides of the outer paper of the plasterboard

INDUSTRY TIP

Working out the area of the plasterboard makes it easier to calculate costs when measuring the amount of plasterboard required for background surfaces.

Base board

Square edge plasterboard

Tapered edge plasterboard

WORKING DRAWINGS

The architect will have produced a series of working drawings and these should be used to extract and interpret the information that will help you complete the work in an appropriate manner and to the specified requirements. The drawings include:

- block plans

- assembly plans

- detail plans

- site plans.

The architect's drawings also include floor plans of the work that contain precise metric measurements which can be used to calculate the surface area of each room. By working out the size of each room you can then calculate the cost and the amount of plasterboard that will be required for the job. For more information on these types of drawings, refer back to Chapter 2, pages 49–51.

SPECIFICATIONS AND SCHEDULES

Performance

In a plasterboard context, this refers to plasterboards that have an extra characteristic compared with standard plasterboard, such as enhanced sound insulation, fire resistance, impact resistance or a combination of these. Their use will improve aspects of the performance of a room/building

When an architect designs a building they take into account the specific types and systems that will need to be used for dry lining. They also decide what type of plasterboard **performance** is required. From all these considerations they produce the specification and the schedule that accompany the working drawings.

SPECIFICATIONS

There are certain factors that can influence which type of plasterboard is selected for its intended use. This is why we need to carefully read and follow the specification. The specification contains specific descriptions of the type of plasterboard required and the fixing procedure to be used, and this must be followed during installation to ensure that the work meets industry regulations.

The specification contains precise descriptions and information about the type of backgrounds to receive the plasterboard, its performance and characteristics, its size and thickness, and the standards of workmanship required for installing and fixing the plasterboard. For more information about specifications, refer back to Chapter 2, pages 52–53.

SCHEDULES

The schedule lists the different types of components and fixings needed to carry out the job, such as nails or screws, various adhesives and compounds, and the number of sheets of different types of plasterboard and their reinforcing materials.

For more information about schedules, refer back to Chapter 2, pages 54–55.

DATA SHEETS

Plasterboard product data sheets are produced by plasterboard manufacturers for every type of plasterboard that they make, and these documents should always be referred to when installing plasterboard. The data sheets provide detailed information about the characteristics of the plasterboard product, including its performance, size, and recommended installation methods, finishing and storage.

Data sheets also provide important health and safety information, such as correct manual handling when moving and transporting the plasterboard, any hazards associated with that plasterboard, and any specific first-aid issues.

SELECTING MATERIALS AND COMPONENTS

Plasterboards can be fixed and installed using a range of fixings, including drywall adhesive, screws or nails. The fixing you use depends on the background, which could be solid, timber or steel. You need to consider these factors when selecting materials and components for fixing the plasterboard.

METHODS USED TO FIX PLASTERBOARD

FIXING TO SOLID BACKGROUNDS

Drywall adhesive is a pre-mixed product for **direct bonding** plasterboard to solid backgrounds. It is mixed with water using a drill and whisk or a handheld mixing wheel until it is the correct consistency which allows you to apply dabs to the wall.

Suitable solid backgrounds for drywall adhesive include blockwork, brickwork, concrete or scratch coated surfaces (keyed) that may have been created to dub out uneven walls. The adhesive contains a polymer additive that improves its adhesion properties, making it a suitable product for direct bonding plasterboard and laminate surfaces to the background.

Direct bond

Applying dabs of adhesive for fixing plasterboard

Drywall adhesive

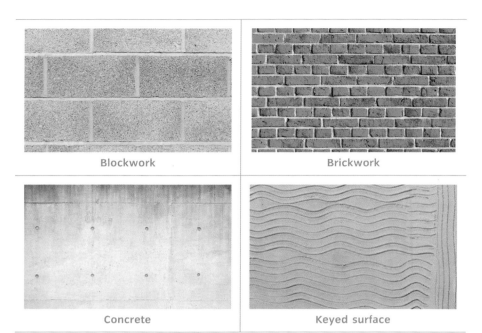

| Blockwork | Brickwork |
| Concrete | Keyed surface |

Once it has been mixed, drywall adhesive has a working time of up to two hours which allows adequate working time for installation and the regular cleaning of tools and equipment. The same rules apply to using drywall adhesive as to any other pre-mixed plaster, and regular cleaning and maintenance of tools and equipment will ensure a longer life span for the adhesive.

FIXING TO TIMBER OR STEEL

Using nails

Galvanised nails are used to fix plasterboard to timber studwork and ceiling joists using a claw hammer or drywall hammer. Galvanised nails are used to prevent rusting. When fixed, the head of the nail should penetrate the board, finishing flush with the plasterboard surface. The nail should penetrate the timber background by a minimum of 20mm. The table below shows the nail sizes you should use for fixing different thicknesses of plasterboard.

Galvanised

A protective zinc coating applied to steel to prevent corrosion or rusting which could cause unsightly staining on the finished plasterboard or cause the fixing to fail

Galvanised plasterboard nail

Thickness of board (mm)	Minimum size of nail (mm)
9.5	30
12.5	40
15	40
19	50

On thermal laminate boards that have been fixed with drywall adhesive to a solid background, a specially designed masonry nail fixing that has a countersunk head can be fixed with a plug as a secondary fixing. Two nails, 60–90mm long depending on the thickness of the laminate, are fixed to each edge on the back of the plasterboard. The nails are fixed so that if a fire occurs and gets behind the plasterboard this would prevent it coming loose, which would make pointless the fire protection given by the plasterboard.

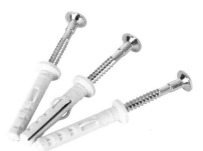

Nailable plugs

SDS drills and masonry bits are used to prepare the holes for nailable plugs

Thermal laminate plasterboard increases insulation values

Using screws

Drywall screws are considered stronger fixings than galvanised nails and have less chance of **popping** through the finished surface. Fixing plasterboards with screws means the plasterboard surface is less likely to move under vibration. Another reason is the higher moisture content in timber studs or joists which have to dry out and, in doing so, can move and twist.

There are two types of screws used for mechanically fixing plasterboard. Timber screws are used to fix plasterboard to timber backgrounds and must penetrate the timber by a minimum of 20mm. They have less thread and give a stronger grip into the timber background compared with metal screws.

Metal screws are used to fix plasterboard to steel studs or linings and must penetrate the steel stud or lining by 10mm. They have a closer thread that gives a strong grip into thin metal linings.

Screws should be fixed firmly home without fracturing the board surface but firmly enough to leave a shallow depression for filling by **spotting** or finishing with setting plaster. Plasterboard screws have Phillips countersunk cross heads that are fixed with a PH2 drill bit. A drywall drill has a built-in clutch that prevents the screws being fixed too far into the board. The screw size varies from 22 to 90mm in length.

Popping

When a nail or screw head pops through the finished surface of the plasterboard because it has not been fixed to the background correctly, or due to vibration or movement if the plasterboard has not been fixed securely to the background

Zinc-plated screw

Spotting

Applying jointing filler over screw or nail head fixings before sanding and priming

INDUSTRY TIP

You can buy drywall attachment bits for ordinary drills that do not have a clutch, which is far cheaper than purchasing a new drywall drill.

Drywall screw sizes for fixing to timber

Size of board (mm)	Minimum size of screw (mm)
12.5	38
15	41
19	51
12.5 double layer	51

Drywall screw sizes for fixing to steel

Size of board (mm)	Minimum size of screw (mm)
9.5	22
12.5	25
15	25
19	42
12.5 double layer	36

Collated screws are a quick way of fixing plasterboard to timber backgrounds, saving time and labour by speeding up the installation process. Collated screws are fixed using a mechanical drywall auto-feeder that is powered by 110V electricity or a battery. These screws vary in length from 25 to 50mm.

Collated drywall screws

A drywall auto-feeder used to fix plasterboard

SELECTING DIFFERENT TYPES OF PLASTERBOARD

One way to recognise and identify the plasterboard's performance and intended use is by its colour: plasterboard is colour coded during manufacture to identify its intended use in the building.

Plasterboard	Description
Standard wall board 	Classed as normal plasterboard. Composed of a core of aerated gypsum plaster bonded between two sheets of strong paper.
Fireline 	Plasterboard with glass fibre and other additives in the core, used in partition, wall lining and ceiling systems to give increased fire protection. Also called fire-resistant.
Sound block 	This plasterboard has a higher density core, designed for use in wall lining and partition systems where greater levels of sound insulation are required.
Moisture-resistant 	Plasterboard that contains water-repellent additives in its core, encased in a special green liner paper and suitable for intermittent moisture applications.

Plasterboard	Description
Impact-resistant 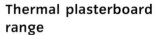	A plasterboard with heavy duty face paper, a higher density core than standard plasterboard, and additives in the core to improve resistance to impact.
Thermal plasterboard range 	Thermal laminate plasterboard manufactured with different types of insulation materials that include polystyrene, phenolic foam or mineral wool. The insulation is glued onto the back face of the plasterboard during manufacture. This type of plasterboard provides enhanced thermal performance on external walls that have limited or no insulation in the cavity. Their intended use is to remove cold surfaces, reducing condensation, cold spots and mould growth which are a constant problem with old buildings that have walls that do not contain insulation.

ACTIVITY

Look at a plasterboard manufacturer's website and make a list of available thermal laminate plasterboards. Provide a brief description of why you would choose to use this type of board in house construction or renovation.

The building regulations state minimum requirements for construction of buildings. Performance plasterboard helps achieve the requirements that relate to fire control, moisture control, sound prevention and impact.

- Privacy rooms such as bedrooms and meeting rooms are best installed with sound block plasterboard which reduces the transmission of unwanted sound that causes disturbance and interference.

- Normal plasterboard is considered a good fire retarder which can withstand the spread of fire for half an hour before it burns through the plasterboard core. Fireline plasterboard has special fire retarders and fibres incorporated into its core to prevent the fire burning through for one hour. Fireline boards are used on multiple occupancy buildings such as flats or on garage ceilings that are incorporated as part of the property. In most cases when fixing this type of board a double layer is applied to increase the resistance of fire to two hours, which meets the strenuous fire standards set by the building control regulations. In the event of a fire this would prevent it spreading and allow more time to evacuate the building safely.

■ Impact-resistant boards, as the name suggests, provide a surface that has greater impact resistance. This type of board can be used in high traffic or pedestrian traffic areas that are prone to constant impact damage.

■ Thermal laminates are used more than ever today because this type of plasterboard can insulate walls from the internal side of the building preventing heat loss, thereby reducing constantly increasing heating bills. They are manufactured with different types of insulation in a range of different thickness. Before selecting this type of board you need to consider its thickness regarding certain areas such as the need to use longer fixings for electrical and telephone sockets. Wider window sills will need to be fixed to overhang the extra thickness of the laminate plasterboard.

Also available is foil-backed plasterboard, which is ideal for installing on ceilings, creating a vapour barrier in loft spaces. In the summer when we get warmer weather it reflects the heat back and keeps the room below the loft space cool. In the winter it prevents heat loss, reflecting it back into the room.

INDUSTRY TIP

Thinner laminates are manufactured to be used when working up to door openings and window frames.

SIZES OF SHEET MATERIALS

When selecting wall boards you need to consider certain factors that will influence the size and thickness of plasterboard to be installed. For instance, installing wall boards using direct bond to solid backgrounds that have openings such as doorways will mean you need to allow not just for the thickness of board but also for the thickness of the drywall dab. When fitting door frames or similar linings you need to allow a thickness of 12.5mm for the dab and a thickness of 12.5mm for the board, so requiring 25mm in total for clearance.

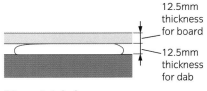

12.5mm thickness for board

12.5mm thickness for dab

25mm total clearance

Standard wall boards have been manufactured to accommodate the standard ceiling height of 2.4m used in modern houses. The centres of timber or steel studs and joists can also be used to define the thickness, length and width of the plasterboard. Studwork that is 400mm apart matches the width of plasterboard which is 1200mm wide (3 × 400mm), meaning it is possible for there to be no cutting and less waste. However, if the studs and joists are 600mm apart then you would have to use a 15mm plasterboard, which is thicker and allows for the span of the joists.

When carrying out refurbishment work, another factor to consider is the thickness and the size of old joists that may need to be strengthened and reinforced to allow for the weight of the plasterboard. If this wasn't done and there was movement due to the weak background or exceeded span, this might cause the board to sag and crack along the joints. Also when making good plasterboard surfaces to existing plasterboard, you need to check the thickness and size of the plasterboard that needs to be replaced so it can be matched.

STORING AND HANDLING PLASTERBOARD

Plasterboard should be delivered flat on pallets or on timber bearers to prevent flexing movement that could damage the core or cause warping. If a delivery contains damaged plasterboard, this should immediately be reported to the driver and your supervisor or someone in a more senior position than you so that it can be resolved.

Manufacturers' data sheets provide specific information about storing and manual handling of materials and components. Identifying the hazards associated with this type of work beforehand can limit the number of accidents and injuries that occur. Plasterboards are heavy, awkward and large. They are best carried on their edge by two people to prevent the board snapping.

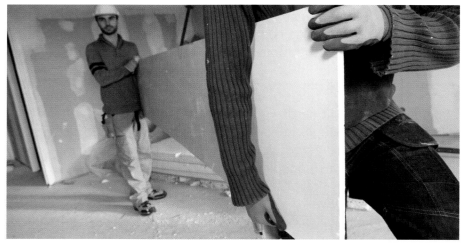
Moving plasterboard by hand

All plasterboard should be stored flat on its face. It should also be stored off the ground in order to prevent it from absorbing moisture from the ground: plasterboards should not come into contact with damp conditions as the plaster core will absorb the moisture and, in time, the paper and core will crumble and perish.

If more than one type of plasterboard is to be stored, they should be stored separately to avoid confusion. For instance, plasterboard with a tapered edge should be stored separately from plasterboard with a square edge.

Any boards that get damaged during handling, cutting or fitting during installation should be removed, replaced and put to one side for disposal. Any components used for fitting and fixing plasterboards that get damaged should be treated the same way, including boxes of fittings, bags of jointing compounds, fixing adhesives, drywall beads, paper tapes, rolls of scrim, nails and screws.

MATERIALS FOR FINISHING

There are two methods used for finishing plasterboard surfaces:

1 applying setting coats of plaster

2 taping joints.

Let's look at the different materials you can use to carry out these two methods.

Method 1: Setting coats

Before applying setting coats to backgrounds, the surface needs to be prepared. This includes applying self-adhesive scrim made of glass fibre matting that has a sticky adhesive, allowing it to bond with ease to all plasterboard joints and internal angles. Once it has been fixed you can then cut it with a sharp utility knife. The scrim will reinforce the weak areas and help prevent cracking along the joints of the plasterboard.

Self-adhesive scrim has replaced the use of traditional materials, such as hessian and cotton, which had to be bedded in plaster before the setting coat was applied. The use of self-adhesive scrim has speeded up the process of reinforcing and finishing plasterboard with setting plasters, saving labour time.

Applying scrim to joints

External angles need to be reinforced using a corner bead manufactured from galvanised steel or plastic. This can be fixed using galvanised nails, drywall screws, staples or adhesive. The beads need to be cut with tin snips.

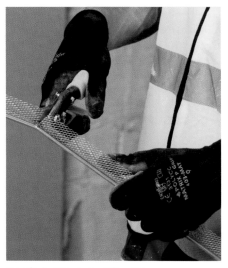
Beads being cut with snips

Beads fitted to a corner

Method 2: Taping joints

Paper tape jointing can be carried out manually or mechanically using a range of accessories and materials. The tape comes in roll form and has perforated holes and a centre crease in its design that helps align the tape to straight joints and internal angles.

Corner paper tape is used on the external angles. It contains two corrosion-resistant metal strips along its length for strength and reinforcement, which means that this type of tape needs to be cut with a pair of tin snips.

Paper tape

Corner paper tape

OUR HOUSE

Look at one of the ground floor rooms in 'Our House'. Measure the amount of paper tape to be used on the joints of plasterboard required for dry lining direct bond to the solid background.

JOINTING MATERIALS

Jointing compound materials are available pre-mixed dry in a bag or ready mixed in tubs, depending on preference and intended use. Ready-mix jointing materials do not need mixing and come in sealed tubs that need to be kept air tight when not in use. There are several types of bagged jointing materials that have different setting times and may set by either exposure to air or through carbonation.

Aerated joint cement can be used mechanically using the speed tape and box system, which is a quick method for applying jointing compound and paper tape at the same time. When you tape and joint plasterboards you also need to spot the screw heads before sanding with grit paper.

Speed tape

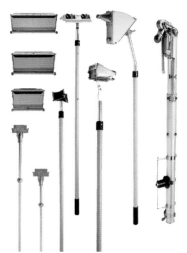

Speed taping tools

Using the speed taping and box system

Joint adhesive is a fine-textured material that should be mixed in clean buckets by hand or mechanically. Avoid using dirty buckets as this can leave grit on the jointing surface that will be difficult to sand smooth and flush with the edge of the board joints. Once the joints and spots have dried out thoroughly, then you can sand the surface, followed by applying a primer to seal the porous surface of the dry jointing material before it receives decoration.

Sealer

SOUND COATS

When dry lining interiors, building regulations standards must be met. These include its requirements relating to resistance to the passage of sound and acoustic standards for separating partition walls and ceiling/floor constructions (Part E) and the rework of Part L (relating to conservation of fuel and power) that raises the bar for energy performance.

Plasterboard manufacturers have developed new systems that comply with the Part E and Part L regulations. For instance, manufacturer British Gypsum has developed a pre-mixed soundproofing plaster parge coat that by minimising air leakage improves the thermal and acoustic performance of masonry walls, such as party walls that divide semi-detached and terraced dwellings.

SEALING MATERIALS

Drywall sealer is another product that is applied after taping and jointing to control vapour in bathrooms and kitchens. If not sealed correctly, the large amount of moisture that exists in these rooms will penetrate the plasterboard surface.

Other sealing materials include special fixing and sealing sealants and mastics that are used with fire and acoustic performance dry lining systems. You can learn more about these products if you search the websites of manufacturers such as British Gypsum, Knauf and Sinniat.

ACTIVITY

Search the British Gypsum website to learn more about Gyproc Soundcoat Plus. Discuss your findings with your tutor.

ACTIVITY

Resilient bars and insulation can also be used for soundproofing walls, floors and ceilings. Research these products at www.soundstop.co.uk

ACTIVITY

Research online and make a list of the different sealants and mastics available.

INTERPRETING INFORMATION ABOUT MATERIALS AND COMPONENTS TO USE

Working drawings provide information about the work to be completed including the various background structures. They will clearly indicate whether the background is solid, timber studs/joists or metal studs/linings. They also provide important information regarding the height of the work and whether low or high level working platforms will need to be used to carry out the work. The drawings can be used alongside the specification to plan the method of work, which should include setting up and preparing the materials and components to be used for specific work activities.

Using the working drawings and the specification is a simple way to plan your work method. When using plasterboard materials and fixing components, you can order the correct quantity of materials and fixing components as and when they are required, reflecting the scheduled work activity and whether you are installing with screws, nails or direct bond bonding adhesive.

Scheduling the work will minimise the storage area required for the plasterboard and prevent materials going out of date and reduce loss due to accidental damage or damp as they absorb moisture.

TOOLS AND EQUIPMENT

Before you install plasterboard you need to gather together the necessary tools from the following list to enable you to measure and cut the board accurately.

Tool	Use
Utility knife 	Before you cut plasterboard, always check that you have a good blade that allows you to score and cut through the paper into the core. If the blade is sharp you will only need to score the board once before snapping and cutting the rear of the board. Blunt blades will rip the paper and cause a rough, uneven cut.

Tool	Use
Straight edge	Straight edges are used as a guide for accurately marking and cutting the length and width of plasterboard.
Surform	This is a good hand tool that allows you to plane and remove rough, uneven edges on cut plasterboard. Also known as a rasp.
Pad saw	This small saw is used for cutting out spaces for services and sockets in the plasterboard surface before fixing to the background.
Tape measure	Essential for taking measurements from the backgrounds and transferring accurately, allowing you to cut the board to the required size or shape.
Claw hammer	Used to fix plasterboard with galvanised nails.

Tool	Use
Drywall hammer	Used to fix plasterboard with galvanised nails.

When you carry out dry lining using direct bond, you will need the appropriate tools to help you complete the task efficiently and accurately.

Tool	Use
Hawk and trowel	Used for applying drywall adhesive to solid backgrounds.
Brushes	Hard and soft brushes are used for cleaning tools and equipment.
Box rule	Used for installing and lining the plasterboard surface against the drywall dabs. It has a wider edge than a normal straight edge or feathered edge rule, so it is less likely to cause impact damage to the board surface when tapped against the plasterboard.
Sprit level	Used with a straight edge for plumbing and levelling plasterboard up to openings such as windows, doors and returns.

Tool	Use
Foot lifter 	Used to lift the plasterboard up to the ceiling line.
Chalk line 	Snapped on floors and ceilings to form guidelines when installing wall boards.
Laser level	This is a popular tool used when setting out guidelines. It is an accurate method of producing horizontal and vertical guides that can be used to work off.

JOINTING PLASTERBOARD

When you tape and joint plasterboard, instead of using the hawk and trowel you could use a drywall knife or a spatula-type blade, which is similar to a scraper but larger. These knives are sometimes preferred instead of a hawk and trowel because their flexible aluminium blade is flat and good for finishing jointing materials but also sharp for cutting paper tape.

Corner trowels, also known as internal angle trowels, are used to form internal angles when applying setting coats or jointing internal angles with tape.

Drywall knife

Corner trowel

HEALTH AND SAFETY ISSUES

TOOLS

Care must be taken when sanding jointing material because of the high levels of fine dust that it creates. You will need to wear health and safety equipment such as a dust mask and safety glasses to protect your lungs and eyes when you use the hand method. Using an electric sander is quicker than working by hand but also causes more dust; it will need an extraction unit to be fitted to the appliance to extract the dust.

Sanding joints wearing PPE

Electrical tools on site must be safe, fit for purpose, well maintained and regularly checked by a competent person. Electrical tools need to pass a regular PAT test (see Chapter 1, page 37). If successful, a sticker will be placed on the appliance with the date when it passed the test and when it needs to be re-tested for safe use. Faulty electrical tools should be reported to your supervisor before they become hazardous and cause electric shock.

ACCESS EQUIPMENT

As with any job in construction you will sometimes need to work at height. Safely setting up the access equipment will allow you to complete your job efficiently and limit any potential hazards that could cause injury to yourself or other operatives working close by.

Low level hop-ups and platforms are preferred when fixing and installing plasterboard to walls with standard ceiling heights of 2.4m. This is because they are easy to work from when you are applying dabs of adhesive or fixing screws or nails. You can easily move along this type of access platform as the work progresses along the length of the wall.

Hop-up

A fully laid out platform might be preferred when working on ceilings. This allows an even platform to cover a larger surface area, which suits the need to lift, fit and install plasterboard and finish ceilings. Smaller platforms would have to be moved constantly around the working area which can be a strain and time consuming.

Moveable tower scaffolding and cherry pickers are used in commercial buildings as the working height increases. Before you can use this type of access equipment you need to be trained to ensure your competency as there are strict health and safety issues surrounding their use.

RISK ASSESSMENTS

Before you carry out your work you will need to read the relevant risk assessments (see Chapter 1, pages 5–6). These identify the risks involved with dry lining and inform you of any potential hazards that may cause accidents. If you plan your work carefully and follow the method statement, you will ensure a safe place of work.

You also have a duty to make sure that you wear the appropriate safety clothing and equipment, and to keep the work area safe and free from potential risks to other operatives.

Any discrepancies relating to the planned work method need to be reported as soon as possible after discovery to a person in higher authority. This could be your supervisor or your employer, who will deal with the discrepancies immediately to ensure they don't cause the work to become problematic at a later stage.

FIXING DRY LINING AND PLASTERBOARDS

PLANNING

Before you start plasterboarding, you need to consider which of the background's services first need to be installed. Planning this can save time and effort and make the work far more efficient to complete.

First fix electrical and plumbing services will need to be installed already. These could include wiring sockets and lighting, telephone and media cables, and pipes for hot and cold water and central heating. All these need to be installed to the background before it can be lined with plasterboard.

Timber joists and stud walls to be covered with plasterboard

Fixtures and fittings also need consideration, as wall cupboards such as kitchen units, sanitary suites or electrical appliances all need to be fixed to plasterboard backgrounds; this would require additional support at the fixing points in order to accommodate the extra load.

SOUND AND AIR TESTS

Buildings that contain dry lining surface linings will be tested for air and sound transmission.

Air tests are carried out on modern new builds. This means that all perimeter surfaces need to be sealed, including internal angles to walls, ceilings and floors, frames to openings, and services. All possible air passage points into the building need to be blocked.

Sound tests are also carried out to check the acoustic performance of the building, identifying the need to reduce or eradicate sound that can have a severe effect on people's privacy in multiple-occupancy buildings.

FIXING PLASTERBOARD TO TIMBER CEILING JOISTS

PREPARATION

Before you start to plasterboard a ceiling you need to take to make sure that the background is adequate and fit for the plasterboard's installation. At this stage all services including ducting, pipes and cables should have been installed.

Modern buildings will have been designed by the architect to meet strict industry standards regarding the type of timber joist used, the **joist centres** and joist spans, and the ability of the joists to take the weight of the selected plasterboard.

The following table shows the maximum joist centres for plasterboard, both with and without **noggins**.

Plasterboard thickness	Maximum joist centres wiith noggins	Maximum joist centres without noggins
12.5mm	600mm	450mm
15mm	600mm	600mm
19mm	600mm	600mm
ThermaLine laminates	600mm	450mm

INDUSTRY TIP

Installation of services is known as 'first fix' by other trades.

Joist centres

The distance from the centre of one joist to the centre of the next

Noggin

Timber fixed between joists or studs to support the edge and end of the plasterboard

INDUSTRY TIP

Joists that are too far apart will cause the plasterboard to sag.

Ceiling joists

Older buildings that need renovation often contain far more problems that need to be resolved before they can have new plasterboard installed. Old timber joists will need to be de-nailed and it is likely that some of the timber will be rotten and need replacing and/or strengthening with additional noggins. Timber can also warp and twist over long periods and may have been fitted to different fixing centres than today's standard distances. A straight edge or string line should be used to check the alignment of the joists: if not corrected at this stage it can later show steps and unevenness in the surface once the plasterboard has been installed.

INSTALLING PLASTERBOARD

The following steps show you the staggered method for installing plasterboard to a timber joist ceiling that is 10m². Before you start plasterboarding, set up a staging that allows you to install your plasterboard safely and efficiently.

1 Mark the wall to indicate the ceiling joists.

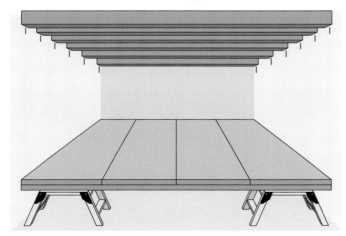

Marked lines for the ceiling joists

2 Mark the width of the plasterboard, allow an extra 5mm on the joists at each end of the ceiling, and snap a chalk line. This will

give you a guide line on the ceiling against which to install the plasterboard edge.

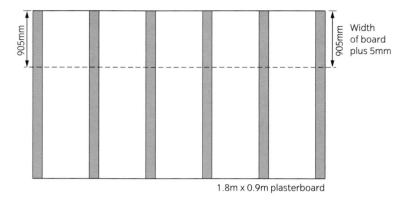

905mm

905mm

Width of board plus 5mm

1.8m x 0.9m plasterboard

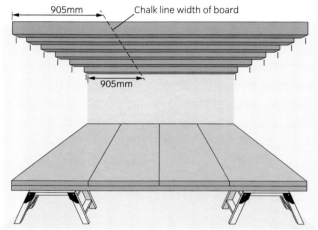

905mm   Chalk line width of board

905mm

Marked width of the plasterboard

3 Measure and cut the first board to the centre of the furthest joist.

4 Rasp the cut edge. This side will be positioned to the wall.

5 Using struts or a **dead man prop**, position the plasterboard along the chalk line, making sure the end of the board sits on the centre of the joist.

Dead man prop

A useful piece of equipment when working on your own. It is a telescopic pole with pads on each end; the pole is adjusted to hold an item above your head just like an extra pair of hands

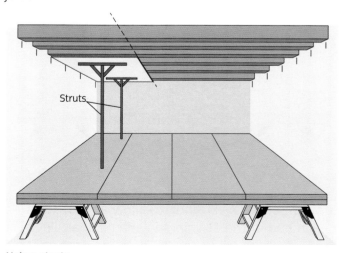

Struts

Using struts

6 Once the board is correctly positioned, it can be fixed to the correct fixing centres using nails at 150mm or screws at 230mm.

7 Continue and fit the next board, leaving a small gap of about 2mm after butting up to the previous board. Make sure you install the board to the chalk line.

8 On the adjacent run you will need to stagger the joints. You can do this by fixing a shorter plasterboard first, followed by a full plasterboard. You have now completed the layout of the staggered ceiling.

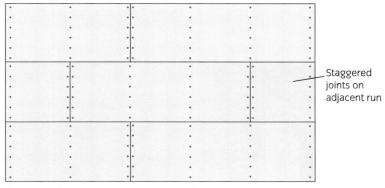

Staggered joints on adjacent run

Completed layout of staggered ceiling

FIXING PLASTERBOARD TO TIMBER STUDS AND PARTITIONS

To fix plasterboard to new or traditional **partitions** you need to follow the same preparation rules as for preparing to fix plasterboard to timber ceilings (see pages 184–185).

There are two methods that can be used when fixing plasterboard to studwork.

1 Fix the plasterboard horizontally across the studs. The adjacent run will need to be staggered, which will increase its strength and help reduce in-line cracks. This method is used more when using 1800mm × 900mm sized plasterboard.

2 Install the plasterboard vertically, in line with the studs. This method is preferred on new buildings that have been designed to accommodate standard wallboards at 400mm centres.

The following step-by-step instructions show you the staggered method for fixing plasterboard horizontally to studwork that is 10m².

Partition

Walls used to separate and divide the overall space within a building into rooms

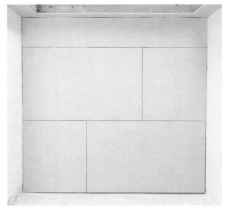

Horizontally plasterboarded wall

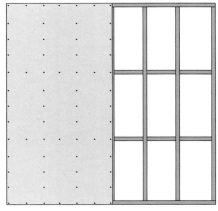

Vertically plasterboarded wall

STEP 1 Mark the floor to indicate the position of the studs.

STEP 2 Cut and position packers to avoid the plasterboard coming into contact with the floor.

STEP 3 Measure and cut the first board to the centre of the nearest stud.

STEP 4 Rasp the cut edge and position this side facing the internal wall, with the good edge to the centre of the stud.

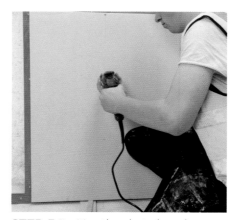

STEP 5 Position the plasterboard, making sure the edge of the board fits to half the stud, and place a level along its edge before fixing with screws every 300mm or with galvanised nails every 150mm.

STEP 6 Continue to fix the boards along the wall, making sure there are no steps in the joints. Stagger the board on the next run and leave a gap of 2–3mm at the joints, which will be filled with plaster and scrim to reinforce.

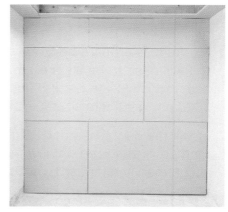

STEP 7 The completed plasterboard partition.

DIRECT BOND PLASTERBOARD

Direct bond dry lining is today used as a backing coat for plasters on new blockwork and brickwork structures far more than traditional cement-based mixes or pre-mixed gypsum undercoats. It is preferred because of its ease of installation and the benefit of increased thermal performance. It also reduces condensation, which is a constant problem with solid plastered walls.

There is a certain procedure for fixing plasterboards to solid walls and if these procedures are not followed precisely then the dry lining background will not perform to its design requirements. Dry lining over damp or painted walls should be avoided unless they can be treated and prepared beforehand, as plasterboard will perish in damp conditions. Backgrounds should be checked with a straight edge to identify whether there are high or low points in the wall, as this will determine how thick or thin you will need to apply the dabs of adhesive.

Drywall adhesive is purpose made for direct bonding plasterboards to solid walls. Before it can be applied as **dabs** to receive the boards, you need to position and line the dabs vertically and horizontally to the top and bottom of the wall. The width of the board is marked on the wall to indicate the line of dabs, which should be 600mm apart. This will mean that each full plasterboard will have three vertical rows of adhesive. A continuous line of adhesive is used at skirting level to provide a solid fixing for the skirting board.

Before any plasterboard is installed, perimeter seals need to be filled with adhesive to prevent air flow from entering behind the plasterboard. Air flow can also come from services, sockets and window and door linings that are fixed to external walls.

Position and line the dabs

Dabs

Drywall adhesive plaster applied to the background in dabs of about 75mm wide and 250mm in length

Perimeter seals

SETTING OUT CHALK LINES

Chalk lines are used as guidelines to fixing points along the floor and the ceiling line. These lines make it easier to fix and line the plasterboard when installing against the dabs. When measuring (see Step 1 below), you need to add up the following measurements:

- the thickness of the box rule (100mm)

- the thickness of the plasterboard (12.5mm)

- the dab of adhesive (allow 12.5mm).

This totals 125mm. Note that this amount will change if you are using a different width box rule or straight edge and if you are using a different thickness of plasterboard. The step-by-steps below show you the method for setting out chalk lines to the floor and ceiling.

> **INDUSTRY TIP**
>
> Cut the plasterboard 15mm shorter than the measured length to allow for tolerances that avoid the plasterboard being too tight and its edges getting damaged during installation.

> **INDUSTRY TIP**
>
> Always cut the plasterboards before starting to mix the drywall adhesive.

STEP 1 From the wall at both ends, measure in 125mm along the floor level. Transfer the marks up to the ceiling line at both ends of the wall.

STEP 2 Snap vertical chalk lines on the ceiling and floor to form marked lines.

STEP 3 Mark the width of the plasterboard on the wall.

INSTALLING THE PLASTERBOARD

The following step-by-step instructions show you the method for installing direct bond plasterboard.

STEP 1 Apply the dabs of adhesive to the wall in three vertical lines. Make sure you place the end dabs about 30mm in from the edge of the plasterboard.

Packers

Small pieces of doubled-up offcut that the boards can sit on to keep them off the floor

STEP 2 Apply dabs of adhesive to the base of the wall to create a solid fixing for the skirting and to the ceiling line for support.

STEP 3 Place two **packers** to the floor. Fit the board onto the wall and check that the edge of the board is plumb.

STEP 4 Use the box rule and tap the board against the dabs and wall until the edge of the box rule is in line with the chalk lines set at the floor and ceiling lines.

STEP 5 Lift the board to the ceiling using the foot lifter and pack underneath the plasterboard. Check the plasterboard surface with the box rule to make sure it is still plumb. Repeat the process for the next board until you have finished the wall.

Installing plasterboard around electrical boxes

If the wall you are plasterboarding has electrical boxes fitted – for plug sockets, light switches or services, for example – then gaps for these need to be cut out of the plasterboard before fixing. The following step-by-step instructions show you how to cut out for electrical boxes.

STEP 1 On the wall, measure from where the bottom of the board is going to sit up to the top and bottom of the box.

STEP 2 Transfer these measurements to each end of the plasterboard. Draw a line between these points to give you two parallel horizontal lines.

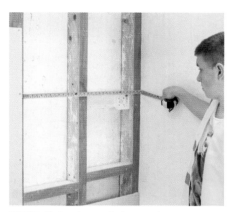

STEP 3 On the wall, from where one edge of the board is to be situated, measure the distance to each side of the box.

STEP 4 Transfer these measurements to each horizontal line on the plasterboard and draw lines between them to form the outline of the box.

STEP 5 Using a pad saw, carefully cut out the outline, taking care to keep to the lines.

Installing plasterboard around reveals

When you have walls with windows and/or door openings, it is best to fix the plasterboard edge 25mm past the **reveal** or return. This allows you to fit a plasterboard sheet and dab in to the reveal or return. It is best to fix the head and sill first as the reveal board can take the weight of the soffit board.

Reveal

Small return to a window or door opening

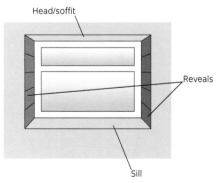

Head/soffit

Reveals

Sill

Fix the head and sill first

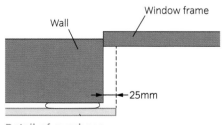

Wall

Window frame

25mm

Detail of overhang

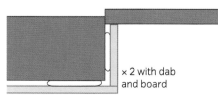

× 2 with dab and board

1 Set out and snap chalk lines to both back walls, allowing a clearance of 25mm for the thickness of dab and plasterboard. Using a square off the main walls mark a right angle to both returns, then mark a line off the face of the pillar.

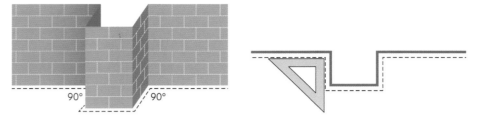

Setting out on the floor off the main wall

Plan view of setting out returns off the main wall

2 Cut and fix the left and right side plasterboard making sure you have the cut end to the wall and the factory edge to the set out mark at the ends of returns. This will also make it simpler to plumb the outer edge of the board.

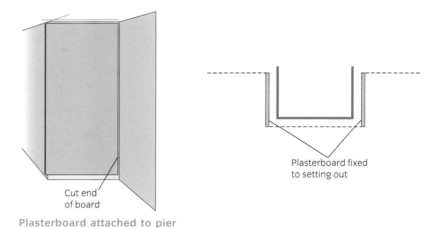

Cut end of board

Plasterboard fixed to setting out

Plasterboard attached to pier

3 Next cut and fix the plasterboard that fits in to the face of the pier between the two return ends, and proceed to cut and fix the plasterboards for the main wall: this will cover your return cut ends at both internal angles of the returns.

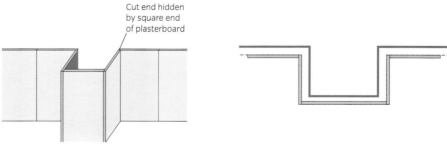

Cut end hidden by square end of plasterboard

Plasterboarded pier and main wall

Don't forget that if you're dry lining direct bond with thermal laminates, you will need to allow for the thickness of the insulation when setting out your chalk lines. You will also need to fix two nailable plugs halfway up the plasterboard, 25mm in from the edge. In the event of a fire breaking out in the building, the insulation would break down and melt with the heat, causing it to separate and fall away from the background wall. This could make evacuation routes difficult to use, causing access difficulties for fire fighters.

Once the walls have been lined with plasterboard, the next stage is to finish the surface with setting plaster (refer back to Chapter 3) or tape and joint.

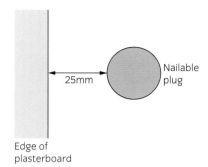

Nailable plug 25mm from plasterboard edge

TAPE AND JOINTING

Before you tape and joint plasterboard, you need to check that the plasterboard fixings have been driven home into the timber or steel, allowing you to fill the heads of the fixings. You should also check that there are no steps in the edges of the plasterboard and that any large gaps in the plasterboard joints are filled.

Tape and jointing is a process that produces a smooth, crack-resistant surface to the joints where tapered edge plasterboards meet. The screw or nail head fixings can be filled over with jointing material and sanded for priming and decorating. The jointing material should be left to dry before sanding and priming.

You first need to apply your jointing material, followed by applying a paper tape over the joint to reinforce it. Before applying a second coat, the tape should be squeezed and flattened, allowing the next jointing application coat to cover the tape's surface.

Before applying another layer of jointing compound, the previous surface must have dried sufficiently as this will make it easier to cover. Some jointing compounds dry and set within one hour, while others are air drying material that take overnight to set.

You can decide on whether to use ready mix or pre-mixed jointing materials, as the same rules apply when applying and finishing. Make sure that the material is feathered out and finished to the edge of the board.

TAPE AND JOINTING ANGLES

Internal angles can be finished by folding and sharing the tape in half and applying to adjacent walls. Care must be taken when finishing opposite walls as the trowel can dig in and damage the surface. A good way to avoid this is to use a corner tool, which is used to finish both internal angles at the same time.

INDUSTRY TIP

Where a cut edge plasterboard is used when butting up to a tapered edge the jointing compound needs to be feathered out further than normal to conceal the surface and allow for the extra thickness where the board steps.

Sanding the jointed surface

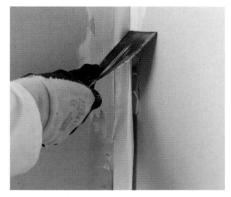

An internal angle

External angles can be finished either by using a drywall bead or by using a reinforced paper tape, depending on the type of reinforcement required. Both are bedded into the jointing material and finished in the same way as paper tape jointing. Once the surface has been jointed, it can then be sanded.

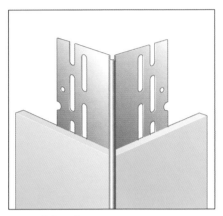

Drywall bead

Reinforced paper tape being used on an external corner

TAPE AND JOINTING METHOD

The following step-by-step instructions show you the method for tape and jointing standard tapered edge plasterboard joints.

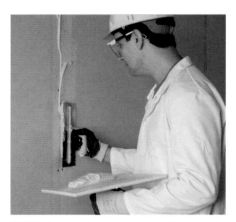

STEP 1 Apply jointing material and apply the paper tape onto the surface, firmly squeezing the tape against the jointing. Make sure that you cover the surface and the small perforated holes in the tape.

STEP 2 Apply further applications of jointing material over the tape, making sure that you feather out each application in turn slightly wider than the first. For example, if the first application is 20mm wide then the second application should be 30mm wide.

STEP 3 Sand the surface to remove any unevenness and imperfections in the jointed surface. Using a roller and brush (as shown), apply a sealer or primer to the plasterboard surface.

Taping needs to be carried out carefully; the following table shows you faults that can occur if it is not performed correctly.

Fault	Issue
Oversanding	The tape will show through.
No filler behind the tape	Will cause the tape to bubble (no adhesive behind it).
Uneven surface	Will cause the tape to be prouder than the board surface.
Fixings that have not penetrated the surface of the board	Will cause bumps and unevenness.

HEALTH AND SAFETY ISSUES

When you carry out tape and jointing, as well as your own safety you also need to consider other operatives who may come into contact with the dusty atmosphere created from sanding the joints and fixing surfaces.

The following measures should be taken.

- Wear appropriate safety clothing to protect yourself from the dusty atmosphere.

- Electrical sanding tools should contain dust bags (or the dust should be extracted with an appropriate extractor) to reduce increased or high levels of dust that can be hazardous to lungs.

- Due to the amount of dust in the atmosphere, adequate environmental protection should be carried out before sanding. Use dust sheets or cling film to protect furniture, flooring and surroundings.

- Warning signs should be displayed to let others know about the dangers and hazards involved with the work in progress. Barriers can be used to keep people away from the work area.

Dry lining dust extraction

Warning sign

Case Study: Jim

Jim recently went to assess a plastering job at the home of a friend's parents. When Jim got there they explained to him that a big crack had appeared over time in their living room ceiling. When Jim assessed the problem he noticed that the ceiling had not only cracked but also sagged down from the laths and that it was likely to collapse at any time. His immediate thought was to clear the room and make the place safe.

Jim cleared all the furniture and laid dust sheets down on the floor to protect the carpet. He explained that the ceiling was plastered over old laths and that it would eventually fall down. This is a common problem in housing that had ceilings plastered before the 1950s. The problem could have been caused by people walking on the floor above, causing vibrations to break the plaster key from behind the laths and the plaster to sag. Jim explained that lath and plaster was not used today in new buildings precisely because of its poor bonding capabilities compared with plasterboard.

Jim provided a quote for the work which was gladly accepted as long as he could start straight away.

The first job was to remove the lath and plaster ceiling. This would cause large quantities of dust. To do this safely Jim opened all the windows, which helped extract the dust and keep it to a minimum. He wore a respirator, glasses, gloves and a helmet to safely carry out the task. Once the dust had cleared, Jim removed the old rusted nails and was left with bare ceiling joists. He advised his friend's parents to insulate between the joists as this would not only keep the heat in but also work as a soundproof barrier between the ground and first floors.

Before Jim installed the plasterboard he checked the alignment of the joists with a straight edge and made sure that the centres were correct. He then measured up and ordered the plasterboard. Jim marked the joists at the wall to indicate the position of the centres and fixed the plasterboard with collated screws. Once this was finished, Jim scrimmed the joints with self-adhesive tape, applied the setting plaster and trowelled the ceiling smooth.

Jim was thanked for the professionalism and manner in which he had carried out the work and was rewarded with a tip on top of what he had been paid.

Work through the following questions to check your learning.

1   Direct bond dry lining is a process of fixing plasterboard using
    a   galvanised nails
    b   drywall screws
    c   jointing compound
    d   drywall adhesive.

2   Plasterboards are staggered when they are fixed to
    a   ceiling joists
    b   door reveals
    c   window heads
    d   beam soffits.

3   Plasterboard joints can be reinforced using which one of the following types of tape?
    a   Masking.
    b   Sticky.
    c   Paper.
    b   Duct.

4   Tapered edge plasterboards can be identified by which one of the following groups of letters on the edge of the board?
    a   TE.
    b   SE.
    c   RE.
    d   BE.

5   Which one of the following plasterboards is used to improve insulation?
    a   Moisture-resistant.
    b   Sound block.
    c   Impact board.
    d   Thermal laminate.

6   A blue coloured plasterboard is used to reduce
    a   heat
    b   air flow
    c   noise
    d   moisture.

7   The number of plasterboards for a dry lining contract can be found on the
    a   schedule
    b   drawing
    c   specification
    d   bill of quantities.

8   Which one of the following tools is used for straightening and fixing plasterboards when using the direct bond method?
    a   Boat level.
    B   Tape measure.
    c   Box rule.
    d   Surform plane.

9   A foot lifter is used for lifting plasterboards up to the
    a   reveal heads
    b   window soffits
    c   ceiling lines
    d   wall edges.

10 When measuring quantities of materials, measurements are taken from the
    a   drawing
    b   schedule
    c   risk assessment
    d   method statement.

11 12.5mm plasterboards are used where joist centres are fixed at

   a 200mm

   b 400mm

   c 600mm

   b 800mm.

12 Before dry lining, direct bond perimeter seals are used to prevent

   a heat

   b vapour

   c suction

   d cold air.

13 Two plasterboard sheets meeting at an external corner can be formed and finished using

   a an angle rule

   b an angle guide

   c a standard angle bead

   d a thin coat angle bead.

14 Plasterboards are stored on pallets to reduce

   a warping

   b storage space

   c waste

   d shrinkage.

15 Collated screws are used to fix plasterboards on which one of the following type of backgrounds?

   a Timber joists.

   b Concrete lintels.

   c Brick walls.

   d Block walls.

16 Which one of the following types of saw is used to cut out openings for sockets and services in plasterboard?

   a Panel.

   b Pad.

   c Circular.

   d Bench.

17 The **standard** thicknesses of plasterboard are

   a 9.5mm and 12.5mm

   b 9.5mm and 13mm

   c 8mm and 12.5mm

   d 8.5mm and 13mm.

18 Drywall adhesive is **best** mixed using a

   a drill and whisk

   b cement mixer

   c gauging trowel

   d bucket trowel.

19 When fixing plasterboard by direct bond, vertical dabs are applied every

   a 300mm

   b 400mm

   c 500mm

   d 600mm.

20 When setting out for dry lining direct bond, chalk lines are snapped on floors and ceilings to

   a ensure accurate installation

   b level the boards

   c stagger the joints

   d show fixings.

Chapter 5
Unit 223: Laying sand and cement screeds

Floor screeds are laid to provide a hard, flat, level and durable surface that forms a base for floor coverings such as carpets, vinyl and ceramic tiles.

Traditionally screeds were laid by plasterers, and if you work in the domestic market for small builders this is a service that you will generally still provide. But these days commercial floor screeding is usually carried out by specialist floor screeding companies, especially since the introduction of pumped, ready-mixed, easy flow materials. The addition of polypropylene fibres in sand and cement mixes to improve reinforcement and flexural strength is now commonplace due to the popularity of underfloor heating.

The basic principles for preparing, setting out and laying floor screeds and curing the materials are always similar.

By reading this chapter you will know how to:

1 Interpret information from drawings and specifications for laying sand and cement screeds.

2 Select materials and components for laying sand and cement screeds.

3 Lay sand and cement screeds.

INTERPRETING INFORMATION

SPECIFICATIONS AND DRAWINGS

As with all plastering operations, the contract specification is the key element for producing work to the required standard. The contract specification will provide information regarding:

- the mix ratio
- the screed materials to be used
- the screed's thickness
- the insulation's thickness
- the type of finish
- falls ratio (if the screed is in a shower room or other sloped floor).

Floor screeding

The inclusion of information about insulation reflects recent government focus on saving energy, with Part L of the building regulations now requiring all properties to supply an energy certificate. This has led to an increased use of insulation to improve **U-values** in screeded floors. Underfloor heating, which is increasing in popularity, also relies on good design and use of insulation.

Alongside the contract specification, the contract drawings should be consulted. The main two drawings required for gathering information about floor screeding are:

- a detailed drawing showing how the screed is built up
- a location drawing showing the position of drainage outlets for shower rooms.

U-values

A measure of heat loss through a building's walls, floors and roof. Higher U-values suggest poor thermal performance. The lower the U-value, the better the building is at retaining heat

ACTIVITY

Search online for 'altro flooring' to see how vinyl sheeting is laid after you have screeded a floor.

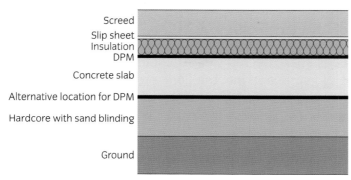

Screed
Slip sheet
Insulation
DPM
Concrete slab
Alternative location for DPM
Hardcore with sand blinding
Ground

Example of a detailed drawing

HEALTH AND SAFETY ISSUES

There are health and safety issues that need to be taken into account when screeds are being mixed and laid. For example, the dust created by the cement when it is being added to the mix can cause respiratory illness. Measures need to be taken to either reduce the levels of dust and/or to reduce your exposure to the dust. These measures can include ensuring that mixing takes place in a well ventilated area, and that fine-particle dust masks or respirators are worn when mixing. Gloves and safety glasses should also be worn, as well as the standard hi-viz clothing and safety boots.

When the mix is being laid, it no longer poses a significant risk from fine dust particles. However, the cement is an irritant and can cause severe chemical burns. This is made worse by the abrasive action of the sand and by the fact that you may well be kneeling in it as you work. To prevent this from being a problem, a long-sleeved, heavy-duty pair of moisture-resistant overalls and a good pair of knee pads should be worn.

Safety glasses

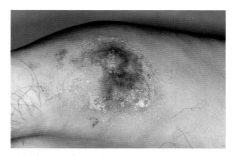

Skin burns from cement

Wearing the correct PPE

By its very nature, laying floor screeds requires you to be working while kneeling, bending over and stretching. This can put a lot of strain on the back, so working for long periods without a break should be avoided. More on health and safety can found in Chapter 1.

ACTIVITY

Using an internet search engine enter 'building regulations for U-values'. Which letter in the building regulations gives advice on meeting the requirements?

ACTIVITY

Using an internet search engine enter 'floor screed insulation'. Find two manufacturers that make insulation.

MIX VOLUME AND RATIOS

Floor screeds are expected to last at least 60 years, so it is important to gauge and mix the floor screeding materials correctly, according to the specification. Failure to do so will result in cracking or weak spots. To minimise the risk of this happening a mix ratio is used; this stops the mix being too strong or too weak. The two most common mix ratios for a traditional floor screed are 3:1 and 4:1.

- **3:1** – three parts of sharp screeding sand to one part of Ordinary Portland Cement.

- **4:1** – four parts of sharp screeding sand to one part of Ordinary Portland Cement.

The materials are mixed by volume to make sure that the consistency remains the same throughout the gauge. It is very important to add the right volume of water to your mix, as too much water will weaken the strength of the floor screed.

Mix ratio of 3:1

CALCULATING MATERIALS

You must know how to calculate the volume of materials to use on a screeding job. Let's look at some examples of how to do this.

Example

If a room measured 5.5m by 3.5m and the screed thickness is to be 75mm with a ratio of 1:4, what is the volume of the materials required?

Step 1

Find out the volume to be filled with screed. Multiply the area of the room by the screed thickness, making sure you are using the same units of measurement.

$5.5 \times 3.5 \times 0.075 = 1.44m^3$

Step 2

Divide the volume to be filled by the total of both sides of the ratio. The ratio here is 1:4, so in total it is 5 (1 + 4).

$1.44 \div 5 = 0.288m^3$

Step 3

Multiply each material by the volume it needs to fill.

Cement: $1 \times 0.288 = 0.288m^3$

Sharp sand: $4 \times 0.288 = 1.152m^3$

Step 4

Work out the weight of the cement needed. Cement weighs 1280kg per cubic metre, written as kgm^3. So multiply the weight per metre cubed by the amount of cement needed in metres cubed. Then divide this amount by the weight of one bag of cement (25kg).

$0.288 \times 1280 = 368.64$

$368.64 \div 25 = 14.74$

Round this figure up to the nearest whole number. In this example, the number of 25kg bags of cement needed is **15**.

Step 5

Next, work out the weight of the sand needed. For our calculations we will assume screeding sand to weigh 1.6 tonnes per metre cubed, or $1600kgm^3$. So multiply the weight per metre cubed by the amount of material needed in metres cubed. Then divide this amount by the weight of one bag of sand (25kg).

$1.152 \times 1600 = 1843.2kg$

$1843.2 \div 25 = 73.728$

Again, round this figure up to the nearest whole number. In this example, the number of 25kg bags of sand needed is **74**.

Step 6

Total up your materials. In this example, to lay a screed 75mm thick with a ratio of 1:4 in a 5.5m × 3.5m room, we need 15 bags of cement and 74 bags of sand.

INDUSTRY TIP

When gauging sand by volume, the sand's water absorption should be taken into consideration. For example, for domestic work most sand is purchased in jumbo bags, which most people assume to weigh 1 tonne. But on average a jumbo bag weighs approximately 850kg. To complicate things even further, a cubic metre of screeding sand has a dry weight of approximately 1.6 tonnes per cubic metre.

INDUSTRY TIP

If we ordered the sand in jumbo bags weighing 850kg, then we would need to divide 1843.2kg by 850kg = 2.16, rounding up to 3 jumbo bags of screeding sand.

TOOLS AND EQUIPMENT

To carry out floor screeding successfully you will require the following tools and equipment.

Tool	Use
Floor laying trowel	These are used to trowel the floor screed smooth. They differ from a plastering trowel as they are made from thicker steel and are at least 450mm long. Some screeding trowels have a pointed end to allow the plasterer to trowel into the corner of a room.
Float	The same as a float used for plastering, floor plasterers prefer to use a larger float to cover more of the surface area when finishing the work and consolidating the material.
Spirit level	At least two good quality levels are required, 600mm and 1800mm long. These are used to ensure a level surface.
Water level	Used to transfer a datum point from one room to another.
Laser level	Easy to use, their accuracy will largely depend on the cost of the machine.

ACTIVITY

Search online to find out how to use a laser level.

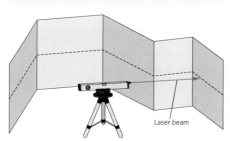

Laser beam

Using a laser level

Tool	Use
Gauging trowel 	Used to mix small amounts of material and position material into tight corners.
Chalk line 	Used to mark out screed lines and datum lines.
Box rule 	Also known as a flooring rule. Used for ruling in screeds and checking the level, as well as to compact sand and cement down to the screeds. This expels trapped air and compresses the sand and cement, making the screed more solid and helping avoid weak spots.
Measuring tools 	Tools such as a tape measure, used to measure lengths of timber battens or floor areas.
Square 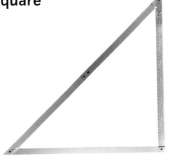	Used to square off frames and walls and for setting the screeds at the datum level.

INDUSTRY TIP

The terms 'tools' and 'equipment' are sometimes used interchangeably but can be used to mean different things. Tools may be handheld but equipment is usually larger items used to carry out the work. If you are employed, they will usually be supplied by your employer.

Tool	Use
Cement mixer	For domestic work, an electric drum mixer (pictured) is the most popular, but on larger sites a pan mixer might be used. Ready-mixed screed is becoming more popular.
Wheelbarrow	For domestic work narrow wheelbarrows are used as they allow you to manoeuvre through doorways.
Large shovel	Shovels are used for mixing and placing mixed material when floor laying.
Buckets	Buckets of various sizes are used to carry water and materials.
Screed rail	To help keep the floor flat, to form a chequerboard framework or to use when forming falls.

ACTIVITY

Look online to find out what a power float is used for.

Power float

MATERIALS

The main two materials used for traditional floor screed mix are:

- Ordinary Portland Cement (OPC)

- sharp screeding sand (washed well-graded sand).

Other materials can also be added in; these are also covered in this section of the chapter.

ORDINARY PORTLAND CEMENT

Ordinary Portland Cement is made from limestone and silica. It is produced worldwide, with the industry growing at a rate of 5% per year. It takes a lot of heat to produce a bag of cement, which has implications as governments are trying to reduce CO_2 emissions by following the **Kyoto Protocol**.

Kyoto Protocol

An agreement between nations to reduce greenhouse gas emissions

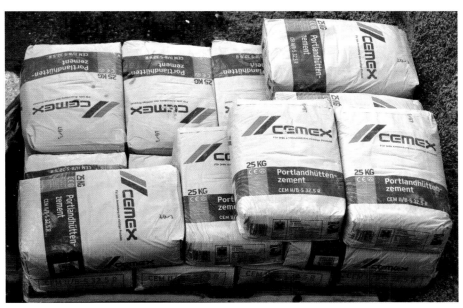

Ordinary Portland Cement

Cement works by wrapping itself around the aggregate (the sand) when mixed together, acting as a binder. Refer back to Chapter 3, page 114, for more information about cement.

SHARP SCREEDING SAND

Coarser than plastering sand, sharp screeding sand has the strength and durability required for a floor screed. The sand works by providing filler to the mix.

When sand is wet it increases in volume, a process called **bulking**. This must be taken into account when gauging materials in order to prevent accidentally creating a weaker mix.

Sharp screeding sand

Bulking

The swelling of sand when it is wet, making it heavy

ACTIVITY

Look online to find out the cost of 1 tonne of sharp screeding sand.

OTHER MATERIALS

Polypropylene

Polypropylene fibres that are 20mm long can also be added to the mix. They help reduce cracking and improve strength. As a proportion of the concrete or screed mix, 1 × 100g bag is used to 1 × 25kg bag of cement. In a standard sized cement mixer (with a 90 litre capacity), one third of the cement bag is used at a time to create a standard concrete/screed mix, so one third of the fibre bag's contents would also be added to each mix.

Polypropylene fibres

> **Curing**
>
> When you keep the cement moist to allow the screed to fully harden

> **Foot traffic**
>
> People walking. The term used when a newly laid floor screed allows someone to walk over the screed without leaving any indentations, usually after about three or four days

SBR

SBR stands for styrene-butadiene rubber. Like a cement slurry, SBR can be added to the mix to improve adhesion to the sub-floor. With SBR added to a screed mix, the polymers in the liquid bond the aggregate and cement together. This allows the production of high-strength screeds and is useful for carrying out patch repairs.

Hardeners

Hardeners can be added either during the mixing process or during the **curing** of the floor screed. They make the surface of the screed more durable and also allows earlier **foot traffic** over its surface.

Waterproofers

Waterproofers may be added to the mix if the screed is to be laid in a wet area.

Reinforcing mesh

D49 mesh or chicken wire can be laid midway in the screed to reinforce the screed and help avoid cracking.

COMPONENT MATERIALS USED FOR SCREEDING

Pre-mixed screed

Using ready-mixed screed has a few advantages over using a traditional sand and cement site-mixed screed. The benefits are:

- consistent batching of materials
- no storage or mixing areas are required on site
- retarders can be added to allow a longer working time
- other additives can be incorporated into the mix, such as polypropylene fibres to reduce cracking and improve flexural strength
- increased productivity as site operatives don't have to spend time mixing materials.

Pre-mixed screed can feed into a mixer with a built-in pump that pumps the mixed screed up many floor heights. This saves on production time and operative fatigue.

Pre-mixed screed used for renovations or small projects

Dry silos

On most medium to large construction sites, dry silos are used to store pre-mixed materials such as mortar, render and floor screed materials. They are connected to the mains water supply, which is regulated to add the right amount of water to mix the materials to the correct consistency. The materials can then be drawn off as needed.

Silos can hold as much as 16 tonnes of material, with some silos having the technology to monitor how full the silo is and trigger a re-order when the supplies drop to a set level.

Expansion strips

To help reduce possible shrinkage and cracking, a large screeded area is laid out in a grid pattern to form **day work joints**. This allows the plasterer to screed the bays in sequence, rather than trying to screed the whole area in one go. Each bay is approximately 14m². Expansion strips are placed and levelled into each bay at its joins. An added advantage of using an expansion strip is that it can be used as a screeding point to rule from. The current guidelines suggest that expansion strips should placed every 8m.

Dry silos

Day work joint

Used when laying large floor areas. Expansion strips are located at the edges of work completed that day. The expansion strips help prevent cracking across the screed

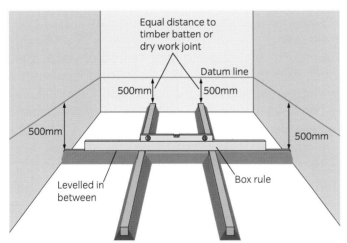

Equal distance to timber batten or dry work joint

Datum line

500mm 500mm

500mm

500mm

Levelled in between

Box rule

Bedded and levelled in sand and cement screed

Working to day work joints

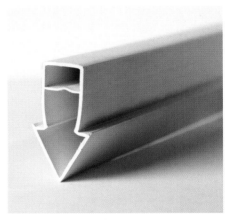
Day expansion strip

Damp proof membrane

Commonly abbreviated to 'DPM', a damp proof membrane can be laid in the sub-floor to prevent moisture rising up from the ground and into the screed. The membrane is lapped up the wall level with the damp proof course.

Materials such as lining paper for decorating and polythene for flooring are sold according to their thickness. The current building regulations state that polythene used for a damp proof membrane must have a thickness of at least 1200 gauge.

Lapped DPM

Compressive strength

The ability of the insulation to take heavy loads, such as furniture and people, without denting or going out of shape

Building sand

Soft building sand can be laid and compacted to an average thickness of 50mm over the sub-base concrete; the DPM is then laid on top of the building sand. The sand minimises the risk of concrete aggregate puncturing the damp proof membrane.

Liquid damp proof membrane

Liquid damp proof membranes are sometimes used in refurbishment work where an existing floor screed is failing. The old floor screed is removed or cleaned to receive a coat of bitumen liquid that is allowed to dry overnight. Once dry, a second coat of bitumen is brushed over the first coat. While the second coat of bitumen is still tacky, clean and sharp sand is scattered over the wet bitumen and allowed to dry. The new screed can then be laid on top to a minimum thickness of 50mm.

Also available is a two-pack epoxy liquid-applied damp proof membrane, which is solvent free and therefore low odour. It is used to provide protection for moisture-sensitive floor finishes where the presence of a satisfactory damp proof membrane is in doubt. The pack is manufactured in two contrasting colours to help identify which areas have been coated.

Rigid insulation

Rigid insulation is used under the floor screed or under the sub-base to help reduce heat loss through the floor. Rigid insulation is available in various thicknesses that allow for horizontal and vertical positioning of the insulation. The insulation is very durable and offers good **compressive strength**.

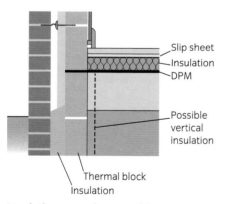
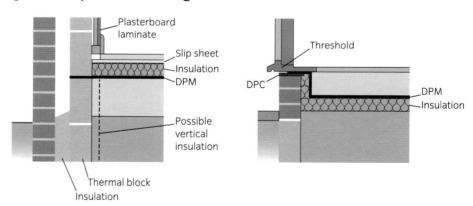

Insulation at various positions

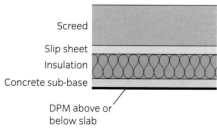

Slip sheet

Slip sheet layer

A slip sheet is laid between the insulation and the floor screed, made from 1200 gauge polythene sheet. It should be lapped 150mm up the sides of the walls to form a vapour control.

Self-levelling compound (latex)

Self-levelling compounds are used to compensate for irregular floor screeds, especially on refurbishment work. The floor which is receiving the compound must be prepared beforehand by removing loose particles and dust. A waterproof PVA can be used to control suction and improve the self-levelling compound's adhesion.

All self-levelling compounds are cement based. The cost of self-levelling compounds varies depending upon the quality of the aggregates and their flow rate (ability to self-level). Better quality self-levelling compounds contain latex which is either incorporated in the dry mixture or added separately during the mixing process. Self-levelling compounds that contain latex flow better when laid and provided a smoother finish if laid correctly. Both compounds that do and do not contain latex are mixed in a bucket with a mixing whisk until they are a creamy consistency and laid immediately with a plastering trowel to the floor to a thickness of between 2 and 5mm.

They are available in slow set and fast set varieties. The fast set variety can have foot traffic after 20 minutes. It is important to lay the self-levelling compound reasonably quickly to allow the materials to flow and self level.

Free flow liquid screeds

Free flow liquid screeds take advantage of modern laying techniques and materials. Calcium sulphate, sand, water and additives are mixed to produce a free flow self-levelling screed.

Instead of marking out the screed using dots or battens, tripods are levelled through from a **datum line**. The screed is poured over the area through a hose up to the underside of the levelling tripod; a dappling bar is then gently moved across the floor to level the floor screed.

This type of screed must be laid over an insulated sub-floor as moisture can affect its durability. It is a quick process which makes it ideal for larger floor areas.

INDUSTRY TIP

Always ensure the sub-floor is clean: slightly dampen the sub-floor with clean water or apply a diluted mixture of PVA. This will control suction and allow the levelling compound to flow easily.

Datum line

Usually about a metre high and running throughout the whole building, from this point measurements are taken to establish the finished floor level

ACTIVITY

Search online for 'liquid screed' to find out about the latest technology in this area.

Dappling bar

Free flow with tripod

TYPES OF SCREEDED FLOOR

There are three main types of sand and cement screed. These are:

- monolithic
- bonded
- unbonded.

MONOLITHIC

When something is described as being monolithic, it means it is made up of a single, unbroken mass. When a monolithic floor screed is laid, it is laid within three hours of the concrete slab substrate having been poured, ie while the sub-base concrete is still green (not fully hardened). The concrete has by then undergone its initial set but has yet to go through its final set. This means that the screed which has been laid on top chemically bonds with the concrete as they both set and dry.

The recommended thickness of a traditional sand and cement screed without fibres is 20mm, but can be from 12 to 25mm. With added fibres, the thickness can be reduced to 10–15mm. This type of screed is often found in commercial settings such as factories and warehouses.

BONDED

As its name suggests, this type of floor screed is bonded to the substrate. The screed is laid when the sub-base concrete has hardened and been **scabbled**, so that it is left with a **tamped finish** that provides a key for the floor screed.

Before laying the screed the sub-base concrete should be soaked with water, ideally overnight, to minimise the risk of bond failure and edge curling. To improve adhesion a slurry of cement and SBR can be mixed together to a ratio of 1:1 and then brushed over the concrete, with the screed laid while the slurry is wet.

Pre-formed concrete slabs and concrete block floors are also suitable substrates for this type of screed. The minimum thickness for this floor is 40mm.

UNBONDED

This type of screed is laid directly on top of either heavy waterproof building paper or 1200 gauge polythene sheeting (DPM) with at least 100mm laps up the outside walls. The only preparation required is that the substrate is swept clean of any debris that might puncture the DPM. The screed is laid to a minimum thickness of 50mm but this increases to 65mm if laid over insulated floor containing heating pipes.

Screed 12–25mm

Concrete sub-base

Monolithic screed

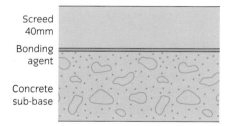

Screed 40mm

Bonding agent

Concrete sub-base

Bonded screed

Scabbling

The removal of the surface finish by mechanical means, producing a suitable key

Tamped finish

The ribbed effect left on the sub-floor's surface once it has been scabbled

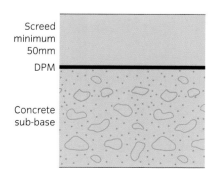

Screed minimum 50mm

DPM

Concrete sub-base

Unbonded screed

Floating floor

The floating floor method is a type of unbonded screed and is becoming more and more common. This type of screed is laid on rigid **extruded polystyrene** insulation to provide an insulated floor area. All walls and pillars must be lined with edging foam or 20mm insulation to protect against shrinkage cracking.

This system is the most commonly used in modern house building, especially those with underfloor heating systems.

Floating floor screeds must be laid to a minimum thickness of 65mm or 75mm if containing heating pipes in domestic flooring. Commercial floating floor screeds are laid to a minimum thickness of 75mm and no greater that 100mm.

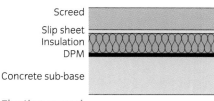

Screed
Slip sheet
Insulation
DPM

Concrete sub-base

Floating screed

Extruded polystyrene

When polystyrene crystals have been heated to high temperatures, along with other additives, and forced through a die. The result is a denser material compared with expanded foam

ACTIVITY

In a small area, practise laying a bonded, an unbonded and a floating floor to see the differences between them.

FLOOR SCREED TOLERANCES

All screeded floors should be level and flat. However, the quality of the finished floor must match what is written in the specification, which will be based on the British Standard BS8204-1:2003.

Lay a 3m rule across the surface of the screed. Any gaps or hollows showing underneath the rule must be within the tolerances shown in the table.

Class	Gap/hollow showing under a 3m rule
SR1 (the highest specified floor screed finish)	3mm
SR2	5mm
SR3 (the lowest specified floor screed finish)	10mm

ACTIVITY

Draw a cross-section of a monolithic floor, a bonded floor and an unbonded floor on DPM. Use the correct symbols for each material found in the floors' construction.

SCREED SUB-BASES

Floor screeds are laid onto the following sub-bases:

- green concrete base (when laying monolithic screed)

- set concrete base (when laying bonded screed)

- **beam and block** (when laying a bonded screed)

- beam and block overlaid with rigid insulation (when laying a floating screed)

Beam and block

Floors made up of standard building blocks laid between pre-stressed concrete beams

- set concrete base overlaid with polythene membrane (DPM) (when laying an unbonded screed)

- set concrete overlaid with rigid insulation (when laying a floating screed).

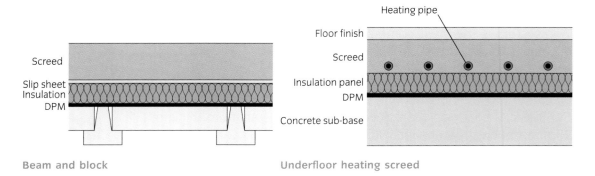

Beam and block

Underfloor heating screed

LAYING SAND AND CEMENT SCREEDS

PREPARING FLOORS

Traditional screeded floors are laid with a **semi-dry** mix. Mixing the screeding sand and cement this way allows the plasterer to rule off, compact and consolidate as the work proceeds. Preparation will depend upon the type of sub-base.

When screeding directly to a concrete sub-base that has been allowed to harden, ie for a bonded screed, the base should be prepared as follows.

1 Provide a mechanical key if screeding directly to the sub-base.

2 Sweep and remove all debris and any signs of **laitance**.

3 Soak the concrete sub-base overnight with water. Remove surplus water the next day with a broom.

4 Mix a 1:1 mix of water and PVA to 50% cement to make a slurry, and brush over the concrete sub-base.

5 Lay floor screed while the cement slurry is tacky.

When brushing a dusty floor, wear a dust mask and spray a light water mist over the floor to help keep the dust down.

Semi-dry

Describes the mix consistency of a traditional sand and cement screed

Providing a mechanical key

Laitance

A layer of weak cement that affects the strength of the floor screed if not removed

Sweeping the floor

SCREED MIXING METHODS

It is important to always gauge materials either by weight or by volume using a gauge box or buckets. Never gauge materials using a shovel as this will produce an inconsistent mix. Always read the specification to ensure that the materials are mixed at the correct mix ratio.

MIXING BY HAND

For smaller quantities, for example for repair work, the sand and cement can easily be mixed by hand. The materials should be proportioned by weight or volume following this sequence.

STEP 1 Gauge the materials with buckets, then place the materials into a single pile.

STEP 2 Then, place the materials into a single pile.

STEP 3 Mix the materials dry (without adding water).

STEP 4 Pour a small amount of water into the centre and gently turn the sand and cement into the water using a shovel. Continue until all of the sand and cement is damp. Turn over the material at least three times until thoroughly mixed.

STEP 5 It is important not to add too much water when mixing; you should be able to clinch a ball of sand and cement in your hand without any water squeezing through your fingers. We describe this as a 'semi-dry' mix.

INDUSTRY TIP

Using a semi-dry mix allows you to compact the sand and cement screed when ruling off, and reduces the risk of laitance forming.

Mixing by cement mixer

MIXING BY CEMENT MIXER

This is where the materials are put in a cement mixer and tumbled until mixed. Care needs to be taken when adding water as the tumbling action of the materials being mixed together can cause balls of compacted materials to form. And always ensure that there are no unmixed materials stuck at the back of the mixer.

The following steps explain how to mix with a cement mixer.

1 If using an electric cement mixer, check that it has a current PAT label (see Chapter 1, page 37).

2 Ensure the work area is uncluttered and that materials are close to hand with a supply of clean water. Check that the mixer is on a firm standing.

3 If using an additive, add it to a large drum of water to ensure consistency throughout the mix. Use water only from this drum for mixing.

4 Add a small amount of water into the mixer drum.

5 Add fibres, if you intend to use them.

6 Add about half of the sand that you intend to use.

7 Add about half of the cement that you intend to use.

8 Add a little more water, followed by the remaining sand and cement.

9 Mix for no longer than five minutes – three minutes is recommended.

10 Pour the mixed material onto a spot board or into a wheelbarrow.

11 Wash out the mixer and clean the equipment.

INDUSTRY TIP

Mix only enough materials that you can use within an hour.

READY-MIXED SCREED

Ready-mixed screed has advantages compared with mixing the screed yourself.

- There is no need for materials storage as the screed can be laid the same day it is delivered.

- Additives that delay the setting time can be added by the manufacturer, allowing you more time to lay larger areas.

- Fibres and hardeners to help reduce cracking can be added by the manufacturer.

- The correct consistency of mixed screed material is guaranteed as the supplier will mix and deliver the screed to the screeder's specified ratio or the architect's design specification.

- There is reduced wastage as only enough materials for the job are ordered.

- Theft of bagged materials from site is reduced as they don't need to be stored on site in the first place.

Using and laying ready-mixed materials

Ready-mixed screed can be laid using battens or from screed dots. Preparation is the same as if it was a traditional sand and cement screed.

To be effective when using ready mix it is important to set up your working area correctly. For example, when working on a domestic extension polythene sheets should be laid out as near to the delivery point as possible so that the material can be stored there, with the sheeting preventing contamination of the delivered materials.

On larger projects ready mixed screed can be pumped as far as 60m; some delivery vehicles can pump as much as 20 tonnes of ready mixed screed.

EFFECTS OF POOR MIXING

Cause	Effect
Lack of preparation of sub-base	Cracking and lifting of screed
Too little water	Materials difficult to lay and compact
Too much cement	Surface cracking
Too little cement	Weak screed prone to wear and tear
Too much water	Weakens screed, causes cement to float to the top of the screed, screed shrinks
Inconsistent mixing	Leaves patches of sand or cement
Over trowelling or trowelling too soon	Attracts water to the surface with the cement, leaves a film of cement on the surface of the screed
Poor curing	The screed dries out too quickly which weakens the screed strength; curing can occur around the edges of the screed
Poor **compaction**	Produces small pockets of air that weaken the floor

ACTIVITY

Using an internet search engine, search for 'source4me building calculator'. Have a look at the ready-mix section and use your own figures to arrive at an estimate to lay the screed in a room in your home.

FUNCTIONAL SKILLS

If a room measures 5.5m × 3.5m and the required screed thickness is 75mm, how much ready-mix material is required, not allowing for wastage?

Work on this activity supports FM2 C2.5 and C2.7.

Answer: $1.4m^3$

Compaction

When the sand and cement screed is consolidated by tamping the screed with a box rule. This action strengthens the floor screed

'Our House' is to benefit from underfloor heating. Remembering this, estimate the following:

1 the total area of the ground floor
2 the volume of ready-mix screed required (if the screed has a minimum depth of 65mm)
3 the amount of horizontal insulation needed for the total floor area (assuming each insulation sheet has an area of 2.88m²)
4 vertical insulation required for the perimeter of each room (hint: measure the perimeter of each room).

If the screed is to receive ceramic floor files, specify the type of floor finish that will be necessary.

Outline how you might promote curing of the floor once it has been laid.

FLOOR SCREED FINISHES

The purpose of a floor screed is to provide a smooth, level surface that can withstand both loads and foot or wheel traffic. There are different ways in which a floor screed can be finished.

TROWEL FINISH

This finish is achieved using a large steel trowel for smaller domestic floors or a power float for larger commercial floors. Trowel finished floors usually receive vinyl tiles/sheets or carpet.

FLOAT FINISH

This finish is achieved using a large plain float. The float leaves a coarser texture that provides a key for tiling adhesive when laying ceramic floor tiles.

LATEX FINISH

This finish is achieved using a levelling compound that is trowelled over an existing floor with a steel trowel to a thickness of about 3–5mm.

METHODS OF LAYING A FLOOR SCREED

The first task when laying a floor screed is to determine the levels to work from. These are taken from a fixed point such as:

- a concrete door step

- the bottom of a door frame for domestic work

- a datum line.

A datum line should always be used for commercial work. Always check that the datum point allows for the floor finish to be laid to the correct floor finish level (FFL).

Once the finished floor level has been determined, timber battens or dots are bedded in, using the screeding material, around the perimeter of the room and at intermediate positions to allow ruling off. Once the battens or dots have been levelled and are able to stand the pressure of ruling off, screeding can begin.

If the timber batten method is used, the floor plasterer will start filling in between the timber battens at the furthest point away from the exit point, ruling and tamping the screed materials as the work progresses. The timber battens are usually about 1.5m long; this allows the screeder to remove the batten as they proceed, fill in with floor screed where the batten was positioned, and then finish the work with a steel or plastic float.

Alternatively if dots are used, screeding materials are laid between the dots and ruled off using a floor rule. As soon as the screed is firm the timber dots are removed. The screeder will start to infill between the wet screeds, ruling and tamping as the work proceeds, finishing the floor with a trowel or steel float. If the floor screed material is initially too wet to finish with a trowel or float, this can be done later in the day when the floor is able to take light foot traffic.

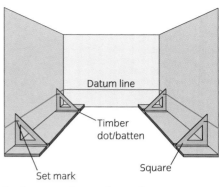

Laying to a datum line using a square

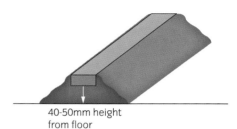

40-50mm height from floor

A dot bedded in the screeding material

> **INDUSTRY TIP**
>
> To make the screed non-slip, carborundum dust can be sprinkled over the surface and trowelled in at the final trowel. For non-slip wet areas, a batten roller is used to produce a dimpled effect.

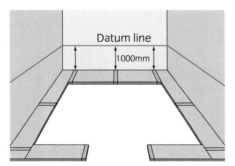

Set the dots and form a perimeter screed

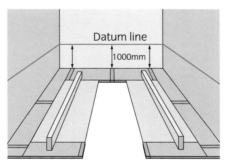

Fill both sides

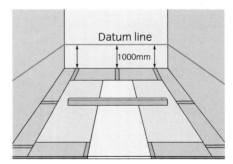

Fill middle and work out of the room

The following step-by-steps show you how to lay the floor to the datum line using dots.

STEP 1 Damp down the floor.

STEP 2 Sweep the floor.

STEP 3 Set out the dots. The first dot should be set in the corner furthest from the door and approximately 300mm from the end of the wall forming the room's longest length. Use a tape measure to make sure the dot is the required distance below the datum.

STEP 4 Set further dots as required. Ensure each dot is the same distance below the datum line. Level the dots across.

STEP 5 Form screeds between the dots. Ensure they are in line and flush with the top of the dots and are level along their length.

STEP 6 Rule in the floor to the dots with a box rule.

STEP 7 Before you lay beyond what you can comfortably reach without over-stretching, remove the dots, fill their holes and float the surface of the floor, filling any misses and hollows, etc. Check the floor with a box rule.

STEP 8 Repeat Steps 5–7 along the opposite wall to form another screed.

STEP 9 You should now have two screeds ruled in to dots and levelled in from the datum.

STEP 10 Fill in between the screeds. Starting at the back wall of the room, empty a wheelbarrow of mix between the screeds. This will need to be compacted down as firmly as possible, then ruled off flush with the screeds.

STEP 11 Follow the same process for the back screed, applying screed and compacting the mix.

STEP 12 Rule in the screed with a box rule and float.

STEP 13 Use a trowel to smooth the screeds.

STEP 14 Continue in this manner, compacting, ruling and floating, working methodically towards the door.

STEP 15 Complete the floor with a trowel.

STEP 16 Carry out a final check for level.

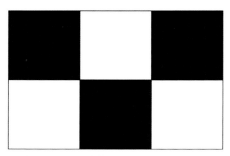

A chequerboard framework

Drainage outlet

FUNCTIONAL SKILLS

A factory floor is to be laid with a constant fall of 1:100 throughout its 15m length from a level base. The minimum thickness is to be 50mm at the drainage point. Calculate the maximum thickness of the floor. Make sure you convert the measurements so that you are working in the same units.

Work on this activity can support C2.7 and L2.2.1.

Answer: 200mm

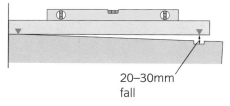

20–30mm fall

Setting out to falls

LAYING SCREED TO A LARGER AREA

Larger areas of floor screed will require a different laying technique to reduce cracking and to allow finishing of the floor. Screed rails are levelled through to form a chequerboard framework; this allows the floor screeder to lay alternate bays. The screed rails are then removed and expansion strips are placed in the gaps to reduce cracking.

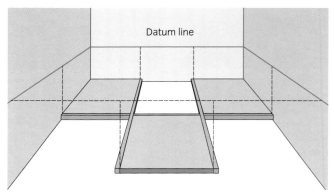

Datum line

Chequerboard framework using day work joints or timber battens

SCREED TO A FALL

All of the basic principles for setting out a sand and cement screed can be applied to laying a screed to a fall (a sloping floor). The purpose of laying screed to a fall is to enable water to drain away to a sunken drainage outlet. This type of floor screed can be found in food preparation areas where washing down is required, in kennels and in walk-in wet shower rooms.

SETTING OUT SCREED TO A FALL

As with a flat floor screed, the finished floor level is established from a datum point or line. The next stage is to check the working drawing to find the fall's ratio. For example, the drawing might state the fall is 1 in 100 or 1:100. This means that for every 100mm in length the screed will slope down 1mm. For example, if the floor screed was 10m long to an outlet, the fall (slope) would be 10cm.

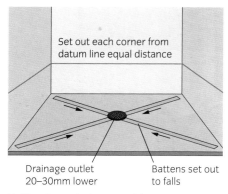

Set out each corner from datum line equal distance

Drainage outlet 20–30mm lower

Battens set out to falls

Falling to a drainage grid

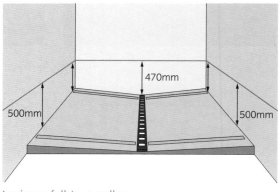

470mm

500mm

500mm

Laying a fall to a gulley

LAYING SCREED TO A FALL

When laying a screed to a fall you have to work from two datum points:

- a horizontal datum line or point to produce the flat part of the floor

- the sunken gully to form the slope that allows the water to drain away.

Before starting work, check with your line manager or the customer that the sunken gully is connected and functioning correctly. As with a flat floor screed you can use screed rails or form wet screeds to establish the slope, working from the gully to the flat screed area. Depending on the design of the gully, the finished floor level will be flush with the gully's rim or just below it; this is to allow for fixing of ceramic or vinyl sheeting.

Always check the drawing and specification as no two floor screeds will be to the same design. Working angled screeds is a difficult job so you will need shorter feather edges or box rules as the floor screed will get narrower as you reach the gully.

This image shows forming falls to a grid gulley, which would mostly be used in public leisure facilities for communal use which caters for more than one person's shower at the same time

Using battens to lay a screed to a fall

The following steps show you how to lay screeds to a fall.

STEP 1 Set up the perimeter level, which is always flat. Place a tile in each corner.

STEP 2 Level the corners across.

STEP 3 Transfer the level diagonally.

STEP 4 Fill in the perimeter.

STEP 5 Rule off with a box rule.

STEP 6 Compact the screeds to create the finished floor level.

STEP 7 Lay battens (or form freehand) towards the gully.

STEP 8 The gully will be lower than the screeds.

STEP 9 Rule off the timber battens and compact.

STEP 10 Form the other side of the gully with battens or freehand.

STEP 11 Compact.

STEP 12 Remove the tiles and battens and fill in.

STEP 13 Trowel or float finish.

STEP 14 The finished fall.

CURING AND DRYING OUT

Curing means keeping cement moist to allow the screed to fully harden. This is different from drying. Curing is an essential part of floor screeding as it allows the cement to reach full strength; the cement shouldn't be allowed to dry too quickly.

To allow time for curing we have two options.

1 Keep the floor screed damp for about seven days by covering it with plastic sheeting or lightly spraying it repeatedly with water. After seven days, remove the plastic sheeting.

2 Spray a chemical curing agent onto the floor screed. After a few days, the chemical agent breaks down and curing is complete.

Curing is an important part of floor screeding. Artificial heat should not be used to promote drying as it needs to be allowed to dry naturally. As a rule of thumb, allow one day of curing for every 1mm of floor screed. As this shows, it takes a long time for a floor screed to dry completely. An easy, rule-of-thumb test is to leave a glass beaker upside down on the floor screed overnight: if condensation appears in the glass in the morning, the floor screed is still drying out.

> **INDUSTRY TIP**
>
> A 75mm screed could take three months to dry completely.

Curing a floor screed

Case Study: Anna and Gary

Anna and Gary had been awarded a 12-month contract with an underfloor heating specialist on a sub-contract, labour-only basis. They received a phone call from the main contractor giving them details about a job in Leeds. It meant an early start for Anna and Gary as they had to travel about 50 miles to get to the job, and the ready mix had been arranged to be delivered between 8.30am and 1.00pm.

When they arrived at 8.15am the plumber was just carrying out a pressure test to ensure there were no leaks in the plumbing system. Where the screed was to be laid, the insulation and the slip layer were already in place, including the perimeter insulation to help prevent cold bridging and allow for expansion and contraction as the floor screed heats up and cools down.

Anna laid a sheet of polythene on the drive to receive the ready mix, while Gary fetched some battens to lay over the water pipes to prevent damage to the heating system. Gary located the datum and marks around the room where the finished floor level should be: he had to make an allowance as the floor was to receive ceramic floor tiling after the screeding was completed, after allowing at least a week for the screed to cure.

The ready mix arrived at 9.30am. As specified, it included a retarder to allow Gary more flexibility and polypropylene fibres to improve the flexural strength of the floor, which is essential to help prevent the floor from crazing as the screed heats up and cools down.

Anna has decided she would barrow the materials to Gary so he could lay the screed to the minimum 65mm depth as recommended in the British Standards. Gary started at the furthest point away from the door opening as he didn't want to trap himself in the room. Gary is an experienced plasterer and floor screeder so he laid the screeds to work from without using battens; he worked around the perimeter of the room and laid a few intermediate screeds in bays of workable sizes.

With the levelling screeds laid, he started to fill in between the levelling screeds, ruling and tamping with a box rule to consolidate the ready mix sand and cement. Checking as he worked that the floor screed was flat and level, Gary used a steel trowel to lay the floor followed by a large plastic float to flatten and provide a textured surface ready to receive the ceramic floor tiles. Anna waited for Gary's instructions before dropping the ready mix onto the insulation as it was important that Gary had control of the laying process.

As Gary neared the end of laying the screed, Anna started to clean and tidy the working area. With the floor screed laid Anna sprayed the floor screed with a curing mixture to ensure the chemical reaction took place: if a floor screed dries out too quickly it can make the screed weaker. Polythene can be used to cure a floor screed but it can only be placed when the screed can take light foot traffic, and by that time Anna and Gary would have started a new job.

Work through the following questions to check your learning.

1   A monolithic floor screed is laid within how many hours of the concrete being placed?

    a   3.

    b   6.

    c   9.

    d   12.

2   Which one of the following is an advantage of using a ready-mix screed material?

    a   Easier to lay.

    b   Cheaper to buy.

    c   Consistent mix quality.

    d   Consistency can be adjusted on site.

3   How much ready mix is required for a floor measuring 6m by 4m with a screed depth of 65mm?

    a   1.56m^3.

    b   1.56m^3.

    c   15.60m^3.

    d   1.56m^3.

4   Floor screed battens

    a   are left in the screed when the floor is completed

    b   are removed as work proceeds

    c   are removed after the floor is completed

    d   can be left in or taken out.

5   Correct PPE must be worn when using sand and cement screed as exposure to cement can cause which one of the following?

    a   Skin burns.

    b   Dry skin.

    c   Cracked nails.

    d   Sore knees.

6   Which equipment should be used to transfer a datum point to another room?

    a   Boat level.

    b   Water level.

    c   Feather edge.

    d   Measuring tape.

7   Laitance is

    a   a cement layer on top of the finished screed

    b   an additive to promote curing

    c   an additive to promote hardness

    d   a type of floor finish.

8   Curing is necessary

    a   for quick drying of the screed

    b   to aid compaction of the screed

    c   to obtain an even float finish

    d   for hardening of the cement.

9   The **minimum** thickness of a floor screed over insulation is

    a   85mm

    b   75mm

    c   65mm

    d   55mm.

10 Perimeter insulation around a room is provided to

    a   prevent cold bridging

    b   give an edge to work to

    c   allow for dry lining

    d   keep the floor warm.

11 A floor screed finished with a trowel is suitable for which type of floor covering?

a   Wood block floor.

b   Ceramic floor tiles.

c   Underlay and carpet.

d   Vinyl sheeting/tiles.

12 Self-levelling latex screed is used to

a   cover up poor workmanship

b   level an uneven floor

c   give a trowel finish

d   cover up cracked floors.

13 Which one of the following is the **minimum** thickness of floor screed if laid over insulated floor with heating pipes?

a   75mm.

b   65mm.

c   55mm.

d   50mm.

14 The strength of a screeded floor can be improved by adding

a   hessian

b   rapid hardening cement

c   polypropylene fibres

d   masonry cement.

15 Poor curing causes the floor screed to

a   dry out too quickly

b   weaken around its edges

c   weaken in its centre

d   dry out too slowly.

16 Adding too much cement to a screed mix will cause it to

a   shrink and crack

b   have good adhesion

c   set quickly

d   be weaker than normal.

17 A common mix ratio for a floor screed is

a   1 sand to 1 cement

b   2 sand to 1 cement

c   4 sand to 1 cement

d   5 sand to 1 cement.

18 Floor levelling compound should be mixed to what sort of consistency?

a   Thick.

b   Watery.

c   Creamy.

d   Weak.

19 Floor levelling compound is laid using a

a   steel trowel

b   plastic float

c   gauging trowel

d   bucket trowel.

20 A monolithic screeded floor has a fall of 1:100 throughout its length of 15m from a level base. Given that the minimum thickness is to be 25mm, what is the **maximum** thickness of the floor?

a   125mm.

b   150mm.

c   175mm.

d   200mm.

Chapter 6
Unit 224: Applying plastering materials to external backgrounds

External rendering is another aspect of your plastering career that you will need to practise hard to develop. This type of work will definitely test your skills when you have to produce straight, flat and smooth surfaces that also contain sharp details to returns of angles and openings.

This chapter covers the materials, tools and equipment required to prepare and apply external rendering. It also explains the procedures and techniques you will need to develop to master this challenging skill.

By reading this chapter you will know how to:

1 Interpret information for external work.

2 Select and prepare materials, tools and equipment for external work.

3 Apply render to external backgrounds.

4 Apply two coat rendering to external backgrounds.

WHAT IS EXTERNAL RENDERING?

External rendering has two main purposes in the building industry:

1 To provide a desirable finish that will enhance the appearance of a building.

2 To provide a protective surface, preventing passage of moisture that can penetrate the external wall and enter the building.

There are many different types of external render finishes. The table below shows the different types of external surfaces and textures that are commonly used in the construction industry. Many of these render finishes will be covered in greater detail at Level 3.

Using a tyrolean finishing machine

Jointer used for forming an ashlar pattern

External render finishes	Description
Plain face 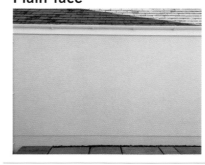	Plain face finish is completed by scouring and consolidating the surface of render that has been ruled with a straight edge and flattened with a darby. It has a flat, smooth, sandy look.
Tyrolean 	A honeycomb finish applied with a tyrolean machine on to plain face backgrounds.
Ashlar 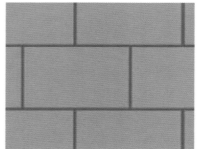	Ashlar is formed with a jointer or similar tool, carving out the shape of blockwork in the surface of plain floated render.

External render finishes	Description
Brush 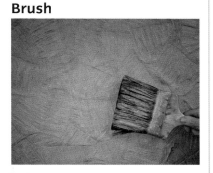	Applied render finished by rotating a large bristled brush flat to its face.
Pebble dash 	Granite, stone or flint spar thrown onto a buttery render mix which is applied to a scratch coat surface.
Rough cast 	A mixture of granite and render material that can be thrown onto a **butter coat** or keyed surface.
Scrape texture 	Achieved by scraping the surface of a pre-mixed render that contains additives.

Jointer used for forming deep V and square joints

Jointer used for forming a pattern with it's teeth

Butter coat

The top coat render mixed to a buttery consistency that is applied to receive dry or wet dash finish onto its surface

INDUSTRY TIP

Pulley wheels are sometimes used for lifting heavy buckets of mixed render onto scaffold lifts.

Pulley wheel

ACTIVITY

Research two types of renders on the websites of manufacturers such as Sto, Weber and K Rend.

External render finishes	Description
Thin coat render 	This external render is applied and finished by scouring the surface with a specialist-made float, forming a textured surface. Also known as 'light texture' and 'rubbed texture', it contains a resin as a binder, allowing the surface to be flexible and crack resistant.

There are also other less common types of renders that are used on older type buildings. These are generally made up to suit the character of the building and can create a very effective appearance; a good example of this is cottage finish. These types have less technique involved in their application and finish.

External renders are popular and can be used on a range of different backgrounds, including insulation. EWI is the abbreviation for external wall insulation, which is fixed to solid backgrounds mechanically, improving the insulation of the building.

Insulation being fixed to backgrounds

Scrim cloth

Lightweight pre-mixed plasters are preferred on insulated backgrounds because render contains polymers and is applied with reinforcing scrim cloth or fibreglass mesh bedded into the render to reinforce the surface.

This chapter focuses on plain face smooth render (see pages 257–259), which is best applied and finished on a scratch coat surface. This type of finish consists of several layers applied onto a solid background surface. It can be described as either two or three coat plastering/rendering work, depending on the unevenness of the background.

Preparing and forming this type of finish will challenge your skills as an operative. Being eager, enthusiastic and keen to practise will help you learn and develop the required techniques to apply and form the required finished surface. You will need to produce high standards of workmanship using various hand tools in order to produce the final product.

To do this successfully you will need to deal with certain factors such as background key, which helps make the render adhere to the surface. You will also need to control and treat **suction** in order to apply the first scratch coat successfully. Another important factor will be selecting suitable materials that will be compatible with the background to ensure there is good adhesion and bond between the two surfaces.

The process of rendering includes laying on several applications of render. The number required will depend on the specification, which will state the background's properties. The specification may state that the background needs to be built up using dubbing out coats before applying the scratch coat and top coat. See the next section of this chapter for more about specifications and other sources of information.

Suction

The rate at which a background absorbs moisture

An uneven external background that needs dubbing out

Dubbing out stonework

INTERPRETING INFORMATION

In order to carry out the work correctly, you will first need to prepare properly by interpreting drawings and reading various contract documents such as specifications, schedules and data sheets, extracting from them the information that will help you carry out the different aspects of the work. More information on these documents is given in Chapter 2.

You can then use the gathered information to select appropriate tools and equipment, evaluate how to prepare the background surface, and prepare for mixing and gauging the materials.

WORKING DRAWINGS

Block plans

Drawings that show the proposed development in relation to its surrounding properties

Elevations

Drawings that show the external walls of the building from different views

Learning how to accurately read drawings such as **block plans** will give you the necessary skills to develop and progress within your plastering career. Drawings provide accurate information and descriptions about the rendering process and provide you with knowledge of the desired outcomes and what needs to be achieved. They illustrate building **elevations**, positions of pre-made profiles, sections of windows, door heads and reveals, and also any special design features that may be included with the rendering work.

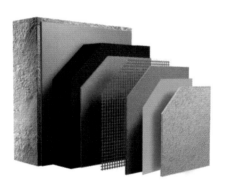

Section of external wall and rendering systems

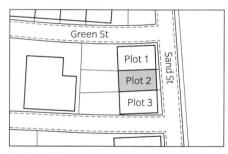

Scale: 1:200

Block plan

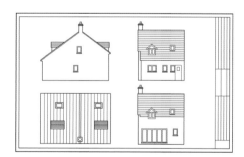

Elevation drawings for a typical house

Tender

To submit a cost or price for work in an attempt to win the contract to do the work

When you work on external rendering contracts, the architect's drawings provide detailed measurements of external wall surfaces. You can use these to calculate areas and volumes of material, as well as linear measurements for pre-made beads or trims. This will help you schedule materials and labour costs when **tendering** for the work.

SPECIFICATIONS

You can use the specification to help you order the correct materials and components for rendering work. The specification provides detailed descriptions of the materials that must be used for the work. It also contains other vital information, including the following:

- the type of background
- the surface preparation
- mix **ratios** and additives
- required standards of workmanship
- method of application
- thickness
- tolerances
- types of pre-formed beads or trims to be used.

Failure to comply with drawings and specifications may lead you to carry out the work incorrectly. There may be other trades working alongside you and any hold-ups in your work schedule will no doubt have a knock-on effect on their work, too.

Any discrepancies found in the drawings or specification should be reported to someone in higher authority as soon as possible to avoid disrupting and delaying the work. For more information on specifications, refer back to Chapter 2, pages 52–53.

SCHEDULES

The schedule is another document used in construction contracts, containing information on the amount of materials and components required for the work. For example, the schedule will list the amount of the different types of pre-formed beads that are required for a rendering contract. For more information on schedules, refer back to Chapter 2, pages 54–55.

MANUFACTURERS' INFORMATION

Manufacturers' data sheets also contain important information about the storage and use of their products, as well as product information and technical guidelines. For more information on data sheets, refer back to Chapter 4, page 167.

You will need to comply with **manufacturers' instructions** and guidelines when using rendering products and components in order to maintain the quality of the completed work. Failure to do this can lead to costly mistakes occurring, which can have a major effect on the outcome of the rendering work.

Ratio

The proportion of materials that are mixed together, eg 6 parts of sand to 1 part of cement, which would be written as 6:1

ACTIVITY

Write a specification for the image used in the Functional Skills activity on page 237. Make sure the specification covers the points above. Your tutor will help you with this task.

ACTIVITY

Search the internet to find a data sheet for cement and lime. Make a note listing the information covered.

Manufacturers' instructions

Manufacturers' instructions say what a product may be used for, how it is to be installed and what conditions it can be exposed to

CALCULATE QUANTITIES OF MATERIALS

At the start of every job you should be aware of the possible effects that poor planning can cause. Every effort should be made to ensure consistently high quality, and these efforts need to be maintained throughout the rendering process.

Materials should be checked for quality and **shelf life** before they are used: using poor quality materials can cause problems in time and reflect badly on your workmanship and professionalism as a qualified operative. Not only this, but you may also incur the cost of having to re-do or repair the work.

It is good practice to order just enough materials to start and proceed with the job. Good planning and storage control, with order points set against your work schedule, will prevent you running out of materials during the work. Running out of materials in the middle of the job not only causes delays but will also become costly if there are no materials for the hired labour to work with.

When pricing for work you will have to work out how much of each material you need for the area specified to be plastered. You can do this by measuring and calculating the wall area from the drawings. Once you have the measurements and calculations, the next stage is to find out the ratio of the mix. This will allow you to work out the amount of each material that you need. Reading the specification will also help you do this.

Shelf life

Use-by date of products such as cement and lime

Poorly set up mixing area and materials

Example

- One 25kg bag of cement will cover 4.5m² at 10mm thick.

- One 25kg bag of sand will also cover 4.5m² at 10mm thick.

If the mix required is 4 sand to 1 cement (a 4:1 mix), at 10mm thick it will cover 22.5m² of wall. The calculation for this is the total number of bags multiplied by the area one bag covers:

5 × 4.5m² = 22.5m²

If you have a wall area that measures 225m², how many 25kg bags of sand and cement applied 10mm thick will you need if you are using the same 4:1 ratio of sand to cement?

To find the answer divide your wall area by the area that the 4:1 mix covers:

225 ÷ 22.5 = 10

So you will need 4 × 10 = 40 bags of sand and 1 × 10 = 10 bags of cement to complete the job.

To allow for minor errors, always add around 10% extra for wastage. You need to work this out for both the sand and cement.

- Sand: 10% of 40 is 4.

- Cement: 10% of 10 is 1.

So you would need another 4 bags of sand and another 1 bag of cement. This brings the total for the job of **44** bags of sand and **11** bags of cement.

FORMULAS

You need to know a number of formulas used for calculating volume. For example, when rendering around the top of a house, you will need to know:

1 the formula for calculating the volume of the triangular part of a **gable apex**: half-length × height × thickness

2 the formula for calculating the volume of the square or rectangular part of the gable wall: length × height × thickness – if there are any window openings, you would need to take the volume of the openings away from your gable wall volume.

Calculating the quantity of beading required can be done from the linear measurements of openings.

Gable apex
The triangular part of a gable wall

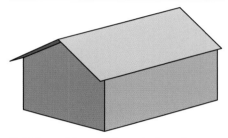

Building with a gable-ended roof

FUNCTIONAL SKILLS

Answer the following questions, using the drawing below.

How many 25kg sand and cement bags will you need to cover the gable elevation with a ratio of sand cement render at 4 sand to 1 cement at 20mm thick, rounded up to the nearest number of bags?

Remember from page 236 that:

- One 25kg bag of cement will cover 4.5m2 at 10mm thick.

- One 25kg bag of sand will also cover 4.5m2 at 10mm thick.

To find the answer you will need to:

1 Work out the area that one bag of sand and cement covers at 20mm thick.

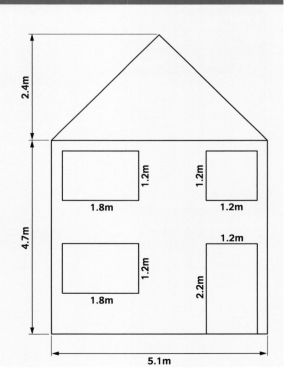

2 Work out the area to be covered. This will involve working out the gable area (the triangular part), the rectangular part of the wall, and adding the two together.

3 You will then need to remove the amount of area of the four openings from the area to be covered.

4 Divide the area to be covered by the area that the 4:1 mix covers.

5 Add 10% extra for wastage for both sand and cement, rounded up to the nearest whole bag.

Work on this activity can support FM2 (C2.2, C2.7 and L2.2.1).

Answer: 13 bags of sand and 4 bags of cement

SELECTING MATERIALS, TOOLS AND EQUIPMENT

RENDERING MATERIALS

Selecting and preparing materials plays a major part in the external rendering process. Knowing what materials to select and how to prepare them will allow you to plan your work methodically.

You need to refer to the specification when selecting materials as this will provide detailed descriptions of the required types.

CEMENT

Cement is used as a **binder** and to provide strength in the mix. It is made from 75% limestone and 25% clay and is used because of its faster setting time compared with lime mixes. Cement mixed with sand and water will begin to set after 45 minutes and will normally be completely set by the next day. Cement-based mixes can take several days to reach their final strength; this process is known as 'curing'. Ordinary Portland Cement (OPC) is one of the most commonly used cements in mortar.

White cement is another type of cement that is used in the render finish coat to enhance its appearance, providing a much lighter look. It is made from limestone (75%) and white china clay (25%). Gauging white cement for rendering should be done accurately to ensure that the mix is uniform in colour and consistent in strength.

Binder

Material that binds the aggregate together and gives the render mix its strength

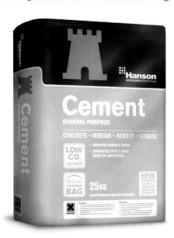

Bagged cement

LIME

Lime is another material that has many uses in plastering mixes. It is made by crushing limestone and heating it in a kiln. Lime comes in bags and should be stored on a pallet in dry conditions. There are two types used in plastering mixes: hydrated lime and hydraulic lime.

Hydrated lime does not set when added to plastering mixes. However, this has many benefits. Lime added to a cement-based mix will improve the mix's workability and adhesion and help prevent shrinkage. Another benefit of lime is that it creates suction.

Hydraulic lime has a 'chemical set' and sets very slowly when mixed with sand. The setting times can be influenced by the temperature – setting will take longer in winter than in the summer, so good planning of the work is required.

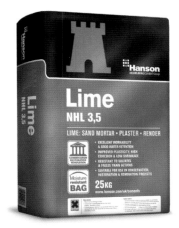

Bagged lime

SAND

Sand is an aggregate used to bulk the mix. Without sand, cement mixed with water would be too hard and would crack. There are many different types of sand used in construction. Sand used for rendering should contain a mixture of small, medium and large grains and contain as little silt as possible. Silt is a very fine grain that can prevent the cement from binding the mix, resulting in the render surface becoming weak and powdery. Refer back to Chapter 3, page 115, for an illustration of sand grains.

Some types of sand should be avoided because of the shape of their grains: the grains of some sands can be too round in shape and will therefore contain too many **voids**.

- *Pit sand* is generally used by bricklayers for building work. This sand is very fine with round-shaped aggregate and also contains too much silt for rendering.

- *Silica sand* and *silver sand* are deemed too fine for plain face rendering. Instead, they tend to be used as a fill-in between paving bricks and for filling in fine seams or joints between the masonry.

- *Loam sand* is a term used for sand containing clay. This type of sand would be used for traditional lime-based renders in the restoration of old buildings, restoring them back to their original state.

Sand

Voids

Pockets of air, common in poorly graded sand

INDUSTRY TIP

Sea sand contains salt and impurities such as shells. It is considered badly graded so should never be used for rendering.

ADDITIVES

Additives play an important part in the render mix and you need to know when and how to use them. They usually come in liquid form in 5 or 25 litre containers. The table below lists the different types of additives and how they can enhance the performance of the render mix.

Additive

A substance that is added to plaster mixes to change their natural properties

Additive	Use
Plasticiser	Used to improve the workability of mix. Without plasticiser, the mixed material would separate and become too heavy to spread. Too much plasticiser in the mix, however, can make it weak and cause the mix to crumble.
Waterproofer	Added to the mix to prevent water penetration.
Frostproofer/accelerator	Added when cold or frost conditions are expected during the work, to speed up the setting time.
Salt inhibitors	Used to prevent the effects of **efflorescence** from penetrating through from the background surface.
SBR bonding slurry	SBR is the abbreviation for styrene-butadiene rubber. Used to increase the bond on poorly keyed surfaces.

Efflorescence

A white powdery deposit on the surface of plaster containing a high proportion of salt

Additive	Use
Mould remover 	Used on backgrounds or render surfaces that have been affected by mould growth such as fungi, mildew, moss and algae. Mould remover is painted or sprayed onto the affected surface to remove and destroy the mould spores and other airborne particles.

Manufacturers' guidance and instructions should be followed when using additives. Measuring the exact amounts to add to clean water is vital: adding too much or too little will cause the mix to lose its strength and adhesion properties.

STORING MATERIALS

You will need to prepare designated areas for storing bagged materials and containers. Poor housekeeping and stock control can result in waste. Consider a solid flat surface for loose materials such as sand, and make sure it is protected with a good heavy cover. Using **contaminated** materials can adversely affect the work, which will be costly to replace or renew.

New deliveries of materials need to be checked to make sure that the delivered goods match the order regarding quantity and quality. Check use-by dates before signing the delivery note. Any materials that are not accounted for, or are damaged or out of date, will need to be recorded on the delivery note and reported to your supervisor as soon as possible. You can check the shelf life of bagged material by looking at the use-by date on the bag.

Sand can be purchased loose, in bags or in sacks. Sand used in plastering mixes should be protected from leaves or animal contamination as this can affect the binding of the material and quality of the surface finish. A good cover or tarpaulin should also be used to protect from rain water as this can **bulk** the sand in weight. Bulked sand affects its weight and volume, which causes problems with inconsistency when gauging and mixing the render mix.

Cement needs to be stored off the ground, under cover and away from damp conditions; contaminated or out-of-date cement will become hard and lumpy and will result in a weak set. If accidentally used in the render mix it may not bind the sand and the render will lose its initial strength. Using poor quality cement may also cause the surface of the render to become powdery and soft.

ACTIVITY

In groups, look at the different types of additives used for external rendering. Read the instructions on their use and feed back your findings to the whole group.

Contamination

When materials have been in contact with something unclean, eg leaves blown into the sand or dirty water used for mixing

INDUSTRY TIP

Always put new deliveries at the back of the stock pile, ensuring that the older materials are used first. This is known as 'stock rotation'.

Bulking

The swelling of sand when it is wet, making it heavy

Sand in bays

INDUSTRY TIP

Some plasterers doing three coat work will add coarse sand to the dubbing out coat to give it strength.

Bagged cement in storage

ACTIVITY

Make a list of the effects of poor storage of materials such as cement, lime and sand and how they can affect the render mix or surface.

Poor quality materials can result in loss of strength, causing mixes to break down and lose their ability to bond and be compatible with the backgrounds.

SELECTING PRE-FORMED BEADS/TRIMS

You will need to select the appropriate type of pre-formed beads for your rendering work. Each one has a specific purpose and use and will need to be fixed in the correct position.

Type of bead	Use
Angle beads	These are used on corners. They form straight arrises and reinforce a vulnerable corner by protecting it from impact.
Stop beads	These are used when a straight stop edge is required. This could be for rendering up against different surfaces, such as cladding or facing brick.

Type of bead	Use
Expansion beads	These are used along straight joints in brick- or blockwork, allowing for slight movement and preventing cracking.
Render/bell beads	These are fixed to bridge the **damp proof course (DPC)**, window and door heads to act as a drip. They are also used to break down large areas of render into more manageable working areas.

Damp proof course (DPC)

A layer or strip of watertight material placed in a joint of a wall to prevent the passage of water. Fixed at a minimum of 150mm above finished ground level

Beads are manufactured either in stainless steel or plastic and come in various lengths and thicknesses. The different sizes help allow for their use when applying render of different thicknesses. Fixing and positioning beads is explained later on in this chapter.

ACTIVITY

Carry out research into different manufacturers that produce beads and trims, for example Expamet, Catnic, ProBead and Renderplas.

SELECTING TOOLS AND EQUIPMENT

Basic tools and equipment such as the trowel and hawk for laying render on to the background surface will be familiar to you by now. However, there are other tools and equipment that need to be used to carry out rendering work.

Tool	Use
Straight edge/feather edge	Straight edges are used to check backgrounds and rule the render surface, removing any high points and filling out low points. This tool can also be used to form the external angles of the render surface and to form the corners of returns.
Darby	This tool is used for flattening and ruling surfaces. You will need to be competent to use this successfully. It can also be used to form the corners of returns.

Tool	Use
Comb scratcher	Used to key the surface of backing coats.
Float	Used to consolidate the final surface of the render finish, removing any high points and filling in low areas in the render surface. A wooden float was traditionally used to carry out this work; plastic floats are now often used.
Tin snips	Used to cut beads to the required length.
Drum mixer	A strong mechanical robust mixer is required to mix the ingredients to make render.

ACCESS EQUIPMENT

When rendering, it is important that the scaffold platform is suitable for the job in hand. The table below details some of the equipment you may use.

Equipment	Use
Independent scaffold 	This is a good type of scaffold to use when rendering outside surfaces because it is erected away from the wall. It is a sufficiently wide and solid working platform, allowing plenty of room to carry out your work.
Trestle staging 	This is a good scaffold for low level buildings and can be erected and dismantled with ease. A firm, flat base is always required for erecting trestles. Some sites will not allow trestles to be used; you should always check what type of access equipment can be used on the site where you will be working.
Hop-up 	This is a good staging to reach low levels up to roughly 2.4m in height.

For more information on using access equipment safely, refer back to Chapter 1, pages 25–30.

INDUSTRY TIP

Scaffolding erected with a series of platforms to the height of the building is called a scaffold lift.

INDUSTRY TIP

Never work on scaffolding unless it has been erected by a competent person and regularly checked as the work progresses. You should always adhere to the Work at Height Regulations 2005 (as amended) when working from access equipment.

ACTIVITY

Make a list of tools and equipment you would need to apply two coat work to brick or block backgrounds that contain a return, require a **bell cast** above a window, and a **plinth** along the base of the wall at DPC height.

Bell cast

Set above openings and the DPC line to form a drip and deflect rain water away from the wall surface

Plinth

The surface area below the bell cast that runs along the DPC

APPLY RENDER TO EXTERNAL BACKGROUNDS

PLANNING THE WORK SCHEDULE

Before you start work on site, you need to read the risk assessment and method statement in order to minimise any risks involved with the work. This will help prevent any accidents and injuries that could occur during the rendering process. Refer back to Chapter 1, pages 5–6, for more information on risk assessments and method statements.

Although method statements are produced to plan a safe method of work, there are other factors to consider before applying external plain face rendering to background surfaces. Not only will you be working at height but you also need to consider how the climate affects the process and how it may cause damage to the surface of the work. Sometimes weather conditions change in minutes and can have an instant effect, causing a wash-down of the applied surface from rain or surfaces to dry too quickly (which could be a result of applying render in direct sunlight or windy conditions). In the winter you need to be aware of frost and freezing conditions as these will cause the mix to become weak or crumble as the material thaws out.

On some renovation work you also need to consider and plan how to deal with TV aerials, satellite dishes, telephone cables, services and pipes – these will need to be removed while the rendering work takes place and then reattached after the work is complete.

Drains and gullies need to be covered and protected to prevent blockages. Windows, doors and ironmongery will need to be covered with sheeting or cling film to protect them from the render mix.

Unauthorised entry and pedestrian traffic areas are important factors to consider when planning your work. Signs and barriers can be displayed to warn other operatives of possible dangers and that the rendering work is in progress. This will also help avoid accidental impact damage to the surface of the work, which would be difficult to repair and costly to replace. **Hoardings** or fences can be used to cordon off the work area, preventing any trespassers or intruders from entering the work area.

> **INDUSTRY TIP**
>
> Always check the latest weather predictions before you carry out rendering work in case it is likely to affect the finished work.

Protect rendering work with hoardings

> **Hoarding**
>
> Barrier surrounding a site to protect against theft and unauthorised entry

PREPARING BACKGROUND SURFACES

The background surface determines many aspects of the rendering process. Its surface forms the base for the render and if it is deemed weak with a poor key it will not be compatible with the applied mix. It is important to understand that not all backgrounds have the same properties and they need to be prepared using different methods and techniques.

Some backgrounds will be soft and weak, some will be hard and dense, or they may be uneven and require building out. Other backgrounds have low suction or high absorption rates.

Checking suction and absorption will tell you if the background is dry and porous. You can check this by applying water to the background with a splash brush to see how quickly or slowly it is absorbed. No or low suction will indicate that the background is hard or dense.

Applying water with a flat brush

Two coat backgrounds are classed as flat and straight and are finished using two applications of render. Some uneven backgrounds will require an additional coat of render; this is termed as **three coat work** (dubbing out, scratch and finish).

Check the background's surface before starting work and remove any mortar snots that may have been left by the bricklayer when they carried out their brick- or blockwork.

BACKGROUND TYPES

Let's examine the surface characteristics of different backgrounds in more detail.

Three coat work

When plastering exteriors, this is applying three distinct layers of render dubbing out/pricking up, scratch and finish render surface

Mechanical fixings

Fixings used to fix EML to composite backgrounds

Type of background	Comment
Composite backgrounds 	Composite backgrounds (backgrounds made up of two or more materials) will need to be prepared with stainless steel EML fixed using **mechanical fixings** and plugs; this will reinforce the render when it is applied to the background, creating a strong surface.

Type of background	Comment
Stone or slate backgrounds 	This is another background that cannot be completed in two coats due to its unevenness, with deep crevasses and recesses that will require dubbing out. Stone and slate have poor key and will need to be prepared by applying a bonding slurry on their faces to improve adhesion when rendering.
Clay bricks 	Clay bricks were very popular at one time and can be found in all types of buildings. A common fault with clay bricks is that they would shell their face, causing the plaster to 'blow' (come away from the background). This background is often uneven due to the fact that the bricks were manufactured in kilns at great heat which made them all a slightly different shape. They were then laid on a lime mortar bed, which is very weak. Clay bricks and lime mortar joints have a high absorption rate that will cause high suction levels. This surface will need to be treated with a bonding adhesive before plastering. Raking out the joints will also improve the key.
Concrete bricks 	These bricks are made from concrete aggregate mixed with cement. This surface is smooth and hard which means the key is poor and the suction is minimal. A bonding agent is best suited for this surface.
Engineering bricks 	This is a hard, dense surface with poor key and no absorption rate. The face of the brick has a glossy surface that makes it difficult to prepare for plastering. It has an enamel look and no suction. This surface needs to be scabbled or roughened to remove the sheen and then an **external slurry** can be applied. Alternatively, you can fix sheets of **EML** to its surface with mechanical fixings – this is a good way to reinforce and form a key on the background.

External slurry

Thin, sloppy mixture of cement and bonding adhesive applied to backgrounds in order to bond render to its surface

EML

Sheet material in the form of diamond-shaped mesh that is used to reinforce a surface. This material can be fixed with screws and plugs, galvanised nails or it can be bedded into the render material

Type of background	Comment
New blockwork 	Newly constructed buildings that have block walling need little preparation before you apply plaster to their surface because they have medium to adequate key. Water can be applied in warm humid conditions to prevent the render from drying out too quickly. The surface is flat and can be rendered using traditional or modern pre-mixed materials. Block walling built to today's specifications and standards need only a scratch coat and finish; this is known as two coat work.

USING BONDING AGENTS

There will be occasions when you will need to prepare the background surface to improve its adhesive properties, otherwise the external render will not bond and will become loose. This would risk developing severe cracks that become widespread over the surface.

ACTIVITY

List five areas or surfaces that would need to be protected on an external contract before applying slurry.

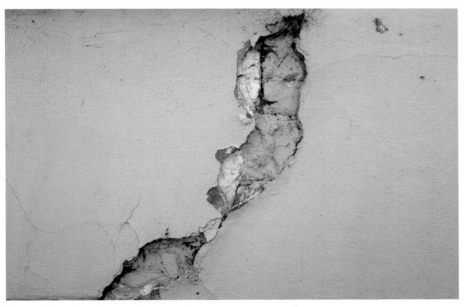

External render with surface cracks

Applying spatterdash to a common brick wall to create a textured surface

Reading the specification will provide you with specific details and descriptions about the background surface and how it needs to be prepared before applying the render. Instructions on mixing and applying bonding agents can be obtained from data sheets; you will need to carefully follow these to avoid breakdown between surfaces and also to prevent invalidating the guarantee of the rendering work.

There are some bonding agents that can be applied to surfaces and left with a textured surface, which forms a good key.

ACTIVITY

Carry out a simple bonding test on a brick surface using different bonding agents. Mix the slurry and apply it onto the brick face, then apply the render while the slurry is still tacky and leave for three days to cure. Repeat the process but this time use the brush to form a stipple pattern with the slurry and leave it to dry on the brick face overnight. Your tutor will help you set up this task.

SBR container

Polymer

Strong glue-like substance used for improving adhesion of render surfaces

Glues are now added to spatterdash slurries

SBR bonding slurry

We touched on SBR on page 208. It is a strong bonding agent that is mixed with 1 part SBR to 2 parts cement to make a bonding slurry. This type of slurry is applied to the background and while it is still tacky the scratch coat mix is applied over the top of it to ensure a good bond between the background and the applied material.

Applying SBR slurry

Polymer-based bonding adhesives

There are many types of **polymer**-based bonding adhesives on the market today, specially designed to overcome problems with adhesion. They contain polymers that have been tested in laboratories to enhance their performance, providing added insurance and a manufacturer's guarantee. Manufacturers' instructions and data sheets provide simple user guides with instructions on mixing and application. Failing to follow these will invalidate the guarantee and cause a breakdown in adhesion between the applied material and the background.

A traditional method for bonding surfaces was to use a spatterdash slurry. This is a mixture of cement and sharp sand made into a slurry and then thrown onto the background with a paddle or small shovel. In more recent years, glues were added to increase and improve the bonding properties.

SETTING UP EQUIPMENT

Reading the specification will help you to set up before mixing, and having the necessary tools and equipment to hand will make the process simpler to complete. You will need equipment for:

- mixing, handling and lifting, such as buckets and tubs

- transporting, such as wheelbarrows and shovels

- access, including scaffolding and ladders

- storing waste, such as skips or bins.

Equipment for external rendering: wheelbarrow, shovel and skip

The next stage is to prepare for mixing, which will include mixing and gauging different materials and additives to specified ratios.

MIXING EQUIPMENT

A mechanical drum mixer (see page 137) powered by electricity or fuel is best for mixing render materials. The mixer should be set up in a designated mixing area away from traffic and pedestrian routes. A suitable place for this work is outside the building and as close to the work as possible, with good access for transporting the render mix.

The materials should be **gauged** and measured in buckets or a purpose-made box to ensure consistent quality and strength throughout the mixing process. Mixing materials such as cement and lime outside can help reduce dust inhalation, but you also need to wear the appropriate safety equipment to protect your lungs and eyes.

Gauging

The technical term for measuring materials

Water and power are essential for mixing efficiently. Storing materials such as sand close to the mixer will reduce physical labour and increase efficiency. Before you start the mixing process, make sure that the mixer you will be using is well maintained and fit for purpose.

MIXING METHOD

Two coat work would normally be mixed to the following ratios:

- *Scratch coat*: 4 parts of sand to 1 part of cement with waterproofer additive.

- *Top coat*: 5 parts of sand, 1 part of cement and ½ part of hydrated lime with a plasticiser additive.

The architect is responsible for designing and writing the specification and will decide the ratio for the mix.

The following step-by-step instructions show you the method for mixing by machine, using the ratio 4 parts sand and 1 part cement with waterproofer.

STEP 1 Set up the mechanical mixer in the designated area. Set up the other equipment and materials near to the mixing area.

STEP 2 Fill a bucket with clean water, add the required amount of waterproofer and mix.

STEP 3 Pour some of the water into the mixer.

STEP 4 Fill one bucket full of cement and add it to the mixer.

STEP 5 Fill four buckets full of sand and add them into the mixer.

STEP 6 Let the mix turn slightly dry rather than wet in consistency for a couple of minutes and the mix will become workable.

STEP 7 When the mix is ready, place it in a clean wheelbarrow and transport it to the work area.

STEP 8 Set up the spot board and stand and soak the board. Empty the mix from the wheelbarrow onto the spot board and you're ready to go.

Accurate gauging of materials and additives reduces the possibility of incorrect ratios, which cause poor surface finishes, and variable strength and colour in mixes.

PRE-MIXED RENDERS

Modern plastering methods and materials have helped to change the way plasterers work. Pre-mixed renders in sealed bags come in a range of different colours that have been specially designed. These renders are less problematic because they have been manufactured and batched in specialised processing plants. Before being bagged they undergo vigorous checks to make sure they meet industry standards. Another benefit of using these renders is that they carry a manufacturer's guarantee (as long as they have been applied in accordance with the installation guidelines provided by the manufacturing company).

Pre-mixed render for external rendering

APPLYING TWO COAT RENDERING

Let's look at the process of applying plain face rendering using two coat work on brick or block backgrounds. This is completed in three stages.

STAGE 1: APPLYING THE SCRATCH COAT

The first application of render for two coat work is known as the scratch coat. This is normally gauged and mixed 4 parts sand to 1 part cement. A waterproofer additive is measured and mixed with the water to form a waterproof barrier in the render when it has set.

The scratch coat provides the base for the top coat and is applied about 9–12mm thick. However, the thickness depends on the unevenness of the background. In some instances the mix can be made stronger, especially if exposed to open areas with severe climate conditions.

If you rule the scratch coat, this will make the base even and easier to apply the top coat to with an average thickness. It also helps the top coat dry evenly, allowing you adequate time to form the finish. Be careful when applying the render because applying it too thickly may cause it to sag and slide.

STEP 1 Check for suction by wetting the background. Set up the spot board and load it with material.

STEP 2 Using a low level working platform, apply the render material, starting from the right-hand side and laying on a trowel length at a time. Spread the render from side to side, flattening the surface to a thickness of roughly 10mm.

STEP 3 Check the surface with a straight edge and remove any high points.

STEP 4 Once you have finished a section of the wall, key the surface using a comb scratcher.

STEP 5 After completing the wall, use the gauging trowel to remove any render that is left on the floor.

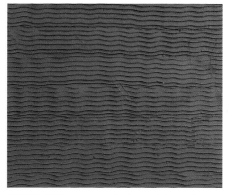

STEP 6 The completed scratch coat surface.

Once you have applied the scratch coat, clean the work area and leave the scratch coat to dry. You will need to let the render surface dry for a couple of days before you start the next stage.

STAGE 2: FIXING THE BELL BEAD

The next stage is to fix the different types of pre-formed beads or trims. Their positions are shown on the working drawing. The total number of beads required for a contract will be listed in the schedule. Relevant data sheets should be referred to and will provide information on precise installation and fixing procedures.

Pre-formed beads

The specification will give specified makes and designs of the beads. They should be made from plastic or stainless steel; galvanised products should be avoided for external work as the coating can wear and corrode, which can cause rust stains in the work.

Bell beads are used to form a bell cast. The purpose of the bell cast is to form a drip along the bottom of the wall, directing rain water away from the render surface below the DPC.

There are two methods for forming the bell cast: with timber battens alone or by using timber battens with pre-made bell beads resting on top.

With both methods the timber batten first needs to be fixed along a level line. Render can be applied to the timber along the length, forming a slight curve on the wall about 150mm from the approximate depth of the curve formed by the bell cast shape, and left to set overnight before removing the timber.

Timber batten used to form a bell cast

Forming the angle at the bell cast with a timber batten

Completed bell cast in place

If using bell beads, this would involve resting and fixing a plastic or stainless steel bead along the timber batten fixed or bedded into position and then rendered to form the bell cast. Before fixing, tin snips and a tape measure are used to cut the bead to the required length and angle of cut. Bell beads are also used above window and door openings for the same reason and provide a rigid fixed profile line to finish the render.

Fixing beads along the timber batten

STEP 1 Using a pencil, mark the position for fixing the bell bead on one side of the wall. This could be 300mm off the floor.

STEP 2 Using a level and straight edge, transfer a level line from the marked point.

STEP 3 Fix a timber batten along the line.

STEP 4 Rest the bell bead along the timber. At this point the bead will need to be fixed with nails, fixed mechanically with screws or bedded with render mix.

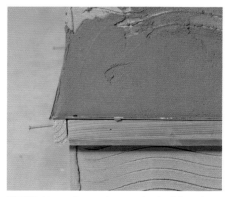

STEP 5 Apply render to the bell bead and form the bell cast shape, cutting back about 10mm along the edge of the bead to allow for the application of the top coat.

STEP 6 The completed bell cast, keyed with the comb scratcher.

Forming timber bell casts above windows

There are several methods used to form drips above openings such as windows and doors, using timber rules or roofing battens instead of using pre-made beads. One method is to cut the timber and notch both ends, allowing the bell cast to project about 75mm away past the reveal.

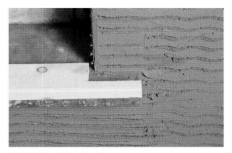

Notching the timber

Notched timber bell cast in position

The other method is to position a timber batten on its edge along the head of the window or opening.

Timber batten fixed on edge

Forming the bell cast up to the timber batten

Both methods need to be supported from below by using timber struts when forming the bell cast. The underside **soffit** would then be finished plain and smooth once the timber has been removed.

STAGE 3: FORMING THE PLAIN FACE FINISH

The top coat is the final coat and will need to be applied and ruled to **tolerances** and standards set out in the specification, which will test your skill. This type of finish will look poor if not ruled accurately; an uneven surface will cast shadows when the sun glares on its face. The same procedure for setting up should be followed as for Stage 1.

The mix for this application includes cement, lime and sand. The ratio is normally 6 parts sand, 1 part cement and 1 part lime, with a plasticiser additive included to improve the mix's workability. Hydrated lime does not set but is added to reduce shrinkage and improve the mix's workability, making it fatty and good for spreading and ruling. Plasticiser also helps improve the workability of the mix; without this the mix would be heavy, dense and very difficult to apply and spread.

INDUSTRY TIP

When consolidating the surface with a float, the sides of internal angles should be formed and finished at different times because the float will dig in and distort the opposite side when consolidating and finishing the face of the work. The opposite side should be left until the following day, leaving the surface to set hard. This will get the internal angle looking straight and sharp.

Soffit

The underside of a window or door opening

Tolerance

Required standards and accuracy of completed work

Top coat

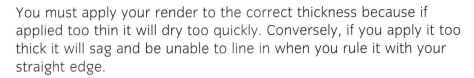

You must apply your render to the correct thickness because if applied too thin it will dry too quickly. Conversely, if you apply it too thick it will sag and be unable to line in when you rule it with your straight edge.

The surface of the render will need to be rubbed and **consolidated** with a plastic or wooden float. This is carried out while the surface is starting to set. A good way to do this is to have some render on your hawk which can be used when you rub the face with the float, filling in minor defects or holes as you finish the surface. If you time this right then the surface will look straight, flat and plain.

If the render dries and sets inconsistently it may be difficult to form the finish and get a uniform appearance to the surface. Poorly prepared surfaces that dry too quickly result in dark sandy appearances that stand out on the face of the render due to over consolidating.

Consolidate

To close in the surface of a floating coat, render or floor screed with a float, which can make the surface flat, dense and compact

INDUSTRY TIP

Care must be taken when using additives with the mix: adding too much will weaken the mix and cause the face of the finish to crack or crumble.

STEP 1 Apply the render mix onto the surface, working from the top right corner. Complete a section of work roughly a metre square or an area that you can rule with a straight edge or darby.

STEP 2 Rule the surface with a straight edge or darby, filling in any hollows as the work proceeds.

STEP 3 Continue to work along the top of the wall, applying and ruling from your previously laid section.

STEP 4 Before you finish, check that the surface is flat and that it lines in with the straight edge.

STEP 5 Complete the bottom part of the wall just above the bell cast and proceed to the other end, using the straight edge or darby to rule and check that the surface is straight.

STEP 6 Apply the render to the bell cast, forming a slight angle in the wall's surface at this level. A darby is best used along this area to make sure the surface is flat.

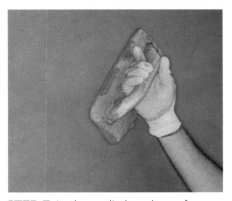

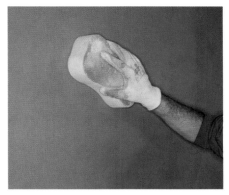

STEP 7 As the applied render surface starts to pull in and set, consolidate the surface with a plastic float to obtain a smooth, plain finish.

STEP 8 A sponge can then be rubbed lightly over the face of the finished surface.

APPLYING EXTERNAL RENDER TO RETURNS USING TWO COAT WORK

Applying render using a scratch and float finish to a return or a pillar can sometimes be a difficult technique to learn if using traditional handheld methods for forming the corner. There are several ways to form the corner of the return, which include forming and finishing two angles at the same time (unless using and fixing pre-made angle beads).

Reverse rule method

One method of forming the angle is to hold a straight edge along the edge of the return to the required thickness of the scratch coat, checking for plumb with a level. Apply the render to the edge and flatten the surface, then key with a comb scratcher, working away from the edge. Remove the straight edge by tilting one side and repeat the process on the other side. This is known as forming the corner free hand or the 'reverse rule' method.

Removing the straight edge

The following step-by-step instructions show you how to form a return to a pillar (ie the top coat finish). This activity needs two people to complete it.

STEP 1 Hold a straight edge to the face of the reveal to a thickness of 10mm, making sure with a spirit level that its position is plumb.

STEP 2 Apply the render mix up to the edge, starting from the top, and rule the surface with a darby or small straight edge. Do not work down to the bell cast at this stage.

STEP 3 Once the face has been ruled, remove the straight edge and clean its face.

STEP 4 Place the straight edge on the other face to the same thickness as the previous one.

STEP 5 Apply the render mix up to the edge and rule the surface with a darby or small straight edge. Do not work down to the bell cast at this stage.

STEP 6 Tilt the straight edge and slide away from the angle. This should leave it sharp.

STEP 7 Form the bell cast in the same way, then leave to set before the next step.

STEP 8 Once the render surface has begun to set and pull in, rub up the face and consolidate the surface with a float.

STEP 9 Hold the straight edge to within 1mm along the edge line and rub up to the edge with the float, consolidating and forming the finish. Again, do not go down to the bell cast until both sides of the return have been finished.

STEP 10 Place the straight edge on the opposite side and repeat the process. Once complete, tilt and remove the straight edge carefully to leave a sharp arris along the edge.

STEP 11 A small plain timber batten can be used to form the edge of the bell, using the same procedure as above.

External angles can also be formed with angle beads which make this job simple and easy to achieve. They can be fixed to the corner, forming and reinforcing a sharp arris that allows you to apply your render and finish flush and flat to the edge of the bead. Once the bead is fixed it will not move, making it easier to apply your render against a solid corner profile.

Fixing angle beads to an external corner

Stop beads are useful profiles that allow the render finish to be stopped against the edge of different surfaces such as face brickwork, timber or plastic cladding. The principle for fixing is the same as for angle beads. Again, once they have been covered with the render material they can't be moved or repositioned so care must be taken when fixing, making sure with a straight edge that the edge of the bead is aligned.

Expansion beads are fixed to straight joints of brick- and blockwork. They allow for slight movement, preventing the surface cracking. Two stop beads are used side by side with a gap in between. It is quite common today to have expansion joints in buildings, especially if the building has a steel frame that contracts and expands.

Plumbing and aligning the edge of a stop bead with a straight edge and level

Expansion beads

Window bands and quoins

External render features

External render features are a good example of how smooth render can be used as a raised feature to produce a classical and elegant look to the wall surface.

Window reveals and heads are rendered smooth, forming a sharp edge for different external renders such as pebble dash and rough cast.

OUR HOUSE

Look at 'Our House' and calculate:

- how many lengths of bell beads are required to form the bell cast at the base of the house
- how many lengths of stop beads are required to form a stop at the height where the facing brick starts above the blockwork
- how many lengths of angle beads are required for each external angle (all beads measure 2.4m)
- the amount of pre-mixed undercoat that would need to be applied at 10mm thick (1 bag covers 1m²)
- the amount of pre-mixed top coat required to form a plain face finish at 10mm thick (1 bag covers 1m²).

Smooth rendering around a window reveal and soffit

COMMON FAULTS IN EXTERNAL RENDERING

Faults occur in plastering work due to a number of factors and issues. The table below describes some faults that can happen in external rendering.

Fault	Description
Poorly prepared backgrounds	Render applied to background surfaces should be slightly weaker; applying render that is stronger than the background will cause stress, leading the plaster to crack and blow.
	Backgrounds that have poor adhesion and low suction will not bond and the render will become loose in time.
	Render mixes applied over high-suction backgrounds will lose their moisture content too quickly and produce a fine crazing surface.

Fault	Description
Climate conditions	Hot and cold climate conditions can affect the set of render mixes in different ways.
	Mixing in freezing conditions will affect the strength of the mix and cause the mix to crumble when set.
	Lime blooming is a phenomenon that can affect the early stage of curing of cement render in damp or cold conditions.
	Applying render in direct sunlight should be avoided as this can draw moisture from the applied render mix, causing it to crumble and become weak.
	Hot conditions can remove the moisture content from the mix; this will affect the **curing** process and can weaken the mix.
	Rain and frost can cause damage to the surface and strength of the render.
Over mixing or using contaminated water	Over mixing rendering materials or using contaminated water affects the setting process and can cause the mix to lose its strength, causing the surface to become powdery.
	Using contaminated water can affect the strength and cause inconsistent colour or colour deterioration.
Incorrect gauging	Incorrect gauging of rendering materials will cause mixes to be inconsistent and have different strengths.

Curing

Allowing the render mix to set and reach its full or maximum strength

Case Study: Chris

When Chris worked for a local building company as a plastering supervisor, one of his duties was to carry out a rendering survey on a detached bungalow in order for the company to tender for re-rendering.

When Chris arrived on site he noticed that the plaster was loose and that it had severe cracks. It would need to be hacked and re-rendered. When Chris removed some of the loose plaster it revealed a lightweight block surface which immediately told him that the background properties were weaker than the render mix. The strength of the mix had caused stress on the background and it had blown from the surface in places. The window reveals had also corroded and had rust staining on the surface of the render caused by using the incorrect type of metal bead.

Chris wrote his report and stated that the background would need to have stainless steel EML mechanically fixed to its surface in order to reinforce it, making it suitable to receive a two coat cement based render. It would also require either plastic or stainless steel bell beads and angle beads to all openings, including reveals and soffits.

During Chris's visit he was able to determine access for scaffolding and identify clear labour and pedestrian routes in order to carry out the job safely. He also made enquiries to the client about services and a designated mixing area.

Chris advised the client to use a pre-mixed render finish which comes in a range of colours and would not need painting. This would ensure a low-maintenance solution. It would also benefit the company, as space for mixing was restricted and it would take less room than mixing a range of traditional render ingredients.

Work through the following questions to check your learning.

1   The reason for applying external rendering to a building is to

   a   prevent stains appearing

   b   prevent paint flaking

   c   prevent uneven surface

   d   prevent water ingress.

2   Dubbing out coats are applied to

   a   uneven backgrounds

   b   flat backgrounds

   c   straight surfaces

   d   poor surfaces.

3   Waterproofer is added to the mix to prevent

   a   quick curing

   b   fast drying

   c   penetrating damp

   d   moisture rising.

4   Renders can be keyed using a

   a   comb scratcher

   b   gauging trowel

   c   bucket trowel

   d   mixing tool.

5   Bonding agents are used to improve

   a   curing

   b   strength

   c   adhesion

   d   consistency.

6   Which one of the following is known as a binder when mixing render?

   a   Sand.

   b   Cement.

   c   Additive.

   d   Inhibitor.

7   Manufacturers' instructions will provide information on

   a   binders

   b   aggregates

   c   application

   d   wastage.

8   Mixing render with contaminated water will affect the mix's

   a   strength

   b   application

   c   thickness

   d   evenness.

9   The number of pre-formed beads needed for a rendering contract can be found on the

   a   schedule

   b   data sheet

   c   specification

   d   bill of quantities.

10   When measuring quantities of materials, measurements are taken from the

   a   method statement

   b   schedule

   c   risk assessment

   d   drawing.

11   Which one of the following tools is used for ruling the surface of external render before it can be finished?

   a   Boat level.

   b   Adjustable staff.

   c   Straight edge.

   b   Timber batten.

12 Pre-mixed render is consistent in

a strength

b thickness

c application

d suction.

13 External render returns or reveals can be formed with which one of the following?

a Angle tool.

b Angle guide.

c Long timber staff.

d Plane timber rule.

14 External render material that sags after application is a result of being applied

a too thin

b too thick

c from the top

d from the bottom.

15 Which one of the following floats is used to form plain face rendering?

a Plastic.

b Sponge.

c Devil.

d Setting.

16 Render surfaces are keyed to

a prevent suction

b allow the next coat to bond

c prevent adhesion

d improve workability.

17 External render bell casts are used to form

a an arris

b an edge

c a recess

d a drip.

18 External renders are **best** mixed using a

a drill and whisk

b mechanical drum mixer

c plunger

d bucket trowel.

19 When gauging render material for consistency and strength it is **best** done with a

a paddle

b bucket

c shovel

d scoop.

20 External render mixes applied to the background surface **must** be

a bulky

b fatty

c stronger

d compatible.

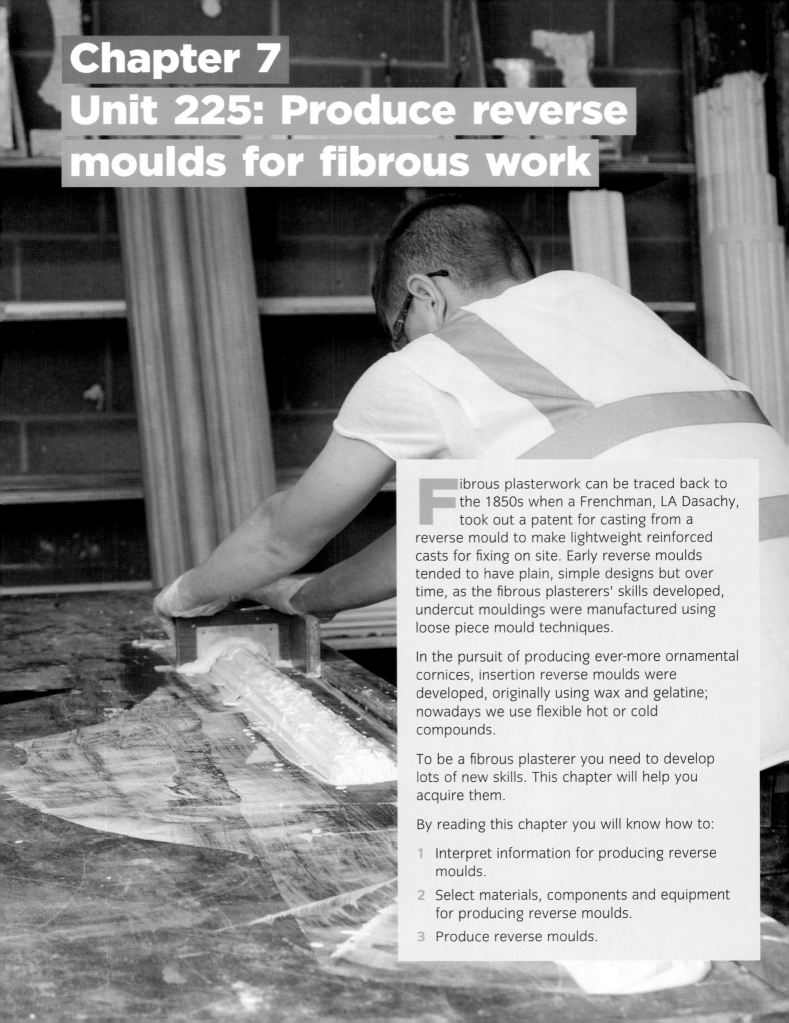

Chapter 7
Unit 225: Produce reverse moulds for fibrous work

Fibrous plasterwork can be traced back to the 1850s when a Frenchman, LA Dasachy, took out a patent for casting from a reverse mould to make lightweight reinforced casts for fixing on site. Early reverse moulds tended to have plain, simple designs but over time, as the fibrous plasterers' skills developed, undercut mouldings were manufactured using loose piece mould techniques.

In the pursuit of producing ever-more ornamental cornices, insertion reverse moulds were developed, originally using wax and gelatine; nowadays we use flexible hot or cold compounds.

To be a fibrous plasterer you need to develop lots of new skills. This chapter will help you acquire them.

By reading this chapter you will know how to:

1 Interpret information for producing reverse moulds.

2 Select materials, components and equipment for producing reverse moulds.

3 Produce reverse moulds.

INTERPRETING INFORMATION

SPECIFICATIONS AND WORKING DRAWINGS

Architectural technician

A draftsperson who works in an architectural practice. They usually prepare the location drawings for a building and detailed drawing for the making of fibrous plasterwork

Examples of fibrous plasterwork

INDUSTRY TIP

On site, if you have a verbal instruction, is it best to have it confirmed in writing, because messages passed on verbally are open to interpretation.

INDUSTRY TIP

The size and shape of the mould outline can be found on the working drawings: no working drawings are available, ie if you are working in an old property, then you can match the pattern by taking a **squeeze** from the original plasterwork.

Squeeze

A way of reproducing a mould outline. It can be taken using clay, a pin template, using plaster to a greased original or making a fine cut into a cornice and inserting a piece of card and copying the outline shape. A zinc template can then be made

Detailed drawing

A drawing that shows the profile or design of plaster moulding in negative or positive view

Profile

The shape and pattern of a mould outline

In order to accurately make and fix into position a manufactured item of fibrous plasterwork, you need to first interpret information from a specification and its associated working drawings. These documents are produced by members of the building team, such as the architect, quantity surveyor and structural engineer. The cornice designer will usually work directly for the architect or **architectural technician**, and the designs will be based on the client's original brief.

Other important information that can be found in the specification and the working drawings includes:

- an overview of the site and any details that may restrict access to the site

- availability of services such as water, gas, electricity and communication systems

- the required standard of workmanship (eg materials to be used, sizes, tolerances, quality)

- information regarding nominated contractors/suppliers and performance criteria.

When preparing to make a reverse mould and take a plaster cast, the plasterer should review the contract specification and the working drawings alongside the manufacturer's literature. This is to check that the finished item can be made and that the materials specified by the architect are suitable for the job in hand. For example, the architect might have specified a timber lath for the new cast, whereas a stainless steel rod or expanded metal would be more suitable. In this instance, a company representative such as the manager of the company would arrange a meeting with the architect to discuss possible amendments to the contract information. The meeting would be documented with a new drawing and specification issued afterwards; the contract value would be adjusted to allow for the extra cost of the material, if significant.

The main drawings used by a fibrous plaster will be:

- **detailed drawings**, for the manufacture of the running mould, including the zinc or aluminium **profile**

- an assembly drawing for the fixing of the cornice into position on site.

The scales used on the drawings will vary depending upon the size and shape of the cornice profile. Typically scales will range between 1:1 (full size), 1:10, 1:20 and 1:50. (Refer back to Chapter 2 for other types of drawings used to communicate information.)

The fixing team will use a document called a schedule; this identifies where the fibrous items are to be fixed. Schedules are covered in Chapter 2, pages 54–55.

MANUFACTURERS' SPECIFICATIONS

When producing a contract specification, an architect will refer to the manufacturers' specifications. These are usually on the back of bags of plaster, on the side of containers of additives such as PVA (polyvinyl acetate), and in manufacturers' literature (which can be found online).

The manufacturer's specification will give information such as:

- a product description

- how to apply the material

- technical data, including limitations on use

- how to dispose of waste material in a safe and environmentally friendly manner

- any health and safety considerations while using the material.

If you look at a manufacturer's specification for Class A plaster, for example, it will give the chemical composition of the plaster ($CaSO_4$ $\frac{1}{2}H_2O$), the hardness of the plaster and the required water to plaster ratio.

ACTIVITY

You have a responsibility for health and safety in the workplace. Enter 'fine casting plaster MSDS' into an internet search engine. Print off a relevant health and safety data sheet and identify any hazards that may affect you and others on site.

WHAT IS A REVERSE MOULD?

Running moulds fall into two basic categories:

- *Positive running moulds* are used to produce a section of the mould on a bench or **in situ**.

- *Reverse or negative moulds* are run on a bench and a positive plaster cast is taken from the reverse mould.

Reverse moulds are moulds that are the 'back to front' version of the shape or pattern that you want to produce.

In situ

When a plaster moulding is run directly to the background, using a positive profile

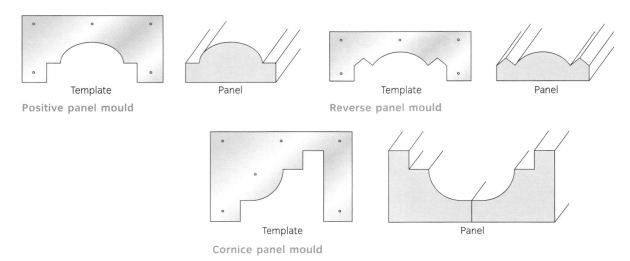

Template
Positive panel mould

Panel

Template

Reverse panel mould

Panel

Template

Cornice panel mould

Panel

The profile designer who creates the detailed drawing and the plasterer who will manufacture and fix the final item must both have the ability to interpret the drawing and visualise the finished product. The plasterer must also have the skills to accurately transfer geometric mould outlines from a drawing onto a sheet of zinc or aluminium.

The geometrical shapes used for most plaster mouldings are based on classic Roman or Greek architecture. They are based on circles and fillets drawn within a series of boxes that are proportional.

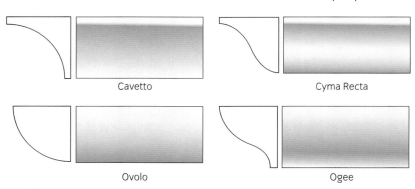

Cavetto

Cyma Recta

Ovolo

Ogee

Moulding outlines

When drawings are not available, for example when working for a domestic client, the plasterer will be required to reproduce the profile from an existing cornice. This can be achieved in a number of ways:

Profile gauge

- taking a plaster squeeze

- using a pin profiler/profile gauge to form the shape of the cornice profile

- cutting into the existing moulding using a fine-toothed saw, inserting a sheet of card and drawing around the profile onto the card

- cutting a small section out of the cornice and transferring the shape directly to a sheet of zinc or aluminium.

Once the fibrous casts have been made, it is good practice to let them hang for a few days so that excess water can evaporate. This helps prevent the casts from distorting. The fibrous items can then be protected, ready for delivery to the site.

CALCULATING QUANTITIES

There are many factors to consider when ordering materials for making fibrous work, including the width, depth and length of the reverse mould or fibrous cast. Many different materials are used in the process of manufacturing a reverse and cornice, such as:

- Class A plaster
- a retarder, such as glue size or trisodium citrate (sodium citrate)
- tallow
- a timber lath
- plywood or timber
- hessian
- fibreglass
- sheet zinc or aluminium
- small tacks
- drywall or wood screws
- shellac.

See later in this chapter (pages 284–285) for more information about glue size and trisodium citrate.

Sometimes you will need to work out the individual cost of an item that is normally sold in packs, including the VAT cost and any delivery costs. Let's look at an example.

ACTIVITY

Using the internet or trade catalogues, find the price and weight of a bag of fine casting plaster.

Example

If a bundle of 100 laths costs £33.00, how much does each lath cost if you also add VAT at 20% and £15.00 for delivery of the bundle?

Step 1

Work out the cost for the bundle with VAT. In your calculator enter the bundle cost and multiply it by itself plus 20%, which is written as '1.20'.

33 × 1.20 = £39.60

Step 2

Add the delivery charge to the total cost so far:

39.60 + 15 = £54.60

Step 3

Divide the total cost by the total number of items in the bundle:

54.60 ÷ 100 = 0.546

Round this up to the nearest pence and the answer is **55p per lath**.

SELECTING MATERIALS, COMPONENTS AND EQUIPMENT

PLANT AND EQUIPMENT TO RUN A PLASTER REVERSE MOULD

The majority of fibrous work is carried out in a plasterer's fibrous workshop. Ideally this will have adequate space to store all the materials used to produce moulding work, as well as drying areas for the finished work. If hot pour compounds are to be used, a fan-assisted ventilation system should also be installed to extract the hot fumes.

To produce fibrous work a plasterer needs a strong workbench to support the weight of the materials used. Traditionally a plasterer's bench was made with solid timber legs and an overboarded top which recieved 50–75mm of casting plaster, producing a hard flat surface.

A plasterer's bench

Nowadays, most plasterers workbenches still have solid timber legs but have 18–25mm thick marine plywood instead of the plaster tops. The most common top size is 1.2m × 2.4m, although the size of the top really depends on the type of work carried out. You could just as easily run a reverse cornice mould from a laminated surface like a worktop.

The essentials of a plasterer's bench are that:

- it is large enough to produce the item required

- it has running rules either side of the bench, made from timber or metal

- if the surface is porous it has been sealed with at least three coats of shellac

- it is sturdy and sits level on the floor.

Some plastering workshops like to use plaster bins for the daily use for fibrous work as they keep the plaster dry and promote an organised working environment.

Plaster bin

HOT MELT COMPOUNDS

Flexible compounds are used to produce ornate plasterwork. They are made out of polyvinyl chloride (PVC), which is a **thermoplastic** material. This means it has to be heated up to between 140–170°C to become a liquid. Always read the manufacturer's instructions for the melting point of the compound.

Once the compound has reached temperature, pour the melted compound into a galvanised bucket and leave to stand for about a minute or so. This allows any air bubbles trapped in the liquid to **dissipate**. The hot compound is then poured over a plaster/clay model surrounded by a temporary fence or a through metal funnel if the model is surrounded by a plaster case. As the compound cools it starts to solidify, forming a flexible rubber compound. The hot melt compound should be left overnight to cool off. Hot melt compounds are environmentally friendly as the compound can be re-melted to produce new flexible rubber moulds.

Thermoplastic

A characteristic of material meaning that it can be re-melted

Dissipate

To disappear

GRADES OF HOT MELT COMPOUND

There are three basic grades of PVC; each manufacturer will have their own colour schemes to designate their grade. We are using Vinamold for our examples.

- Vinamold Red is a general-purpose PVC and the most flexible compound, suitable for most plaster applications.

Vinamold

- Vinamold White is both flexible and tough, so it is ideal for concrete and polyester resin.

- Vinamold Yellow is the least flexible of the three, so it is used with large moulds and thin sections, and is recommended for use with all casting materials.

Different grades can be mixed together if required, for example if you are running short of materials or are just topping up – the different grades are compatible with each other when heated.

HOW TO USE HOT MELT COMPOUNDS

Follow the steps below when using hot melt compounds.

1 Check that the heating equipment has a current PAT label.

2 Visually check the heating equipment before switching it on. Ideally the heating equipment should be situated under an extractor system, or at least in a restricted, safe and ventilated area.

3 Set the thermostat to the manufacturer's recommended melting point.

4 Estimate the amount of PVC that you will need to complete the pour in one attempt.

5 Cut the PVC into small cubes, about 25mm^2, as this helps the melting process.

6 Remove any air present in the plaster model by pre-soaking it in water. Do not over soak as any visible water on the model surface will be detrimental.

7 Depending on the style and size of the model, form a fence or a case around the model. This is a dangerous operation: ensure you wear appropriate heat-resistant PPE including arm-length gauntlet gloves.

8 Pour the hot melt compound (HMC) into a metal bucket and allow it to stand for a few minutes to lose heat. The cooling lets any bubbles in the HMC dissipate. If you pour too quickly any air bubbles present will appear on the flexible mould.

9 Then pour the hot PVC liquid in one continuous stream, from the lowest point of the model.

Case moulds

If pouring rubber into a case mould, place a funnel at the base of the model. The length of the funnel must be higher than the model otherwise the rubber will not rise to the top. Breather holes at the top of the case will ensure that the HMC will push to the top. Cap off the breather holes with clay when the rubber has cooled down.

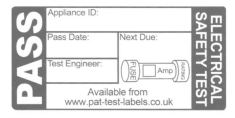

PAT label

INDUSTRY TIP

Minimise any possible suction to a bare plaster model by soaking it in water.

HMC heater

Flood moulds

If pouring rubber into a flood mould, remember to make sure that all the porous surfaces have been sealed with a suitable sealer. Pour a steady continuous stream of rubber at the lowest point at the base of the model until the rubber is a few millimetres short of the clay, plasterboard or timber fence that surrounds the model. Once the rubber is set, carefully remove the fence and the rubber from the model and wash the rubber reverse. Plaster casts can then be taken using one gauge of casting plaster.

COLD POUR COMPOUNDS

Cold pour uses a flexible silicone two-part moulding compound consisting of a colour-coded liquid and a **catalyst** to visually aid thorough mixing. It is important to read the manufacturer's instructions before mixing as each silicone compound will have a different mix ratio depending on the weight of the material. Working time can vary from 15 minutes up to 90 minutes depending on the selected silicone. Curing/de-mould time is at least 10 hours for most silicone compounds.

Catalyst

Commonly used when using fibreglass materials or cold pour rubber, the catalyst in liquid form is carefully measured into the bulking liquid. It reacts with the other liquid: in fibreglass it hardens, whereas in cold pour it forms the liquid into a flexible rubber

Cold pour rubber compound

Latex rubber is also a cold pour compound. This material does not use a catalyst to activate the set and is brushed over the model to build up as many coats as required. Because of its **thixotropic** properties it can be applied vertically.

Thixotropic

Material that remains in a liquid state in its container, but when brushed vertically or horizontally forms into a gel-like state and hardens into position

RUNNING MOULDS

MATERIALS

Running moulds are constructed from timber. They use a **zinc** or aluminium template that forms the profile shape of the moulding. You will need the following materials to make a running mould.

Zinc

A non-ferrous metal, zinc is easy to cut and forms its own protective layer called patina, so it does not rust

Material	Use
Timber or plywood	To make the running mould.
Zinc or aluminium	To make running mould profiles.
Small tacks or panel pins	Used to fasten zinc profiles to timber.
Drywall or wood screws Wood screw	To assemble running moulds.
Shellac	To seal porous plaster.

TOOLS

You will need a workbench with a vice to hold the timber and zinc steady whilst the materials are cut, shaped and assembled. As well as this, you will need the tools in the table below for the running mould making process.

Tool	Use
Tin snips	Basic or avionic tin snips are used to shape the zinc or aluminium into a mould profile.
Files	A range of files is required to form both the timber and the zinc. Files come in a variety of styles and sizes. You will need at least a flat and a half round fine metal file for shaping the zinc or aluminium, and similar wood rasps for forming the timber.
Wood saw	A sharp wood saw is used to cut the timber or plywood **horse**, **stock** and **brace** to size.
Coping saw	Once the profile has been cut to shape, the outline of the mould is placed on the timber/ply stock and the outline is extended by approximately 3–5mm. The coping saw is then used to shape the timber.
Tenon saw	This fine-toothed saw is useful for cutting rebates into timber.
Pein hammer	This small lightweight hammer is useful for securing the zinc profile onto the timber stock with nails. Also known as a pin hammer.

Bench with vice

Horse

Runs against the running rule on the bench

Stock

Holds the zinc profile and is attached at a 90° angle to the horse

Brace

Is fixed to the top of the horse and stock at a 45° angle; it stops the running mould from twisting when it's in use

Tool	Use
Drill/driver	A small lightweight drill/driver is essential to drill pilot holes and secure the running mould, together with suitable screws.
Try square	Also known as a carpenter's square, is useful for ensuring the horse is square with the stock, and if you decide to cut a housing joint into the horse instead of a butt joint.
Sandpaper/wet and dry	Sandpaper is used to smooth down rough edges of timber. Wet and dry emery paper can be used to smooth out high spots on zinc or aluminium profiles.
Busks	Sometimes known as 'drags', busks are small pieces of thin flexible metal that are available in three shapes: square, kidney and rectangle. Their main use is for cleaning mouldings and for making good joints.
Small tools	An essential part of the plasterer's tool kit, available in various shape and sizes, the most popular are trowel and square, and leaf and square. Useful for mixing small quantities of plaster, making good damaged plasterwork and mitre, and very handy for working behind pipes.

Tool	Use
Gauging trowel 	Also known as a 'bull nosed trowel', gauging trowels are used to mix small quantities of plaster and feed plaster into awkward areas.
Splash brushes 	Traditional splash brushes have coarse bristles and are circular, unlike standard paint brushes which have various types of bristles and are oblong in shape. A splash brush is used to brush plaster into **enrichments** in reverse moulding and then to brush and splash plaster when casting.
Shellac brushes 	Any good quality paint brush can be used to apply shellac. Any size can be used but 50mm is perhaps the most common. The most important issue is not to leave the shellac brush exposed to the air for too long or the brush will be ruined; always leave the brush in water after use or in a shallow container with shellac in it.
Mixing bowls 	Used for mixing small quantities of plaster. Designed to be flexible (unlike plastering buckets), it is okay for casting plaster to set hard in the bowl because the plaster will just pop out.
Scraper 	Used to clean plaster from floors. However, their blades can be used as a joint rule/busk for cleaning plaster slabs and mouldings.

Enrichment

Decorative sections of plasterwork, for example egg and dart or acanthus leaves

PLASTER REVERSE MOULDS

MATERIALS

Plaster of Paris

Retarder

A chemical additive that slows down the setting time of gypsum plasters, casting plaster and cement

The plaster used in fibrous work is commonly known as casting plaster although its proper name is Class A hemihydrate plaster. It is made from gypsum, a fairly soft rock containing calcium sulphate and waters of crystallisation. The rock is obtained mainly by drift mining, after which the crushed gypsum is fed into containers called kettles. The crushed material is then heated for about two hours at a temperature of 170°C until three-quarters of the waters of crystallisation have been driven off. The resulting material after grinding is the hemihydrate plaster, also known as 'plaster of Paris'.

When water is added to plaster, the reverse chemical action takes place and the waters of crystallisation re-form to convert the plaster back into gypsum. Chemically, the plaster will accept back only the exact amount of water that was driven out during the calcining or heating process; any excess water will be left to dry out later.

You will notice that the plaster gets warm as it sets; this is all part of the chemical reaction. Do not attempt to re-mix any gypsum plaster as it sets because the crystals will not lock together, resulting in a weak final set.

Class A plasters set too quickly for normal plastering uses so **retarder** is added by manufacturers to convert the plaster to Class B retarded hemihydrate plaster, which we use for internal plastering.

Types of casting plaster

In Europe, the major manufacturer of Class A plaster is Formula, part of British Gypsum and Lafarge. The characteristics of Class A plaster depend on its water/plaster (W/P) ratio, hardness and compressive strength. As a rule of thumb, the more water required to mix the plaster the more fluid the mix will be, but the strength will be reduced and the setting time extended. Conversely, with less water the setting time is shorter but the hardness and compressive strength are greater.

- Fine casting plaster 100/70 = 100 parts by weight of plaster to 70 parts by weight of water – this is a *weaker* plaster.

- Crystacal Alpha K 100/21 = 100 parts by weight of plaster to 21 parts by weight of water – this is a *harder* plaster.

The method of manufacture also determines the ultimate strength and water ratio of the plaster. If the plaster is manufactured in open pans under atmospheric pressure, it is classed as a beta plaster. This plaster will be cheaper but weaker. Alpha plaster is heated to the same temperature as beta plaster (200–392°C) but is made in an autoclave oven under steam pressure which gives the plaster its hardness.

Trade names

- *Prestia Classic Plaster (100/70)*: A consistent general-purpose castings plaster, ideal for fibrous plasterwork and sculptural work.

- *Prestia Normal Plus Plaster (100/66)*: Similar to Prestia Classic but with a slower setting time, useful when a longer working time is required.

- *Prestia Casting Plaster (100/68)*: Ideal for general casting, cast moulds and curving.

- *Formula Fine Casting Plaster (100/70*: Probably the most common general-purpose plaster, it is a versatile and economical beta plaster and is used in numerous industries.

- *Formula Super Fine Casting Plaster (100/70)*: A general-purpose beta plaster that has better working characteristics than fine casting plaster. It can be used to model and for carving applications.

- *Prestia Traditional Plaster (100/70)*: A slow setting general-purpose beta plaster.

- *Prestia Creation (100/50)*: A good quality hard plaster useful for most casting and modelling applications.

- *Formula Helix Plaster (100/50)*: A hard plaster used for high strength and surface durability.

- *Formula Herculite 2 (100/42)*: Similar to Helix plaster but with more strength and surface durability.

- *Formula Crystacast (100/28)*: An exceptionally hard plaster, used where exceptional detail is required.

- *Formula Crystacal R (100/35)*: An extra hard plaster used for its high strength and hardness.

- *Formula Crystacal Alpha K (100/21)*: Ultra high strength casting plaster that can be used for industrial modelling.

Prestia Casting Plaster

Formula Herculite 2

Flexural strength

Allows the plaster mould or cast to bend slightly without cracking or breaking

Materials used for reinforcement

Class A plaster can be brittle. To improve the overall strength of fibrous work, timber, hessian and fibreglass strands can be used to improve **flexural strength**.

Reinforcement material	Use
Hessian 	Hessian comes from the jute plant and is woven into coarse fabric that is available in many sizes, usually in 200m rolls and in widths of 75mm, 100mm, 150mm, 300mm and 450mm. It is still the most common material used in traditional fibrous work. Hessian can be wrapped around damp timber laths or wire to improve flexural strength. Hessian ropes and wads can be formed by dipping hessian into wet Class A plaster; the excess plaster is then removed by running fingers loosely over the hessian. The hessian is then placed in positions from fibrous slabs to suspended fibrous slab ceilings.
Sisal 	Sisal comes from the sisal plant. Its main use is to manufacture twine and for rope making. Like hessian, sisal is a popular choice as fibrous reinforcement material.

Reinforcement material	Use
Fibreglass 	Chopped fibreglass is a more modern material used to reinforce fibrous plaster. It is useful to tuck into awkward places, where hessian may be difficult to drape. Chopped fibreglass can be bought in lengths from 3mm to 20mm; 15mm is the most popular size. Other uses including adding it to backing and finishing plasters to help prevent cracking and to floor screed mixes. Chopped fibreglass and matting are most often used in acrylic resin-based plasters that can be used externally, such as Jesmonite or Fibrocem.
Timber lath 	Softwood timber lath can be used along with hessian to reinforce fibrous casts, providing a strong, rigid skeleton and preventing casts or mouldwork from snapping. The two thicknesses of timber lath are 3mm and 5mm. Widths vary to 10mm, 13mm and 22mm, and lengths are either 2.4m or 3m. The most popular size for fibrous cornice work is 3mm thick by 22mm wide by 2.4m long. Laths require soaking overnight to prevent the cast from cracking when dry out.

Sealants and release agents

As well as casting plaster and reinforcements, you may need to use some of the following sealants and release agents.

Shellac

Shellac is a traditional material used to seal plaster. It is a resin secreted by the female lac bug on trees in the forests of India and Thailand. It is processed and sold as dry flakes.

When the plaster reverse mould has been run on the bench, before any casting can take place the plaster needs to be sealed because the plaster surface is porous. Shellac flakes are mixed with methylated spirits to dissolve the shellac flakes, usually overnight. The shellac is then brushed onto the plaster surface and left to dry.

ACTIVITY

Search online to find out the most common sizes that fibrous laths are purchased in.

INDUSTRY TIP

Always cut your laths at least 10–20mm short when casting. This allows for the hessian to be tucked in and stops bulges on the back of the cast.

Shellac

INDUSTRY TIP

It's better to have the shellac weaker rather than stronger because it needs to be absorbed into the porous plaster reverse mould.

ACTIVITY

A 1 litre container is half filled with shellac flakes. How many millilitres of methylated spirit will be required to give a 50/50 ratio?

Tallow/plasterer's grease

INDUSTRY TIP

Tallow can be used in solid block form to grease the plasterer's workbench. Because it is not as slippery as oil, the plaster tends to stay in place when running.

Wax

Glue size plaster retarder

Subsequent second and third coats of shellac are applied after the previous coat has dried. More coats of shellac can be applied to plaster reverse casts, depending on the viscosity of the shellac and the porosity of the reverse cast.

You can also use shellac to seal your workbench.

Tallow

Tallow is solid animal fat from beef or mutton. The solid fat is warmed up gently by heating it in a pan. As soon as the fat has softened and becomes runny, it is removed from the heat and paraffin is added at a ratio of approximately 50/50. At this stage in the process it is known as 'plasterer's grease'.

Plasterer's grease is used as a release agent to help prevent plaster sticking to the workbench or the plaster cast sticking to the reverse mould. During cold weather the plasterer's grease may start to solidify; conversely, in summer months the plasterer's grease may become too runny. To solve this problem, adjust the amount of paraffin at the making stage, or store the grease in a warmer or chillier area of the workshop.

As an alternative to plasterer's grease, other materials such as lard, vegetable oil and linseed oil can be used. For exceptionally fine detail cornice works, oil-based materials are a better choice as a release agent because of their thinner consistency.

French chalk

This chalk is a fine powder, similar to talcum powder. It is used when the reverse is greased to find any misses.

RL247 Wax

This type of wax is a brush-on liquid wax release agent, which is also available in an aerosol canister. Release agents are substances applied to the surface of a mould to ease its removal after the plaster has set.

Retarders

Retarder can be added to casting plaster to slow its setting time.

Glue size plaster retarder

A traditional **retarder** used within the ornate plasterwork industry, glue size plaster retarder is made from animal skins and hooves. When added to gauging water it slows down the set of the plaster, allowing you more working time.

To make a batch of 'size', add 1kg glue size crystals to a gallon bucket of very hot water. Dissolve and stir the crystals in the hot water; do not allow the water to cool. While the water is still warm, add approximately 25g of hydrated lime and stir until fully dispersed. The mixture can now be allowed to cool.

Keatin is very similar to glue size and is also used as a retarder.

Trisodium citrate

Trisodium citrate is a retarder that is very easy to make. Simply add 1kg to a gallon of very hot water, mix until fully dissolved and then allow to cool down. As with size, you now have to sample batches to add to your gauging water to determine the delay of the set.

OUR HOUSE

1   Measure the perimeter of the living room in 'Our House'.

2   Calculate the number of timber laths required to produce enough 3m lengths of fibrous cornice if two length of laths cover 3m of cornice.

INDUSTRY TIP

When making 'size' it is difficult to gauge its strength. Use a small pot and measure the amount you add to your gauging water and adjust accordingly.

INDUSTRY TIP

Be careful when using trisodium citrate as a retarder: add too much to your gauging water and the plaster will take too long to set, which affects the hardness of the plaster.

INDUSTRY TIP

If no glue size or trisodium citrate is readily available, a small quantity of pink plaster may be added to the water before adding casting plaster to the water – the retarder in the pink plaster will slow down the set of the casting plaster, too.

PRODUCING REVERSE MOULDS

All plastering work carried out on a plasterer's workbench falls in to the category of fibrous plastering. Moulding carried out on a bench has certain advantages over solid in situ moulding work because fibrous work:

■ can be manufactured while the building is being constructed, saving time

■ is manufactured to manageable working sizes, allowing easy transportation and easier fixing on site

■ is lightweight, uses less material and reduces fatigue when fixing

■ allows more elaborate moulding to be manufactured, using various moulding techniques.

We need to remember the difference between a positive and a negative mould. As mentioned earlier in this chapter (see page 269):

■ positive moulding is run on a bench to the shape of the finished product, such as a panel mould or a dado rail

■ negative moulding is run on a bench to the reverse (see overleaf) of the finished product and a fibrous cast is then taken from the reverse mould, such as a cornice.

Negative moulding run on a bench

COMPONENTS OF A RUNNING MOULD

Running moulds can be made to a variety of shapes and sizes. Regardless of whether they are a positive or negative profile, the basic principles of constructing a running mould are similar. Only the size of the profile design and the practicalities of use determine the final running mould features, such as a loose piece mould for undercut profiles. The basic components of a running mould are as follows.

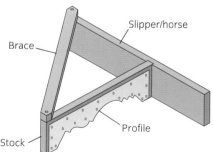

Parts of a running mould

- *Horse* or *slipper*: These are two different regional words used to describe the same part. The stock is fixed to the horse with nails or screws. The horse then rides down the bench against the bench's running rule.

- *Stock*: The stock is fixed at 90° to the horse/slipper with a butt or housing joint (see illustrations opposite). The stock is approximately 3mm larger than the profile. This helps prevent a build-up of plaster on the back of the profile when running the plaster mould.

- *Brace*: The brace is fixed to the horse/slipper and the stock at an angle of 45°, using nails or screws.

- *Profile*: Sometimes known as a template, this is made from zinc or aluminium to the shape of the mould (positive or negative) and is then fixed to the stock using small tacks or screws.

Refer back to page 276 to see the materials needed to build a running mould.

INDUSTRY TIP

It important to smooth the outline shape of the profile/template using 180 or 220 grade wet and dry abrasive paper. This will remove any file score marks. You can use the side of a nail if you run out of wet and dry.

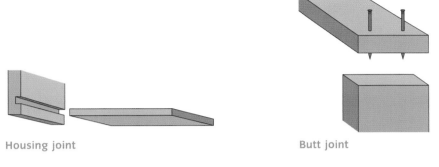

Housing joint　　　　　　　　　　　　Butt joint

TYPES OF RUNNING MOULDS

The list below shows just some of the types of running moulds and their uses.

- *Plain panel/dado mould*: A small positive mould run on a bench or in situ.

- *Plain reverse mould*: A negative cornice mould.

- *Loose piece reverse mould*: A negative cornice mould with an undercut profile.

- *Loose piece insertion reverse mould*: A negative cornice mould with ornate detail.

- *Extended stock running mould*: To run circular moulding.

- *Gig stick running mould*: To run circular moulding with a larger radius.

- *In situ running mould*: To run a mould direct to the wall or ceiling, in situ.

The following step-by-steps show you how to construct a running mould. The photographs show a positive panel mould being constructed, but the principle is the same for making either a positive or negative mould.

STEP 1 Design the basic shape of the profile on graph paper and stick it onto a piece of aluminium or zinc.

STEP 2 Cut out the shape of the profile with tin snips to within 2mm of the profile line.

STEP 3 Using a smooth metal file, shape the zinc to match the paper template.

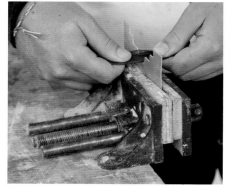

STEP 4 Any burrs can be removed with wet and dry (emery paper).

STEP 5 Cut your stock. This should be wider and longer than the profile metal (5mm bigger in both directions) in order to fit the profile on its surface. This allows for any swelling that might occur when in contact with wet plaster. Fix your aluminium/zinc profile to the stock using tacks.

STEP 6 The stock and profile can now be fixed to the slipper. For strength, the stock can be notched then glued and screwed into position. Make sure that the stock and slipper sit flat on the bench before fixing them together. For stability when running on the bench, it is normal for the slipper to be longer than the stock.

STEP 7 Braces can be fixed to support the stock and slipper. Use a square to make sure the stock is set at a right angle to the slipper before fixing.

STEP 8 The running mould has been constructed but you may want to seal the timber with shellac before it comes into contact with wet plaster. This will increase the running mould's life span and prevent distortion of the timber.

LOOSE PIECE MOULD

Some cornices may incorporate an **undercut** design; this design feature makes it difficult to release the fibrous cast from the reverse. To resolve this problem the plaster reverse profile should include a detachable loose piece profile.

To run a loose piece mould, the bench is prepared in the usual way and the reverse mould is run with the detachable loose piece profile in position. When the reverse mould is run, two to three coats of shellac are applied to the section that the loose piece ran over, and this is lightly greased to prevent plaster sticking to the loose piece channel. The reverse mould is run again, filling the loose piece channel. It is wise to strengthen this section with lath, hessian or fibres. Once completed, the whole of the reverse mould is sealed with shellac three times.

When a cast is taken from this reverse mould the loose piece will separate from the reverse mould, allowing the cast to be removed without any problem.

WASTE MOULDS

Waste moulds are used to produce a one-off moulding from a clay model where the sculptor wishes to retain exclusiveness. The clay model is prepared with a thin coat of a release agent such a linseed oil or Mac Wax spray. Class A plaster is then mixed with a coloured tint, such as vegetable dye used in cake making. The mixture is then lightly splashed onto the clay model to a thickness of approximately 5mm. Care must be taken to ensure that no air is trapped between the clay model and the tinted plaster. It is essential that the model is completely covered with the tinted plaster.

As the plaster starts to set, a weak mixture of clay water is brushed over the tinted plaster, just enough to discolour the surface. Ordinary Class A plaster is then mixed and applied over the clay wash to an approximate thickness of 12mm, depending upon the size of the model.

Undercut

A model or mould with overhanging patterns. They can be difficult to remove when cast unless the reverse mould is made from flexible material or loose piece mould

Undercut cornice

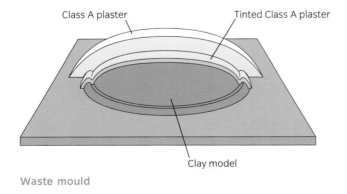

Class A plaster

Tinted Class A plaster

Clay model

Waste mould

Once set, the mould is turned over and the clay original is picked out carefully. The inside of the mould is rinsed with clean water; a mixture of soft soap and water is applied to the mould, making sure all of the crevices have a coating of soft soap. Once coated, a creamy gauge of Class A plaster is poured to the top of the mould and gently shaken to remove any trapped air.

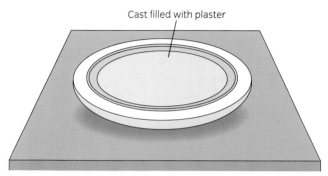

Cast filled with plaster

Mould turned over with clay model removed and Class A plaster inserted

The plaster cast must be fully set before removal of the outer case is attempted. To remove the outer case, sharp chisels and cutting tools are used to cautiously cut and chip away until the tinted plaster is reached. This indicates that the cast has nearly been reached, so the tinted plaster is gradually removed with blunt tools to avoid potential damage to the cast.

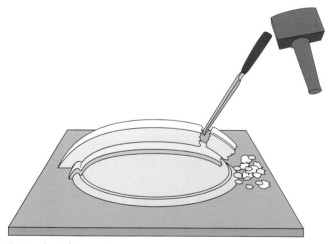

Removing the case

Large, more intricate waste moulds are best made in several sections to ease the removal of the clay and then the waste plaster.

INSERTION MOULDS

Insertion moulds can be manufactured in the following two ways.

Method 1

A cornice is run in situ with a channel in the profile. Enrichments are cast separately from a rubber mould. The enrichments are bedded into the channel with casting plaster or a suitable plaster adhesive and jointed as required.

Run cornice with sinking channel

Method 2

The more popular method for producing a decorative cornice with enrichment moulding is to run a reverse mould with channels and fix decorative moulding in place, then take a rubber reverse moulding from which plaster casts can be taken.

First, a modeller will create a clay model of a decorative section of the plasterwork on a sheet of plywood. The next stage is to make a clay fence around the model, which should extend to at least 10–20mm from all parts of the model including its highest part: this is to allow for the pouring of the hot or cold pour compound. The thickness of the clay fence will depend on the size of the model; the fence must be robust enough to be free standing and to hold the pressure of the poured compound. Other materials, such as timber or plasterboard, can be used to form the fence around the model as long as they are sealed with shellac.

In a clay model, a small section is made first and a rubber reverse is taken. As many plaster casts as are needed to cover a sufficient length of a panel mould are made from the small rubber reverse. These are jointed together to provide a seamless plaster model; again, a fence is built around the plaster model ready to receive hot or cold pour compound. These small castings are called flood moulds because the plasterer just 'floods' the rubber reverse with plaster.

Reverse mould with rubber insertion

Should the cornice design incorporate a decorative moulding, an insertion mould may be used within a reverse mould. A reverse

Reverse mould with enrichment

mould would be run with a loose piece template. Once the loose piece template is removed, a channel is left for placing the reverse mould rubber or decorative plaster cast.

Using a backboard

A backboard is formed by securing a length of timber vertically on the plasterer's workbench. It can be used to run a short section of positive cornice which is too difficult to run in situ, or a section of cornice which includes decorative plasterwork, such as egg and dart, that cannot be run due to enrichments. The running mould would be designed to accommodate decorative inserts; a rubber reverse mould would be taken from the model.

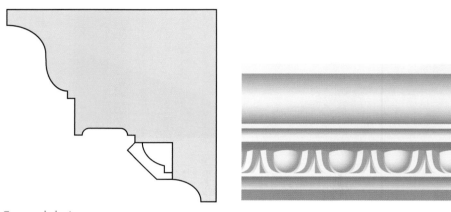

Egg and dart

FORMING A BEAM CASE

Cast beam cases are used to:

■ improve the appearance of concrete or steel beams that support upper floors but divide the lower-floor room

■ form part of a **coffered** ceiling

■ be part of a false ceiling to give the impression of a beamed ceiling.

Coffered

Formed with intersecting beams

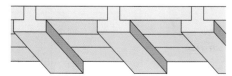

Bare ceiling beams

Coffered ceiling

The design of a beam cast can vary, from plain sides (cheeks) and bottom (soffit), to panelled and moulded with inserts. Like the fibrous cornice, beam cases can be run on a backboard or as a bench reverse mould with channels for the fixing of enrichments.

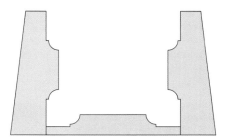

Panelled beam case

RUNNING A REVERSE MOULD

PREPARATION

The bench should be scrapped and swept with a brush to remove any loose materials. Check that the running rules are firmly in position and free from any sticking plaster, as this would hinder the smooth movement of the running mould along the bench. Repair any indents on the bench surface and apply a few coats of shellac to seal the surface of the bench.

Cleaning the bench with a floor scraper

Check the sturdiness of the running mould and the sharpness of the profile to prevent any unwanted drag lines that would spoil the finished work.

Get together two buckets of clean cold water, a brush to clean the running mould, and at least two clean flexible mixing bowls. Apply some barrier cream or wear a pair of disposable latex-style gloves to protect your hands.

It is important to mix enough plaster to run the full length of mould. Failure to do so will cause uneven expansion along the length of the mould, which will create difficulties at the later stages of running the mould when smaller quantities of plaster are mixed to finish the run section.

A reverse mould requires a **core** to help reduce expansion of freshly mixed plaster during running by using less plaster (see illustration on next page). This is a good opportunity to recycle offcuts.

INDUSTRY TIP

When bagged materials are delivered, always check the use-by date on the side of the bag: it's not uncommon for suppliers to deliver materials that are out of date or nearly out of date.

INDUSTRY TIP

Remember when you store bagged materials to rotate the stock so that they are used on a 'first in, first out' basis.

Core

Old moulding or plasterboard used to help reduce expansion

INDUSTRY TIP

A running mould can be made either left- or right-handed; however, the principle of using the running mould is the same.

INDUSTRY TIP

Don't be tempted to add the plaster to the water and mix it straight away as your mix will be lumpy and inconsistent.

INDUSTRY TIP

Keep your working area and running mould clean as you work to prevent unnecessary build-up of plaster.

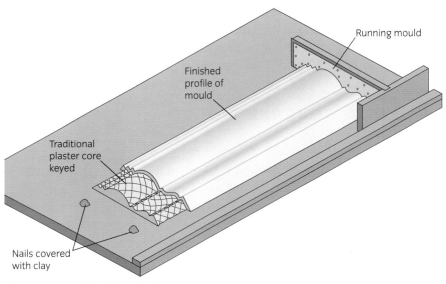

A reverse mould with a plaster core

RUNNING THE MOULD

STEP 1 Position the core on the bench.

STEP 2 Fix the core in place.

STEP 3 Apply plasterer's grease to the bench. This will allow the running mould to move freely and act as a release agent.

STEP 4 Lightly grease the running mould before use to help prevent the plaster from sticking.

STEP 5 Add some clean cold water to a mixing bowl and then sprinkle through your fingers small quantities of casting plaster until the plaster sits just below the water line. Let the plaster soak for a minute or two. Then gently mix the plaster through your fingers to produce a smooth lump-free creamy consistency.

STEP 6 Pour the creamy plaster mix just longer than the required length of the finished mould. This is to allow for wastage.

STEP 7 Place firm downward pressure on the horse against the running rule and the nib of the stock. This ensures the running mould has full contact with the bench and helps prevent plaster building up beneath the running mould.

STEP 8 The zinc or aluminium profile should always face the direction you are working. With one hand on the nib and the other on the brace, walk backwards, pulling the running mould. As you are walking backwards feed the surplus soft plaster from in front of the profile back into the low spots.

STEP 9 As the running mould is gradually built up, smaller wetter quantities are mixed to finalise the running.

STEP 10 Wash the mould. Repeat Steps 8–10 several times. Once you are satisfied the running mould is complete, leave the mould for 20 minutes or so until the plaster has set. During this time, take the opportunity to clean up and get ready to run the next cast.

STEP 11 Gently run the blade of a small tool to both edges of the reverse mould. This will release the mould from the bench.

STEP 12 Brush the sides of the mould.

STEP 13 When the reverse mould is complete, trim off the rough ends.

STEP 14 Apply three coats of shellac to seal the porous plaster surface. Once sealed, the reverse mould can be used many times to produce fibrous cornices.

Gently tilt the panel mould on its edge to move it to a suitable storage area.

To speed up the running process, a false profile can be built up from plaster, or a zinc plate can be fixed temporarily to the stock profile. The false profile should extend the original profile by approximately 5mm and can be made up from casting plaster or any sheet material such as zinc, plywood or hardboard. In plastering terms we call this false profile a **muffle**.

Muffle

A temporary extension to the profile by 5–6mm with plaster, thin ply or a zinc sheet

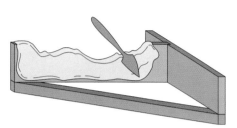

Using a small tool to build up the muffle gradually (view from inside the running mould)

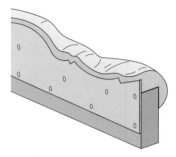

Scribing the set plaster to the shape of the profile

The process for casting a reverse mould is covered in Chapter 8.

RUNNING A PLASTER POSITIVE PANEL MOULD

The method used to produce a bench panel mould is similar to that for making a plaster reverse mould. The only exception is that a panel mould is smaller in size and does not require a core.

Drive two headless nails into the bench, approximately 500mm apart, leaving about 10mm of each nail projecting out of the bench at the deepest section of the mould. A small cone of clay is built around the projecting nail heads; this prevents the plaster moulding from moving when being run and the plaster from sticking to the nail head.

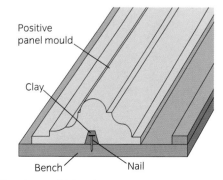

Positive panel mould
Clay
Bench
Nail

Bench mould in place

Running a panel mould

Depending on the size of the running mould, reinforcement can be incorporated by using cotton, fibre or hessian scrim.

To run a panel mould, refer back to pages 294–295 as the step-by-step instructions are the same as for running a reverse mould.

CHECKLIST FOR RUNNING A PANEL MOULD

- Prepare the bench and running mould, checking for any defects and repairing.

- Grease the bench and running mould.

- Secure headless nails and clay domes every 500mm.

- Select clean buckets, bowls, water brushes and water.

- Select a small joint rule.

- Mix plaster to a creamy consistency and pour just beyond the length of the finished mould.

- Build up the running mould shape with creamy plaster mix as quickly as possible.

- Finalise the running mould shape with smaller, wetter quantities.

- Clean up and leave the plaster mould to set.

- Carefully remove the plaster mould from the workbench.

- Place the panel moulds flat in a well ventilated area.

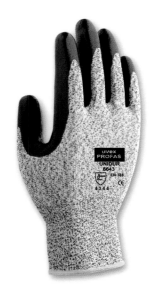

Nitrile glove

ENVIRONMENTAL AND SAFETY CONSIDERATIONS

Class A plaster is considered a safe material to use. However, care should be taken against inhaling its dust by mixing in a well ventilated area and wearing a dust mask. Barrier cream or nitrile gloves should be worn to help prevent absorption into the skin, and safety glasses should also be worn.

Never cast body parts on raw skin especially hands: skin burns can occur at 45°C and the cast can reach 60°C when setting.

Class A plaster should be disposed of in a separate skip for recycling. Dirty plaster water should be tipped down a filtered trap but the plaster slops at the bottom of a bucket should be scraped into the plaster skip.

FUNCTIONAL SKILLS

Imagine you are working for a fibrous plasterwork plasterer. A new contract has been awarded to your company to make 840 lengths of cornice for a hotel chain. On average, you can make three lengths of cornice an hour and you have a 35-hour working week.

a How many weeks will it take to you to make 840 lengths of cornice for this contract?

b If the contract value is £14,700.00, what is the unit cost for a length of cornice?

Work on this activity can support FM2 (L2.1.2–3 and L2.2.1).

Answers: a) eight weeks, b) £17.50

Case Study: Becca and Jamie

Becca has been given a work placement in a fibrous workshop and hopes to be taken on as an apprentice fibrous plasterer. She has been assigned to Jamie, who has 25 years' experience of manufacturing and fixing fibrous components.

After familiarising herself with health and safety in the workshop, during the first few weeks Becca's role was to watch Jamie produce fibrous cases and assist him when instructed. She also had to keep the work area clean to help prevent slips, trips and falls, and keep mixing bowls and buckets clean and ready for use.

As Jamie worked he explained the process of making a fibrous cast to Becca. Jamie was pleased with Becca's progress and wanted to see if she had observed and understood the casting process. He gave Becca a short section of a reverse mould and asked her to produce a cast unassisted.

Becca set to work to produce a plaster cast, keeping the work area tidy and gauging just the right amount of materials to reduce wastage. When the cast was finished, Becca was keen to show Jamie her completed fibrous cornice. As she pulled the fibrous cornice away from the reverse, a small section stuck to the reverse. Becca panicked as she wanted to prove her worth. She was concerned she might get told off.

Jamie on the other hand was pleased to see Becca had some pride in her work and asked Becca what she felt had caused the problem. Becca thought back over the stages she had gone through to produce the fibrous cast and was sure that she had not missed out any of the stages. Then she looked down the reverse and noticed a small area that had not been brushed with the release agent plasterer's grease.

Jamie reassured her that it was an easy mistake to make when new to the job, especially if you're under pressure or trying to rush.

Work through the following questions to check your learning.

1   Who is responsible for the overall design of a moulding profile?

   a   The architect.

   b   The client.

   c   The technician.

   d   The plasterer.

2   A copy of a cornice can be taken with a

   a   squeeze

   b   slurry

   c   clasp

   d   clutch.

3   What type of working drawing would a plasterer use to make a running mould?

   a   Component drawing.

   b   Assembly drawing.

   c   General drawing.

   d   Scale drawing.

4   When fixing a cornice, it is measured by

   a   girth

   b   volume

   c   length

   d   depth.

5   The plaster to water ratio information is found in the

   a   bill of quantities

   b   manufacturer's specification

   c   plaster gauge scales

   d   supplier's delivery note.

6   On site, a verbal instruction is **best** confirmed

   a   in writing

   b   by text message

   c   by shaking hands

   d   by phone.

7   Manufacturers' data sheets give information about

   a   the safe use of the material

   b   how much plaster they sell weekly

   c   the date the plaster was made

   d   how much plaster is made weekly.

8   The approximate length of the horse/slipper is

   a   the same size of the stock

   b   one-and-a-half times the length of the stock

   c   just smaller than the stock

   d   two-and-a-half times the depth of the stock.

9   Mould profiles are made from zinc because it is

   a   cheaper than tin

   b   long lasting

   c   easy to cut and shape

   d   lightweight.

10   The purpose of the gap between the stock and the zinc or aluminium profile is to

   a   make the zinc or aluminium profile easier to fix

   b   stop plaster gathering when running a mould

   c   stop the timber stock from expanding

   d   allow the zinc or aluminium to cool off when running.

11   Hot pour compounds are more economical than cold pour because they

   a   can be heated very quickly

   b   are easier to use compared with cold pour

   c   are cheaper the more you buy

   d   can be re-melted and used again.

12 Shellac is used to

a improve the look of a plaster reverse mould

b look like hessian

c seal a plaster reverse mould

d help prevent plaster from sticking.

13 Autoclaved plasters

a are no different from other Class A plasters

b require more water to mix properly

c set slower than other Class A plasters

d are harder than any other Class A plaster.

14 Water driven off during the manufacture of gypsum plaster is known as

a vaporisation

b hydration

c evaporation

d crystallisation.

15 Which one of the following is used to form a moulding on a bench?

a Joint rule.

b Small tool.

c Steady mould.

d Running mould.

16 The preferred method for a small cast is

a mix firstings, mix seconds, apply firstings, apply seconds

b mix seconds, mix firstings, apply seconds, apply firstings

c mix firstings, apply firstings, mix seconds, apply seconds

d mix seconds, mix firstings, apply firstings, apply seconds.

17 A reverse mould is a

a mould run backwards

b negative mould

c positive mould

d mould run forward.

18 What is the name of the timber fixed to each edge of the fibrous bench that the horse runs against?

a Box rule.

b Running rule.

c Bench rule.

d Measuring rule.

19 Plasterer's grease is made from

a linseed oil and paraffin

b linseed oil and animal fat

c animal fat and paraffin

d shellac and paraffin.

20 Which one of the following plastering materials is highly flammable?

a Shellac.

b Class A plaster.

c French chalk.

d Size.

Chapter 8
Unit 226: Casting and fixing fibrous plasterwork

In this chapter we look at the process of casting and fixing fibrous plasterwork.

Casting and fixing fibrous plasterwork is perhaps the most rewarding aspect of fibrous work. You will need to able to interpret information from a working drawing and specification: by using these contract documents you will be able to produce a reverse from plaster, a clay model or silicone mould. Your skills will be on display for all to see for many years.

By reading this chapter you will know how to:

1 Interpret information to cast and fix fibrous plasterwork.

2 Select materials, components and equipment to cast and fix plasterwork.

3 Cast fibrous plasterwork.

4 Fix and finish fibrous plasterwork.

INTERPRETING INFORMATION

WORKING DRAWINGS, SCHEDULES AND SPECIFICATIONS

Having made the plaster reverse mould in the plasterer's workshop (see Chapter 7), the next stage is to make a fibrous cast from the reverse mould and then transport the finished items to the client for fixing. In order to prepare for doing this, the plasterer needs to interpret information from the following contract documents.

CONTRACT DRAWINGS

Contract drawings show the cornice design and vital measurements, such as depth and projection. For fibrous work the most common drawings used are:

- detailed drawings (usually at 1:10, 1:5 or 1:1 scales)
- assembly drawings (usually at 1:20, 1:10 or 1:5 scales).

For information on other types of drawings used, refer back to Chapter 2, pages 49–51.

CONTRACT SCHEDULE

The schedule identifies the room location to ensure that the right cornice is fitted in the correct room. This is especially important if the site has multiple rooms that all have different fibrous plasterwork designs to be fitted in them.

CONTRACT SPECIFICATION

The specification gives guidance on the required fixing method and the materials to be used for fixing the cornice or other fibrous work, such as a niche. For example, guidance on the required fixing method might include instructions such as:

- Depth and projection of cornice.
- Mark out to prepare ceiling and walls to receive fibrous cornice by scoring to improve mechanical key.
- Drill **pilot holes** every 600mm through timber lath bearers.
- Apply approximately 3mm of Fibre Fix adhesive to back leading edge of cornice.

Niches are a type of fibrous work

Pilot hole

A small pre-drilled hole bored to help prevent splitting

- Firmly push cornice into position and fix with 50mm drywall screws into plugged or timber background.

- Remove excess Fibre Fix. Make good and joint as work proceeds.

On receipt of the contract drawing and specification, it is good practice to review the information to check whether the item on the drawing can be made and that the specification reflects the job to be carried out. Also check that the materials specified comply with the manufacturer's own guidelines. Any discrepancies should be reported to your line manager if you are employed or, if you are a sub-contractor, to the main contractor or the architect.

ACTIVITY

Have a look at the decorative plaster frieze in the illustration. What type of mould would you use to produce this decorative fibrous plasterwork?

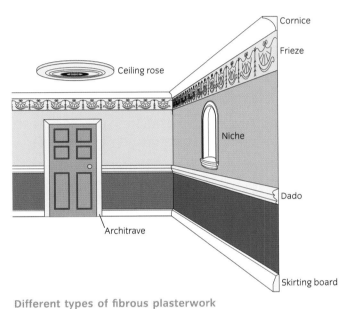

Different types of fibrous plasterwork

The picture above is an artist's impression of a room showing various types of plaster moulding. Although not a working drawing as such, architects often use this type drawing to illustrate to a client how a room might look once it is completed. You will notice the picture does not include the measurements and other information that a plasterer will need to make and fix fibrous work.

RISK ASSESSMENTS

As with manufacturing fibrous work in the workshop, fixing fibrous plasterwork requires a risk assessment to be carried out. The risk assessment can be done by anyone who is competent in that field of work. A useful document to consult when writing a risk assessment is the manufacturer's own data sheet, which will outline any known risks when using their materials and suggest control measures to minimise any potential health hazards.

For more about risk assessments, refer back to Chapter 1, pages 5–6.

ACTIVITY

Search online and find prices and measurements for the following:

- plain plaster ceiling rose (find cost and diameter of ceiling rose)
- plain plaster cornice ogee (find cost and depth and projection of cornice)
- egg and dart plaster cornice (find price and depth and projection)
- decorative plaster frieze (find depth of frieze)
- solid based plaster niche (find cost and width and length of niche)
- egg and dart plaster dado (find cost).

ACTIVITY

Sketch or describe the egg and dart design in your own words.

DATA SHEETS

Data sheets are produced by the plaster manufacturer and are usually available online. If an employer is planning to use new materials for the first time, the employer is responsible for informing their workforce how to use them safely. This could be done during a tool box talk. (See Chapter 1, page 6 for a reminder about tool box talks.)

Data sheets provide lots of information about the use of the material and usually contain at least 15 important headings:

1 *Product name and company information*: Provides a general description of the material and its use, plus the name and address of the manufacturing company.

2 *Hazards identification*: Outlines any known hazards when using the material, which can be used when creating the job's risk assessment.

3 *Composition of material*: States the ingredients used in the product.

4 *First-aid measures*: Gives first aid advice, such as how to deal with skin exposure or inhalation/ingestion of the material.

5 *Firefighting measures*: States whether the material is flammable and how to deal with the materials in the event of a fire.

6 *Accidental release measures*: Gives advice on what to do should the materials be spilt on the floor.

7 *Handling and storage*: Covers how best to handle and store the material.

8 *Exposure control*: States limits of exposure when using the material and engineering controls to minimise the risks when using the material.

9 *Physical and chemical properties*: Gives the properties of the material under various conditions.

10 *Stability and reaction*: Provides information about the stability of the material in various conditions and how it reacts when mixed with other materials.

11 *Toxicological information*: Gives advice on whether the material is poisonous.

12 *Ecological information*: Covers information about the effects of the material on wildlife and the natural environment.

13 *Disposal considerations*: Recommended methods for safe disposal of the material.

14 *Transport information*: Provides information about whether the material requires any special delivery precautions, ie whether it is a **DOT** hazardous material.

15 *Regulatory information*: Outlines regulations that might apply to that material.

DOT

Transported materials are given a DOT (Department of Transportation) rating to indicate how hazardous they are. Material such as sand is low risk whereas petrol might be considered high risk should an accident occur. The back of most lorries carries a notice with a number on. If the lorry is involved in a traffic accident, the number helps the fire service choose the best option for dealing with the spillage or fire

ACTIVITY

Search online for a data sheet for plaster of Paris. How long should you wash your eyes out for if you get plaster in them? Discuss your findings with your group and tutor.

BENEFITS OF FIBROUS PLASTERWORK

Fibrous plasterwork has benefits that appeal to architects and project managers:

- the fibrous items can be manufactured by specialist plasterers in a controlled factory environment (as well as on site)

- fibrous plasterwork is durable and lightweight

- the skill and efficiency of the specialist plasterer save time

- the project manager can plan the work's manufacture and delivery to meet contractual timescales

- the quality of finished work can be maintained by following proper fixing procedures.

MOULDING OUTLINES

GEOMETRICAL SETTING OUT OF MOULDING OUTLINES

As mentioned in Chapter 7, page 270, geometrical outlines for cornice moulding are based on either Greek or Roman architecture. Although many of the shapes are similar, the Greek style is more flowing whereas the Roman style is proportional and based on squares.

In order to understand descriptions of the fibrous plasterwork you are installing, you need to learn the geometrical shapes shown below and their names.

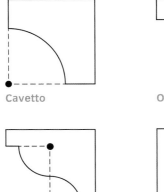
Cavetto

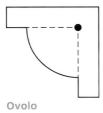
Ovolo

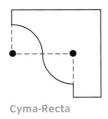
Cyma-Recta

Cyma-Reversa

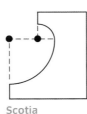
Torus

Scotia

Casting a ceiling rose

SUITABILITY OF MATERIALS

It is essential that all the materials used are compatible with each other, including the background that the fibrous work is being fixed to. Manufacturers' data sheets and the contract specification should be referred to in order to make sure that the correct Class A plaster is selected for the project. If you refer back to Chapter 7 you will see that the method of the plaster's production determines its strength and hardness, which in turn is reflected in the price of the material selected.

Mechanical fixings must be rust free to avoid staining the finished work. All types of drywall screws are suitable, but zinc-plated screws offer better all-round performance. Similarly, if any fibrous components are used to fix fibrous work with the wire and wad method (see pages 321–322 and 329), the wire used must have sufficient strength to support the fibrous component and be galvanised to prevent rusting.

Coving adhesives can be bought in powder or pre-mixed form. However, their properties vary immensely in respect of setting times, fineness of the materials and their adhesive strength. Generally, ready-mixed adhesives are slower at setting whereas powdered adhesives offer quicker setting times and greater strength. With some powder adhesives there is no need to prepare the background with PVA.

MEASURING PLASTER AND FIBROUS WORK

Plastering work is measured using standard units of measurement which are as follows.

- *Area*: Used to measure most plastered surfaces, for example two coat plasterwork, dry lining, finishing plasters, external rendering, floor screeding. As plasterers we know this as 'a metre square'. The common unit icon is m².

- *Volume*: From a costing point of view we don't use volume, but plasterers use volume all the time when gauging plastering materials. The common unit icon is m³.

- *Linear*: With the exception of very deep or complex cornice moulding, the majority of cornice is measured by the linear metre run. The common unit icon is m.

MANUFACTURERS' SPECIFICATIONS

As discussed in Chapter 7, the fibrous plasterer would refer to the manufacturer's specification for information about the materials used, reading this in conjunction with the client/architect's specification to make the fibrous work.

For fixing the fibrous plasterwork the process is similar. You should refer to the client/architect's specification to check whether the fibrous work is to be mechanically fixed or fixed using adhesive. It could be a combination of both fixing methods. If fixing cornice work you should also check projection and depths and the position of dado or panel mouldings.

How to prepare the background to receive the fibrous work will also be covered in the manufacturer's instructions and the client/architect's specification.

For installation instructions, the contract schedule states fixing locations and positions of the fibrous work.

Measuring projection

INDUSTRY TIP

Anticipate deliveries and plan for safe unloading and storage of materials to minimise labour costs and material wastage.

You should also consider protecting the finished work once it is fixed, especially exposed items of work such as dado or panel mouldings. Any work damaged on site without being signed off could lead to a contractual dispute over payment.

Part of the challenge of working on site is planning to receive materials from stockists. These materials can include fibrous work for fixing, if they are not being manufactured in house, and fixing materials such as adhesive, wire and fixing screws. On larger sites there will usually be a designated person to receive all inward goods and materials; on smaller sites the delivery driver would more than likely deal directly with the sub-contractor. Regardless of whether the site is large or small, the principles for receiving goods are the same.

- Check the delivery note against the official order. Check especially that the quantity and grade delivered match the quantity and grade ordered.

- Check the goods for any signs of damage and, if there are no problems, sign the delivery note to acknowledge receipt.

- Any discrepancies found with the delivered goods, such as damaged goods or shortages, should be reported to your line manager so that they can decide whether to take part delivery or return the full consignment. It is worth remembering that once you sign for the goods your company is responsible for payment under the terms and conditions of the supplier's contract.

- Store materials in a secure location that is appropriate for the type of goods received. High value goods should be stored in a lockable container; it's wise to store less valuable but equally desirable items such as screws in a lockable container, too, as these items have a tendency to slip into overall pockets. Perishable goods, ie bagged materials with a use-by date, must be stored in rotation, so that older materials are used first ('first in, first out'). Other materials, such as timber, fibrous work and sheet materials, are usually stored off the ground, horizontally or vertically, in a dry and well ventilated secure storage compound.

SELECT MATERIALS, COMPONENTS AND EQUIPMENT

The following materials are used to cast fibrous plasterwork:

- casting plaster
- release agents
- sealing agents/shellac
- reinforcement (eg timber laths, hessian, fibreglass).

Refer back to Chapter 7 for information on these materials.

Mixing Class A plaster in a bowl

TOOLS AND EQUIPMENT

The tools used to fix fibrous work are as follows.

Tool	Use
Tape measure	Used for measuring lengths. The most common sizes of tape used by plasterers are 3m and 5m.
Pencil	Used to mark out, it's impossible to work without one!

Tool	Use
Timber or metal square	Used to square up reveals, soffits and beams.
Fine-toothed saw	Used to cut plaster and timber for moulding.
Rasp	Used to clean down and reduce the size of cornice and plaster board.
Mitre box	Used to cut **mitres**.
Claw hammer	Used to fix (and remove) nails.

Mitre

A cut joint to an internal or external angle. The joint is then made good (the gaps are filled) with casting plaster or fixing adhesive, using a joint rule and a small tool

Tool	Use
Battery-powered drill	Used to drive screws into timber mould and for mechanically fixing fibrous work into plastic plugs or timber grounds.
Hand screwdriver	Can be used instead of using a battery-powered drill/driver.
Tin snips	Used to trim zinc profiles and cut metal trims.
Laser level	Used to determine a level or vertical line to work from.
Spirit level	As with a laser level, used to determine a level or vertical line to work from.

Tool	Use
Water level 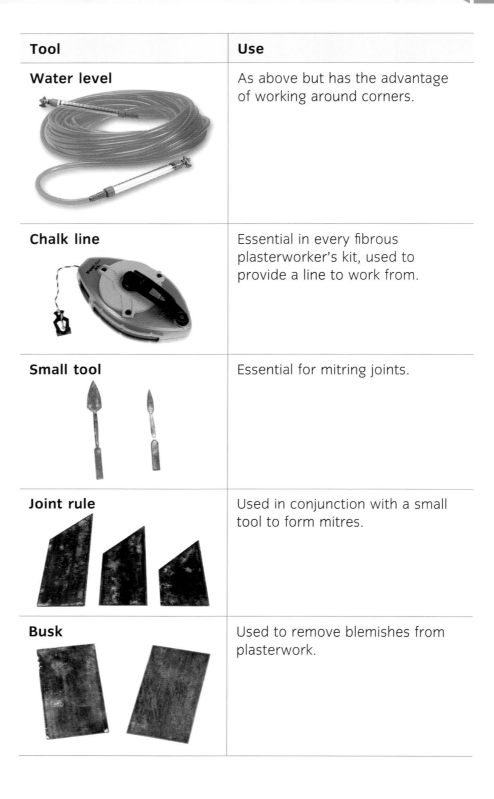	As above but has the advantage of working around corners.
Chalk line	Essential in every fibrous plasterworker's kit, used to provide a line to work from.
Small tool	Essential for mitring joints.
Joint rule	Used in conjunction with a small tool to form mitres.
Busk	Used to remove blemishes from plasterwork.

Tool	Use
Gauging trowel	Used to mix small quantities of materials and apply materials to awkward areas.

Other equipment required includes:

- buckets and flexi bowls

- access equipment

- benches (if making fibrous work on site).

For information on the tools and equipment used to cast fibrous plasterwork, refer back to Chapter 7.

Using a bench and a bowl to mix Class A plaster

CAST FIBROUS PLASTERWORK

The most common fibrous plaster casts are taken from a plaster, rubber or fibreglass reverse.

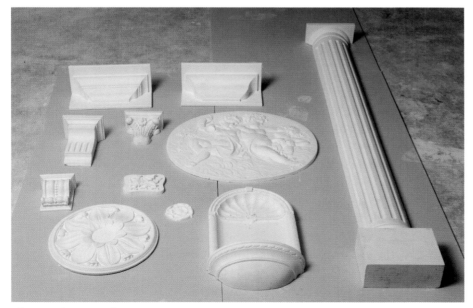

Fibrous plasterwork

SETTING UP TO CAST FROM A PLASTER REVERSE

Chapter 7 covered how to run a plaster reverse on a bench. The next stage is to prepare the plaster reverse to take a fibrous cast.

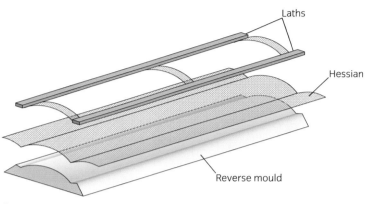

A reverse

MATERIALS AND SEQUENCE OF WORK

Sealing the plaster reverse with shellac

Cutting hessian

1 *Sealing the plaster reverse*: Traditionally, shellac is used to seal the plaster reverse. Other products can be used but shellac is tried and trusted. Ideally the plaster reverse will have had some time to dry out slightly as this helps the shellac dry. Apply three coats of shellac, leaving each coat to dry before applying the next.

2 *Casting plaster and equipment*: While the shellac is drying, gather the necessary casting plaster, hessian cloth, timber lath, plasterer's grease or linseed oil, mixing bowls, brushes and hand tools.

3 *Hessian and lath*: Once the shellac has dried, lay the hessian along the length of the plaster reverse, ensuring that at least 50mm extends at each end and both sides. (Remember that hessian comes in various sizes.) Cut some small pieces of hessian to use as cross braces; small pieces of timber lath can be used in conjunction with the hessian to improve strength. Cut the timber lath just short of each end of the plaster reverse; this is to allow for turning back the hessian cloth to the end and sides. Cut a small piece of lath for cleaning the plaster reverse strike off and set it aside for later. Soak the timber laths in water as this helps to reduce cracking in the fibrous cast.

4 *Release agent*: The most commonly used release agents are linseed oil and plasterer's grease, although other products are available. For our reverse we are using linseed oil. A thin coat of linseed oil is applied to the plaster reverse using either a brush or an oil-soaked hessian cloth.

5 *Bowls and buckets*: You will need at least three mixing bowls and two buckets. One of the buckets should contain clean water for mixing, the other water for cleaning the splash brush during the casting.

MAKING THE FIBROUS CAST

Before you start:

- make sure everything you need is to hand and that the working area is clear of debris and clutter

- look down the length of the plaster reverse to check that you have applied a release agent to all of the plaster reverse mould

- check that the casting plaster is within its use-by date

- half fill two mixing bowls with water, adding retarder to the second if you feel you will have insufficient time to position hessian and timber lath reinforcement.

This is the step-by-step procedure for using the two gauge system to produce a cast from a plaster reverse mould.

<table>
<tr><td>
INDUSTRY TIP

If you look along the length of the plaster reverse you should see the oil glistening or a slight sheen. If it doesn't, you have missed a bit!
</td></tr>
</table>

Strike off

The built-up plaster area on the back of a cast that will come into contract with the background surface when the plasterwork is fitted in place

STEP 1 Cut the hessian and laths to the required length.

STEP 2 Apply grease to the face of the reverse mould.

STEP 3 Mix the firstings.

STEP 4 Apply the firstings to the reverse mould with a brush. Remove air from the cast by vibrating it, then leave it to pull in.

STEP 5 Wash the bowl as soon as possible, before the plaster sets.

STEP 6 Clean off the **strike off** before applying the seconds.

STEP 7 Mix the seconds and apply to the tacky firstings. Place the hessian/canvas in position, overhanging the strike offs.

STEP 8 Apply plaster over the hessian/canvas.

STEP 9 Bed the laths on the back of the cast.

STEP 10 Fold back the hessian/canvas over the laths to strengthen and reinforce the cast.

STEP 11 Build up the strike offs with the remaining plaster, then leave to set.

STEP 12 Use a lath to form the strike off.

STEP 13 The cast will curl and lift slightly at both ends. However, it should not be removed from the reverse until it has completely set.

Leave the plaster to set and then gently prise the fibrous cast away from the plaster reverse. Store it vertically on a hook or loop, if possible. If storing it flat, make sure that the cast is kept completely flat otherwise it will distort.

If casting from a rubber reverse mould, silicone release agent must be applied instead of grease. The process and procedure for casting are otherwise the same.

CASTING FROM A FLEXIBLE MOULD

Casting from a flexible mould is similar to casting from a plaster reverse. The major difference is that there is no need to apply a release agent because the hot and cold compounds are self-lubricating.

It is important to ensure that the flexible mould sits firmly on the workbench as any distortion will show on the finished work. With larger flexible moulds it is wise to form a plaster or fibreglass case over the back of the flexible mould; this ensures that the flexible mould sits firmly on the bench.

Flexible rubber ceiling rose mould

A finished ceiling rose

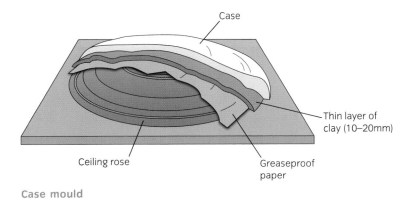

Case mould

CASTING FROM A FLEXIBLE CEILING ROSE MOULD

Follow the step-by-steps for the process of casting from a flexible ceiling rose mould.

STEP 1 Set up the workbench area, select the necessary casting plaster, hessian, lath, buckets, bowls and tools. Wash the flexible mould and pat it dry to remove surplus water. Place the flexible mould flat on the workbench. Check that the flexible mould is clean and dry.

STEP 2 Cut the hessian to overlap the ceiling rose by at least 50mm all round, snipping around the outside to help prevent gathering. Cut extra hessian to cover the timber lath.

STEP 3 Cut the timber lath for the centre and the strike off.

STEP 4 Sift plaster into two plaster bowls to just under the water line, setting aside the second bowl without mixing.

STEP 5 Mix the first bowl of plaster to a creamy consistency and brush it into the decorative sections of the mould. Brush and then splash to cover to a depth of approximately 3–5mm.

STEP 6 Clean off the strike off and allow the firstings to **pick up**.

STEP 7 Place a large piece of hessian on top of the firstings, then mix and pour a cup full of the seconds into the centre of the flexible ceiling mould.

STEP 8 Brush from the centre out towards the perimeter of the flexible mould. This action will minimise the build-up of air bubbles and ensure the hessian adheres firmly to the firstings.

STEP 9 Work around the perimeter of the ceiling rose, tucking in the hessian overlap as you go, allowing for a 10mm band around the perimeter of the ceiling rose.

Picking up

When the materials start to stiffen

STEP 10 With the large piece of hessian in position, lay the timber lath over the hessian and brush both sides of the timber lath with plaster, and lay it into position. Dip the short pieces of hessian into the seconds, then tuck and lay the wet hessian over the laths, making sure there are no pockets of air.

STEP 11 Start to build one of the centre laths flush with the perimeter; this will allow the ceiling rose to fit flush with the ceiling. Splash the back of the ceiling rose and clean off the strike off for the last time.

STEP 12 Leave the plaster to set and then gently peel the rubber mould away from the plaster.

STEP 13 The finished ceiling rose. Remember to lay the plaster ceiling rose flat otherwise it will distort.

INDUSTRY TIP

Wet the laths before use.

Wet the laths

Bearers

Small blocks of wood placed between and underneath materials to keep them separate and promote drying

STORAGE AND DELIVERY TO SITE

Manufactured fibrous work should be stored in a dry, well ventilated room, ideally with an ambient temperature of about 15°C. The important thing is to not let the room get too cold or too hot, otherwise the fibrous work could freeze, form mildew or dry too quickly.

Cornices are best stored upright; during casting, hessian loops can be incorporated into the cast so that they can be hung vertically. If you decide to store the cornice flat, use plenty of **bearers** to promote drying; don't scrimp on bearers as wet fibrous work will sag between the supports if they are not close enough together.

Other manufactured items should be stored flat to prevent any possible distortion.

All fibrous work must be protected from accidental damage caused by to poor handling or poor transportation. Most cornice work is transported face to face and tied together. Using bubble wrap is a good option as it can be used to completely wrap the work and can accommodate all shapes and sizes.

MOVEMENT AND DISPOSAL OF MATERIALS FROM STORAGE TO SITE

Always follow current applicable health and safety legislation when moving and transporting materials. They are:

- Health and Safety at Work Act (HASAWA) 1974

- Control of Substances Hazardous to Health (COSHH) Regulations 2002

- Manual Handling Operations Regulations 1992

- Personal Protective Equipment (PPE) at Work Regulations 1992.

You should also pay attention to the Environment Agency's requirement that plaster waste be disposed of separately, and the need to plan for deliveries and storage on site.

For more information about health and safety legislation, refer back to Chapter 1.

FIX AND FINISH FIBROUS PLASTERWORK

HOW TO FIX FIBROUS PLASTERWORK

The first task is to consult the contract schedule and contract drawings to determine precisely where the fibrous items are to be fixed. You will also need to refer to the contract specification to determine the specified fixing methods and materials. Remember:

- the contract schedule identifies the fibrous items and where they are to be fixed

- the contract drawings identify the fibrous items in detail, with fixing dimensions

- the contract specification identifies fixing methods and materials.

FIXINGS

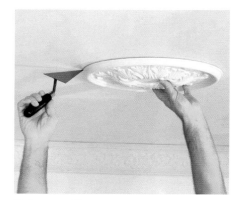

Fixing a ceiling rose

Most fibrous work is fixed into position using adhesive, although larger, heavier items may require additional support using mechanical methods. The length of the fixing will depend on the thickness of the fibrous item being fixed and the depth of the background it is being fixed to.

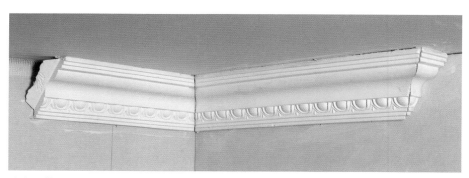

Fixing fibrous plasterwork

ACTIVITY

Search the internet and find the best price for a box of 1000 coarse phosphate 50mm-long screws (current price).

Suitable fixings include:

- adhesive

- nails and screws

- wire and wad.

Adhesive

Coving/fibrous cornice adhesive is available ready mixed or in powdered form. It can be purchased in 1kg, 5kg, 10kg, 15kg, 20kg and 25kg bags. Ready mixed adhesive has a slower setting time as it is air setting, whereas the powdered adhesives have specific setting times that range from 45 minutes up to 120 minutes, depending on the manufacturer. The adhesives are used for jointing internal and external mitres; the more expensive adhesives incorporate a PVA that improves adhesion to the background.

Nails and screws

Any nails used must be rust proof, such as galvanised, aluminium or zinc plated nails. Those with annular shanks offer better fixing as they grip the timber better. Nails usually come in 25mm, 30mm, 40mm and 50mm long sizes.

Nails are a less popular fixing option as they tend to lose their fixing strength over time, resulting in for example nail popping with plaster-boarded ceilings. In contrast, screws offer a more secure fixing and in most cases are cheaper to buy than galvanised or zinc-plated nails.

Drywall screws are commonly used because they are phosphate or zinc plated, which makes them rust proof. They are available in most sizes from 25 to 75mm, which covers the majority of fixing situations.

When fixing into masonry, plastic plugs will be needed to secure the screw fixing enough to carry the weight of the fibrous work. Guidance on the size of the screw and the diameter of the masonry drill bit needed to drill the hole in the masonry can be found on the plastic strip that joins the plugs together when they're bought.

The size and weight of the cornice dictate how much fixing is required. Heavy cornice should be mechanically fixed with a plastic plug and screws every 300mm, while lighter cornice can be mechanically fixed every 600mm in conjunction with a suitable fixing adhesive.

Wire and wad

Wire and wad is a traditional method of hanging fibrous slabs from joists and steel beams. Basic wadding involves soaking hessian in casting plaster to fix or joint fibrous work together or to a background. To improve the strength, galvanised wire is tied to the fibrous work and to a fixing point, and then wrapped with plaster-soaked hessian.

Galvanised wire is used because it is easy to work with and does not rust. The choice of wire thickness depends on the size and weight of the fibrous slab, but typically it will be 1.6–5mm thick.

As soon as the fibrous slab has been levelled and secured, plaster-soaked hessian is wrapped around the wire to form a strong support

Annular nails

Drywall screw

Plastic plug

mechanism. It is import to make adjustments to the fibrous slabs before applying the plaster wads because as soon as the plaster wads set no further adjustments can be made.

MARKING OUT AND PREPARATION

Take the following measures to mark out and prepare for installing fibrous plasterwork.

1 Lay protective sheeting to the floor area and select suitable access equipment.

2 Check that the background and the item to be fixed are both free from dust.

3 Determine the projection and depth of the coving or cornice.

4 Using a level and chalk line, mark out the position of the fibrous item to be fixed.

5 Provide a mechanical key by lightly scoring the background with a craft knife or a scutching hammer.

6 Adjust the suction of the background and the fibrous item using clean water or a weak solution of water and PVA.

7 Have ready some temporary support such as nails or props to hold the fibrous item in position until the adhesive has set. (If permanent mechanical fixings are to be used in conjunction with adhesives, these temporary supports are not so important.)

FIXING CORNICES

Before starting the work, have a final check of the drawing and manufacturer's information to determine the **projection** and **depth** of the cornice.

Scutching hammer

INDUSTRY TIP

Always carry fibrous work on its edge to stop it from flexing.

Projection

The distance from the wall to the outer edge of the top of the cornice

Depth

The distance from the ceiling to the lowest edge of the cornice

INDUSTRY TIP

Always scan the wall with a pipe/electric detector before tapping nails into a wall.

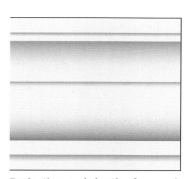

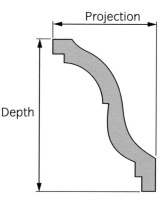

Projection and depth of a cornice

Although the following text refers to cornices, the same steps should be followed for fixing coving.

The walls and ceilings should be plumb, level and true. If they run out slightly it is better to have straight projection lines, as these lines are more noticeable when looking at coving or cornice work.

Once you're ready, follow these step-by-steps.

INDUSTRY TIP

When joining straight lengths together, the best method is to mitre the joint as opposed to creating a butt joint, which would tend to show through on finished work.

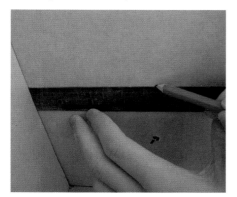

STEP 1 Measure the projection of the cornice on the ceiling line (100mm).

STEP 2 Measure the depth of the cornice on the wall (100mm).

STEP 3 Snap chalk lines to the ceiling projection and depth marks to indicate the position of the cornice on the ceiling and wall.

STEP 4 Place the cornice in position between the set lines and mark the cornice to indicate the mitre cut.

STEP 5 Position the cornice in to the mitre box making sure the ceiling line of the cornice lies to the base of the mitre box.

STEP 6 Cut the cornice using a fine tooth saw to your previously set mitre marks making sure that you cut to the front and not from the rear.

STEP 7 Cut a stop end on the other side. This will be the same cut as an external mitre.

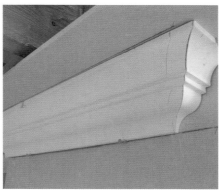

STEP 8 Fix the stop end in position.

STEP 9 Repeat the process when cutting the next length which starts with a left internal mitre cut, followed by the opposite external mitre on the opposite side.

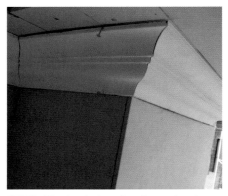

STEP 10 Check that this fits and tack in place.

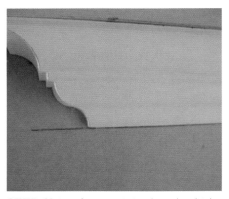

STEP 11 Cut the remaining length which has an internal right mitre and on the opposite side a return stop end.

STEP 12 Now you have cut all the cornices and checked their position you need to remove them and prepare them for fixing.

STEP 13 Prepare the cornice by sealing the strike off with diluted PVA; this will control the suction.

STEP 14 Mix the cornice adhesive to a creamy paste and apply the strike offs with a gauging trowel.

STEP 15 Position the cornice directly in place and firmly squeeze; this will cause excess adhesive to spread out.

STEP 16 Use a busk to remove the excess adhesive.

STEP 17 Use a brush and clean water to remove any surplus adhesive whilst cleaning the wall and ceiling line.

STEP 18 Continue to fit the remaining lengths and both stop ends making sure that all the moulding members line in with no steps.

INDUSTRY TIP

When cutting a mitre block, always have the ceiling line of the cornice on the bench with the face of the cornice facing you.

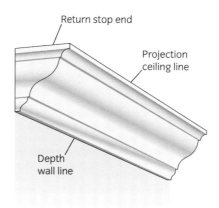

Cornice in position

Plan view of stop end

Cutting splayed joints requires a different technique, with the projection and deep chalk lines marked out.

- For an internal splayed joint the cornice is cut to the wall length and held into position. Where the ceiling line chalk lines cross, the cornice is marked and cut to the end of the cornice meeting the wall line.

- For an external splayed angle the cornice is cut to the wall line and the length of the projection is allowed for. Again, the cornice is held in position and, where the chalk lines cross, the cut is made to the end of the cornice on the wall line.

INDUSTRY TIP

If the fibrous cornice is dry, adjust the suction by applying a weak solution of PVA. If you apply weak PVA to joints and mitres it improves adhesion and helps prevent hairline cracks.

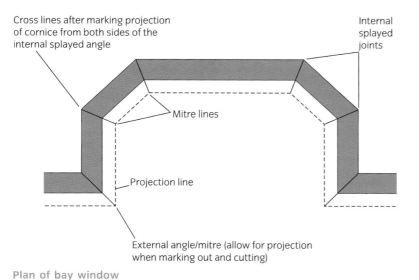

Plan of bay window

1   The quantity surveyor suggests that a single plasterer will fix a 3m length of fibrous cornice, including all jointing, in 40 minutes. How long will it take the plasterer to fix all the fibrous cornice in the living room of 'Our House'?

2   The fibrous cornice for the living room has been manufactured by another supplier at a cost of £26.35 per 3m length. The fixing contractor has priced the job at £36.23 per metre of run, including all labour and material costs. How much is the job worth to the fixing contractor?

3   A Victorian style ceiling rose is to be fixed to a single central light. Write a specification on how best to fix the fibrous ceiling rose to the ceiling.

4   The ceiling rose is an afterthought, and is to be fixed while the property is occupied. Write a method statement for the work.

PANEL AND DADO MOULDS

Panel and dado moulds are usually smaller and lighter than cornice mould and only require fixing with adhesive. Temporary support will still be required to hold mouldings in position.

The background should be clean and free from debris. Having marked out fixing positions with a level and chalk line, lightly score the background and the back of the moulding to provide a mechanical key. Test suction of both the background and the moulding with a splash of water and adjust accordingly with water or a weak solution of water and PVA.

As with the cornice, the moulding must sit firmly and squarely in the mitre box. Try not to cut the mitre exactly; a small mitre gap of 5–8mm allows adhesive to be pushed in and forms a stronger mitre.

Some panel moulds feature a quadrant mould running into a straight length, similar to cutting a splayed joint to a cornice. A bit of skill is required to produce a mitre as they cannot be cut in a mitre block. To overcome this problem the shape of the panel mould needs to be outlined on the wall or ceiling. Mitre lines will need to be made longer so that you can see where to mark the panel moulding for cutting. Draw a line through the outer and inner lines and extend the lines by about 5mm to allow for the mitre joint.

Cut all of the panel mould lengths and hold them in position to check that they fit before mixing any adhesive.

Mix a small amount of adhesive to a thick, creamy paste and apply with a gauging trowel to a thickness of about 3mm to the back of the moulding. Press firmly to the outer or inner outline and remove any surplus materials with a joint rule or a damp sponge. Work all mitres with a small tool and joint rule, remove temporary support when appropriate and make good as necessary.

BEAM CASES

Beam cases can be manufactured in one unit, ie up stand cheeks and a soffit, or they can be manufactured in three sections, ie two up stand cheeks and one soffit. Alternatively, timber laths can be fixed to the steel beam or concrete beam with suitable fixings to allow the beam case to be fastened to them using suitable screws.

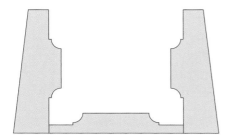

Beam case

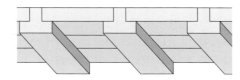

Bare structural concrete beam floor

Beam casts in position

The method of fixing a beam case will depend on the beam it is surrounding. A structural beam will be formed from concrete or a steel joist; imitation beam background may be formed with timber or metal studding. Therefore fixing beam cases is a combination of adhesive or mechanical fixing, or both.

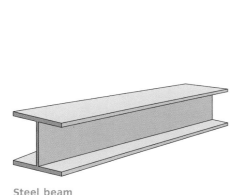

Steel beam

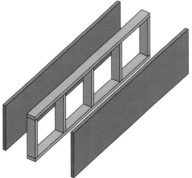

Built-up timber beam

FIBROUS SLABS

The method for fixing fibrous slabs depends on the type of ceiling, whether it is:

- timber joist or metal stud
- suspended.

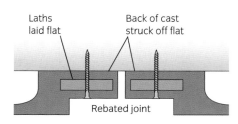

Laths laid flat — Back of cast struck off flat

Rebated joint

Fixing a fibrous slab with drywall screws

When fixing to a timber joist background, the finished ceiling height datum line would have been formed by a carpenter. The fibrous slabs should have been manufactured to fit to the joist centres, with slabs being mechanically fixed to the ceiling joist using drywall screws or galvanised nails into timber joists. The starting point will vary depending on the size and layout of the room. During fixing, pilot holes should be drilled through the slab at fixing points to minimise the risk of cracking the slab; the pilot holes are usually just smaller in diameter than the fixing screw or nail.

Consideration should be given to the weight of the fibrous slabs before attempting to hold and fix them in position. Two people working together will make the job easier. If working on your own a **dead man prop** can be used.

Dead man prop

A useful piece of equipment when working on your own. It is a telescopic pole with pads on each end; the pole is adjusted to hold an item above your head just like an extra pair of hands

Slabs must be checked for alignment as the work proceeds, similar to plasterboarding a ceiling.

Suspended ceilings are used to lower a ceiling's height and to conceal services. The architect will specify a datum point from the finished floor level or a datum level. A metal grid is formed which hangs from the concrete floor slab or structural beams. Fibrous slabs are usually wired and wadded into position.

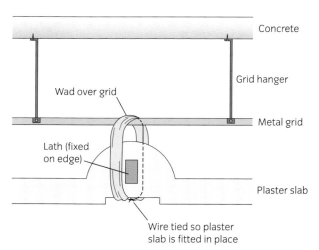

Concrete

Grid hanger

Wad over grid

Metal grid

Lath (fixed on edge)

Plaster slab

Wire tied so plaster slab is fitted in place

Detail section of fibrous slabs fixed with wire and wad

SEQUENCE OF WORK

1 Set out ceiling grid centres.

2 Pull the string line tight along the first line of slabs.

3 Drill holes each side of the lath diagonally at 70–80mm centres to line up with the fixing points of the grid.

4 Form slotted grooves or rebates between the holes below the surface of the slabs.

5 Working in pairs with one person supporting the slab, thread a suitable length of 18g wire through the slab and twist the wires.

6 Adjust the wires if required using wire cutters until the slab is level and in line.

7 Wrap the wires with plaster-soaked hessian to form a solid plaster fixing.

8 Repeat the steps above for the other slabs in the line.

9 Re-position the string for the next row of slabs and repeat the process untul the ceiling is complete.

JOINTING FIBROUS SLABS

Joints should be wetted with a weak solution of water and PVA. Hessian soaked in plaster is then pushed into the rebated joint, making sure that the hessian does not protrude. As the hessian stiffens in the rebate, mix a small quantity of casting plaster and work it into the joint with a small trowel. Finish the joint with a joint rule or busk; the hessian will strengthen the joint and reduce the risk of cracking.

Fibrous slabs

Case Study: Becca and Jamie

Becca and Jamie are fixing some fibrous cornice for a client. Becca gets the clean dust sheets out of the van and lays them in the room where the cornice is to be fitted. Jamie gets the tools and equipment out of the van and sets up a working area. Reading the specification, Jamie checks the projection and depth of the cornice and the fixing method. Using a working platform to reach the ceiling line, Becca measures out the projection across the ceiling and the depth down the wall from the ceiling. At various points around the room's perimeter she snaps a chalk line to the ceiling and wall line.

Wearing the correct PPE, they carefully create a mechanical key by lightly scoring the plasterwork with a utility knife, sweeping the dust away as they proceed. Becca then mixes some PVA to a 1:5 ratio to seal the plaster surface. They are using ordinary powder coving adhesive as the coving is lightweight.

Becca taps in some small nails just below the chalk line on the wall, while Jamie measures and cuts enough cornice for the first wall. Becca mixes a small amount of adhesive to fix these lengths. Jamie applies a thin coat of adhesive to the fixing edge of the cornice, to an average thickness of 4mm with a gauging trowel. Together they carefully lift the cornice into position and squeeze it against the wall and ceiling chalk lines. Jamie taps a few nails along the ceiling line edge to temporarily hold the cornice in place and cleans away the surplus adhesive with a joint rule.

They both continue to work in sequence around the room until all of the cornices are fixed in position. Becca proceeds to remove the temporary support nails as the adhesive starts to set, while Jamie mixes a small amount of adhesive to make good the internal mitres using a joint rule, small tool and small brush. Becca uses a joint rule to fill the holes where the nails temporarily held the cornice in position, then wipes the ceiling and wall joints with a moist sponge to clear away any dirty plaster marks.

They both walk around the room checking the cornice is fixed and clean. Satisfied, Jamie cleans all the tools and equipment while Becca carefully removes the dust sheets, shaking them in the back of the van to minimise mess in the client's property.

As soon as the room is clean and tidy Jamie asks the client to look at the complete work. The client is pleased with the work and compliments both Becca and Jamie on the clean and efficient way that they worked.

Work through the following questions to check your learning.

1   To find information for fixing a cornice, which contract document could you refer to?

   a   Bill of quantities.

   b   Block plan.

   c   Detailed drawing.

   d   Risk assessment.

2   An alternative to plasterer's grease is

   a   linseed oil

   b   shellac

   c   plasticiser

   d   size.

3   Fibrous moulding can be reinforced with

   a   timber and tallow

   b   fibreglass and tallow

   c   fibreglass and size

   d   timber and hessian.

4   A contract requires 122m of cornice to be fixed. How many 3m lengths are required? Add 10% for wastage and round up your answer.

   a   44.

   b   45.

   c   46.

   d   47.

5   When casting a ceiling rose from a flexible mould, plaster is brushed away from the centre in order to

   a   even out the spread of plaster

   b   build up the thickness of plaster

   c   expel possible air pockets

   d   build the sides up.

6   A working drawing is to a scale of 1:20 and a measure from it is taken of 200mm. How long is that section of cornice?

   a   4m.

   b   40m.

   c   2m.

   d   20m.

7   When casting a length of cornice, reinforcement is bedded

   a   when applying the firstings

   b   when applying the seconds

   c   after the seconds have set

   d   after the firstings have set.

8   Shellac contains

   a   methylated sprits

   b   turpentine

   c   linseed oil

   d   plasterer's grease.

9   It is **best** to carry a fibrous cornice

   a   on its edge in pairs

   b   flat in pairs

   c   over your shoulder in pairs

   d   upright in pairs.

10   When cutting mitres, it is **best** to have

   a   no gap between mitres

   b   a big gap to fill with bonding compound

   c   a gap of 5–10mm

   d   a gap of 10–20mm.

11   When jointing two straight cornice lengths together, joints are **best**

   a   butt jointed without a gap

   b   mitre jointed without a gap

   c   butt jointed with a small gap

   d   mitre jointed with a small gap.

12 Which one of the following would be used to cast, using a semi-dry mix?

a   Well-graded fine sand and cement.

b   Well-graded coarse sand and bonding plaster.

c   Well-graded sand and casting plaster.

d   Well-graded sand and wet cement.

13 Cement mouldings are reinforced with

a   timber laths

b   steel rods

c   hessian

d   angle beads.

14 Fixings for fibrous work **must** be

a   rustproof

b   flexible

c   expandable

d   compressible.

15 The purpose of the 'firstings' in a two gauge casting system is to

a   allow sufficient time to do the job

b   prevent canvas from coming through to the face

c   give an even coating to the face

d   speed up the work.

16 The purpose of a specification is to provide information on the

a   required workmanship and materials

b   time taken for the work

c   cost of the contract

d   health and safety requirements.

17 Fibrous cornice is fixed in new building construction immediately after finishing the

a   external framing

b   studding and partitioning

c   internal plastering

d   painting and decorating.

18 The **main** advantage of fibrous plasterwork is that it is strong, light and it

a   can be prefabricated

b   needs no decoration

c   needs no waterproofing

d   can be load bearing.

19 The **last** job carried out to the reverse mould before making a fibrous cast is to

a   shellac it

b   wet it

c   grease it

d   dry it.

20 The average thickness of adhesive when applied to the cornice edge for fixing is

a   16mm

b   12mm

c   8mm

d   4mm.

TEST YOUR KNOWLEDGE ANSWERS

Chapter 1: Unit 201

1   c   Risk assessment.
2   d   Blue circle.
3   b   Oxygen.
4   a CO_2.
5   b   Control of Substances Hazardous to Health (COSHH) Regulations 2002.
6   c   75°.
7   c   Glasses, hearing protection and dust mask.
8   d   Respirator.
9   a   400V.
10 b   80 dB(A).

Chapter 2: Unit 202

1   a   Specification.
2   a   1:5.
3   a   Door.
4   b   Insulation.
5   a   A point of a known height used for setting out.
6   c   Trench.
7   b   Raft.
8   c   Coarse aggregate.
9   a   Insulation.
10 b   English.

Chapter 3: Unit 221

1   a   Sharp.
2   d   Vermiculite.
3   a   Devil float.
4   a   Clean water.
5   d   Dirty water.

6   b   Compatible.
7   c   High suction.
8   a   Plasterboard ceilings.
9   a   Stone.
10 b   Sagging.
11 b   Two.
12 c   Plasterboard.
13 a   400–600mm.
14 c   External corner.
15 a   Thickness of plaster.
16 a   Dot and screed.
17 b   Door frames.
18 b   3mm.
19 d   10mm.
20 d   Scraping to remove snots.

Chapter 4: Unit 222

1   d   Drywall adhesive.
2   a   Ceiling joists.
3   c   Paper.
4   a   TE.
5   d   Thermal laminate.
6   c   Noise.
7   a   Schedule.
8   c   Box rule.
9   c   Ceiling lines.
10 a   Drawing.
11 b   400mm.
12 d   Cold air.
13 d   A thin coat angle bead.
14 a   Warping.
15 a   Timber joists.

16 b Pad.

17 a 9.5mm and 12.5mm.

18 a Drill and whisk.

19 d 600mm.

20 a Ensure accurate installation.

Chapter 5: Unit 223

1   a 3.

2   c Consistent mix quality.

3   a $1.56m_3$.

4   b Are removed as work proceeds.

5   a Skin burns.

6   b Water level.

7   a A cement layer on top of the finished screed.

8   d For hardening of the cement.

9   c 65mm.

10 a Prevent cold bridging.

11 d Vinyl sheeting/tiles.

12 b Level an uneven floor.

13 d 50mm.

14 c Polypropylene fibres.

15 a Dry out too quickly.

16 a Shrink and crack.

17 c 4 sand to 1 cement.

18 c Creamy.

19 a Steel trowel.

20 c 175mm.

Chapter 6: Unit 224

1   d Prevent water ingress.

2   a Uneven backgrounds.

3   c Penetrating damp.

4   a Comb scratcher.

5   c Adhesion.

6   b Cement.

7   c Application.

8   a Strength.

9   a Schedule.

10 d Drawing.

11 c Straight edge.

12 a Strength.

13 b Angle guide.

14 b Too thick.

15 a Plastic.

16 b Allow the next coat to bond.

17 d A drip.

18 b Mechanical drum mixer.

19 b Bucket.

20 d Compatible.

Chapter 7: Unit 225

1   a The architect.

2   a Squeeze.

3   b Assembly drawing.

4   c Length.

5   b Manufacturer's specification.

6   a In writing.

7   a The safe use of the material.

8   b One-and-a-half times the length of the stock.

9   c Easy to cut and shape.

10 b Stop plaster gathering when running a mould.

11 d Can re-melted and used again.

12 c Seal a plaster reverse mould.

13 d Are harder than any other Class A plaster.

14 d Crystallisation.

15 d Running mould.

16 a Mix firstings, mix seconds, apply firstings, apply seconds.

17 a Mould run backwards.

18 b Running rule.

19 c Animal fat and paraffin.

20 a Shellac.

Chapter 8: Unit 226

1   c Detailed drawing.

2   a Linseed oil.

3   d Timber and hessian.

4   b 45.

5 c Expel possible air pockets.

6 a 4m.

7 b When applying the seconds.

8 a Methylated sprits.

9 a On its edge in pairs.

10 c A gap of 5–10mm.

11 d Mitre jointed with a small gap.

12 a Well-graded fine sand and cement.

13 b Steel rods.

14 a Rustproof.

15 b Prevent canvas from coming through to the face.

16 a Required workmanship and materials.

17 c Internal plastering.

18 a Can be prefabricated.

19 a Shellac it.

20 d 4mm.

INDEX

PICTURE CREDITS

Every effort has been made to acknowledge all copyright holders as below and the publishers will, if notified, correct any errors in future editions.

Achim Raschka: p282; **Actionplastering.co.uk:** p232; **beesleyandfildes.co.uk:** p232; **Alamy:** auremar p174; ©BUILT Images p292; ©Caro pp 298, 330; ©Caroline Eastwood p113; ©Dimitar Mitev pp xxiv, 232; ©Fabricate p185; ©Gaia Moments pp 129, 248; ©Justin Kase zfivez pxix; ©LatitudeStock p236; ©Lilyana Vynogradova p182; ©Malcolm Park p140; ©Nik Taylor p119; © Paul Carstairs p128; © PHOVOIR p320; ©Simon Hart pp xxxii, 183; ©worldthroughthelens-RF p136; ©67photo pp xxx, 113; **Alexander P. Kapp:** pp xxii, 209; **Anthony King:** p291; **APL:** p25; **Axminster Tools:** pp xix, xxi, xxiv, xxv, xxvi, xxix, xxxi, xxxiii, xxxiv, xl, xli, xlii, xliii, xliv, xlv, xlvi, 20, 22, 23, 34, 36, 123, 124, 125, 179, 180, 183, 204, 205, 230, 244, 270, 277, 279, 297, 310, 311, 312; **Bosch:** pp 169, 170; **Brandon Tool Hire:** p195; **Britannia Fixings:** p182; **British Gypsum:** pp xx, xxii, xxxiii, xxxv, xxxviii, xl, 116, 117, 140, 164, 169, 171, 172, 177, 189, 190, 193, 194; **Caledonia Signs Ltd:** p195, Safety sign image supplied by Caledonia Signs Ltd to BS ISO 7010:2012 Standard; **Cardinalsystemsinc.com:** p209; **Celotex:** p100; **Conservation Resources UK:** p273; **Construction Photography:** © Adrian Greeman pp 21, 56; © Adrian Sherratt pp 89, 230; © BuildPix pp 11, 33; © Chris Henderson p34; © CJP p89; © Damian Gillie pp 85, 193; © David Burrows p85; © David Potter pp 92, 249; © David Stewart-Smith p91; © Grant Smith p13; ©imagebroker pp xv, xviii, xxxii, 89, 114, 207; © Image Source pp 15, 16, 85, 97; © Jean-Francois Cardella p47; © MakeStock p43; © Paul McMullin pp 229, 261; © QA Photos/Jim Byrne p85; © Xavier de Canto p1; **CSC Screeding Ltd, screedscientist.com:** pp xx, 225; **www.collywobbles.f2s.com:** p246; **Darley Classics Period Mouldings Ltd:** pp xvii, 317; **E H Smith:** pp 129, 248; **engineeringfiber.com:** p208; **Everbuild Building Products Limited:** p134; **Family Handyman:** p177, Copyright © 2005 The Family Handyman magazine. All Rights Reserved; **Fibre Hand Shop:** pp xvii, 279; **Fotolia:** © Alan Stockdale p39; **greenhus.co.uk:** p234; **Grŵp Llandrillo Menai:** pp xi, 107, 115, 116, 118, 125, 126, 131, 133, 134, 135, 136, 137, 138, 139, 140, 141, 142, 143, 144, 145, 146, 147, 148, 149, 150, 151, 152, 153, 154, 155, 156, 157, 163, 175, 187, 188, 191, 200, 214, 215, 216, 220, 239, 244, 247, 250, 252, 253, 254, 255, 256, 257, 285, 259, 260, 261, 267, 268, 272, 274, 275, 282, 283, 284, 286, 288, 296, 308, 313, 314, 315, 316, 323, 324; **Hackney College:** p34; **hamiltonfirst.co.uk:** p230; **Hawes Plant Hire:** p18; **HSE.gov.uk:** © p9; **HSS Hire Service Group Ltd:** pp xxxvii, 132; **If Images:** © Michael Grant p47; **iStock:** © Banks Photos p95; **Knauf:** pp xvi, xliv, 165, 167; **Lafarge photo library:** © Franck Betermin p242; **lihuastainlesssteel.com:** p321; **lockerandriley.com:** pxxxv; **Marshall Town:** p122; **mbfg.co.uk:** pp xxxvi, 284; **Mediscan:** p23; **Merlwood Timber:** p86; **Meteor Electrical:** pp 35, 90; **Mike Gashe:** pp 128, 231, 233, 323, 324; **Multi Marque Production Engineering Ltd:** p xxxii; **The NBS (NBS Create specification system):** p51; **Neil Plume:** pp xxiii, 233; **Numberger13:** p283; **PAT Training Services Ltd:** pp 37, 274; **ppconstructionsafety.com:** p52; **ProFormConcrete.co.uk:** pp xxxvii, 206; **randmwilliams.co.uk:** p262; **redbanduk.co.uk:** p206; **Refina Ltd:** p231; **renderplas.co.uk:** p261; **Restoration UK:** p240; **RIBA Product Selector:** p78; **Science Photo Library:** © Dr P. Marazzi/Science Photo Library pp 23, 201; **Screedflo Ltd, screedflo.com:** p211; **Screwfix:** pp xviii, xxvi, xxxiv, xlii, xlv, 120,178, 179, 181, 205, 309, 310; **3services. co.uk:** p209; **Shutterstock:** © Alena Brozova p95; © alessandro0770 p93; © Alexander Erdbeer p13; ©Anatoliy Kosolapov pp xxi, 124, 244; © aragami12345s p18; © auremar pp 18, 45, 65, 75; © Barry Barnes p41; ©bikeriderlondon p160; © Bokic Bojan p46; ©Bugtiger p xxx; ©cam p168; ©Chad McDermott p xv; © Cynthia Farmer p18; © Darkkong p15; © daseaford p41; © DeiMosz p41; © demarcomedia p15; © DenisNata p22; ©Dirk Ott pp xxviii, 245; © Dmitry Kalinovsky pp 31, 60, 226, 264; © DmitriMaruta p90; © Fireco Ltd p40; ©Ford photography pp 41, 231; © gyn9037 pxxxviii; © Igor Sokolov (breeze) p3; ©Israel